Scholastic Success With
4th GRADE
WORKBOOK

SCHOLASTIC

NEW YORK • TORONTO • LONDON • AUCKLAND • SYDNEY
MEXICO CITY • NEW DELHI • HONG KONG • BUENOS AIRES

Cover design by Anna Christian; Cover art by Rob McClurkan

Interior illustrations by Elizabeth Adams, Jon Buller, Reggie Holladay, Anne Kennedy, Kathy Marlin, Bob Masheris, Sherry Neidigh, and Marybeth Rivera

Interior design by Quack & Company

Charts, Tables & Graphs (pages 159–198) copyright © Michael Priestley

Maps (pages 199–244) copyright © Linda Ward Beech

Photos ©: 248: Paula Bronstein/Getty Images; 251: Chase Swift/Getty Images; 252 left: CreativeNature_nl/iStockphoto; 252 center: GlobalP/iStockphoto; 252 right: GlobalP/iStockphoto; 256: AVAVA/iStockphoto; 267 all: U.S. Geological Survey; 272: Peter Gudella/Shutterstock; 275 center right: Robert Kemp Graphics; 275 bottom left: U.S. Geological Survey; 280: SlipFloat/Shutterstock; 283 left: Kalauz Zsofi/Shutterstock; 283 center: Valentina Razumova/Shutterstock; 283 right: Surrey NanoSystems Ltd; 289: duckycards/iStockphoto; 292 top, 293: kyoshino/iStockphoto; 292 bottom: rbv/iStockphoto; 298: donatas1205/Shutterstock; 298 top right: 4kodiak/iStockphoto; 300: Looker_Studio/Shutterstock; 302: Dr_Microbe/iStockphoto; 304: Mikołaj Tomczak/Dreamstime.

ISBN 978-1-338-30661-3

Scholastic Inc., 557 Broadway, New York, NY 10012
Copyright © 2018 Scholastic Inc.
All rights reserved. Printed in the U.S.A.
February 2019

2 3 4 5 6 7 8 9 10   56   24 23 22 21 20 19

Table of Contents

READING COMPREHENSION

GRAMMAR

WRITING

CHARTS, TABLES & GRAPHS

MAPS

SCIENCE

ADDITION, SUBTRACTION, MULTIPLICATION & DIVISION

"Nothing succeeds like success."

Alexandre Dumas the Elder, 1854

Dear Parent,

Congratulations on choosing this excellent educational resource for your child. Scholastic has long been a leader in educational publishing—creating quality educational materials for use in school and at home for nearly a century.

As a partner in your child's academic success, you'll want to get the most out of the learning experience offered in this book. To help your child learn at home, try following these helpful hints:

★ Provide a comfortable place to work.

★ Have frequent work sessions, but keep them short.

★ Praise your child's successes and encourage his or her efforts. Offer positive help when your child makes a mistake.

★ Display your child's work and share his or her progress with family and friends.

In this workbook you'll find hundreds of practice pages that keep kids challenged and excited as they strengthen their skills across the classroom curriculum.

The workbook is divided into eight sections: Reading Comprehension; Grammar; Writing; Charts, Tables & Graphs; Maps; Science; Addition, Subtraction, Multiplication & Division; and Math. You and your child should feel free to move through the pages in any way you wish.

The table of contents lists the activities and the skills practiced. And a complete answer key in the back will help you gauge your child's progress.

Take the lead and help your child succeed with the *Scholastic Success With 4th Grade Workbook!*

FOCUS SKILLS

The activities in this workbook reinforce age-appropriate skills and will help your child meet the following standards established as goals by leading educators.

Mathematics

★ Uses a variety of strategies when problem-solving

★ Understands and applies number concepts

★ Uses basic and advanced procedures while performing computation

★ Understands and applies concepts of measurement

★ Understands and applies concepts of geometry

★ Understands and applies properties of functions and algebra

Writing

★ Understands and uses the writing process

★ Uses grammatical and mechanical conventions in written compositions

Reading

★ Understands and uses the general skills and strategies of the reading process

★ Can read and understand a variety of literary texts

★ Can understand and interpret a variety of informational texts

Geography

★ Understands the characteristics and uses of maps and globes

★ Knows the location of places, geographic features, and patterns of the environment

Science

★ Plans and carries out investigations to answer questions or test solutions

★ Recognizes the interdependent relationships in ecosystems

★ Identifies basic structures and functions of plants and animals, and their classifications

★ Analyzes patterns of weather, natural hazards, and geological events and how these affect people and animals

★ Recognizes that objects can be seen only when light reflected from their surface enters our eyes

★ Understands the basic relationship between pressure, density, and gases

★ Recognizes basic details of our solar system and space travel

★ Understands the human body and its needs

Scholastic Success With

READING COMPREHENSION

Mail Call

*The **main idea** tells what a story or paragraph is mostly about.*

Read the letters Tyler wrote from camp and those he received. Write the main idea for each letter.

Dear Mom and Dad,   Saturday, June 7

Camp is great! I have met a lot of new friends. Jimmy is from California, Eric is from Iowa, and Tony is from Missouri. We have a great time together, swimming, canoeing, hiking, and playing tricks on other campers! Every night, we sneak over to another cabin. We then try to scare the other campers either by making scary noises or by throwing things at their cabin. It's so funny to see them run out screaming! Now don't worry, Mom. I'm not going to get caught like I did last year.

One thing that is different from last year is how many bugs there are! I know that scientists discover 7 to 10 thousand new kinds of insects each year, and I think they could discover even more here! I have at least 100 itchy mosquito bites and about 20 fire ant bites. Every time I go outside, horseflies chase me, too! Other than all these buggy bugs, I'm having the best time!

Love,
Tyler

Main idea _____

Dear Tyler,   Tuesday, June 10

Are you sure you are okay? All of those bugs sound awful! Have you used all of the "Itch-Be-Gone" cream I got you? You know how your feet swell if you don't use the cream! How about the "Ants 'R Awful" lotion for the ant bites? You and your Aunt Ethel have always seemed to attract those nasty fire ants.

Now Tyler, I am very happy that you have met some new friends and that you are having fun together. However, you MUST stop trying to scare other campers. Remember, honey, some campers may frighten easily. I want you to apologize for any anxiety you may have caused them and start being the nice, polite boy that I know you are. Do you hear me, Tyler? Please be careful. I want you home safely.

Love,
Mom

Main idea _____

Dear Steven,   Saturday, June 7

Camp is amazing this year! Our guides help us do the coolest stuff. Like yesterday, we hiked for six miles until we found this awesome spring. Then we used a rope hanging on a tree to jump in the water. I went so high that I made a huge splash! Thursday, our guides took us rowing. We rowed to this little island where we made a bonfire. We roasted the fish we had caught. My fish was the biggest, of course!

Last night, we collected a big bunch of frogs in a bag. Then we put the bag under a bed in another cabin while they were all at the campfire. When they got back, the frogs were all over their cabin. We laughed so hard! I know they're going to get us back. I've seen them planning. I can't wait to see what they try. Hey! How's the leg? Sure wish you were here!

Your friend,

Tyler

Main idea _____

Dear Tyler,   Tuesday, June 10

That's great you're having so much fun! I wish I were there. All I do is sit around bumming out, thinking about all the fun you are having. I can't believe I broke my leg two days before camp started. My mom keeps renting me movies and video games, but I think I've seen everything and played everything. I just know I won't be happy again until this cast is off.

Your new friends sound great! Sure wish I was there helping you guys play tricks on the other campers. Remember last year when we smeared honey all over another cabin and all those bees came? That was so funny—except the part where we had to scrub all the cabins clean wearing hot, protective gear. I'm still surprised they let you come back this summer!

Hey! What's up with all the bugs? Your mom called my mom all worried about a bunch of bugs or something. Have fun and write soon!

Your friend,

Steven

Main idea _____

 Read a newspaper article about a foreign place. On another piece of paper, write the main idea for each paragraph.

From Boy to President

*The **main idea** tells what a story or paragraph is mostly about. **Details** in a story provide the reader with information about the main idea and help the reader better understand the story.*

Do you know any 9-year-olds who have started their own museums? When Theodore Roosevelt was only nine, he and two of his cousins opened the "Roosevelt Museum of Natural History." The museum was in Theodore's bedroom. It had a total of 12 specimens. On display were a few seashells, some dead insects, and some birds' nests. Young Roosevelt took great pride in his small museum.

Born in New York in 1858, Theodore Roosevelt was not always healthy. "I was a sickly, delicate boy," he once wrote. Roosevelt had a health condition called asthma. He often found it hard to breathe. Instead of playing, he observed nature and then read and wrote about it.

Roosevelt's interest in nature sometimes got him into trouble. Once, his mother found several dead mice in the icebox. She demanded that the mice be thrown out. This was indeed "a loss to science," Roosevelt said later.

Because Roosevelt was often sickly as a boy, his body was small and frail. When he was about 12, his father urged him to improve his body. Roosevelt began working out in a gym. He didn't become strong quickly. But he did decide to face life's challenges with a strong spirit. That determination stayed with Roosevelt his whole life. And eventually his body did get strong. As an adult, he was an active, healthy person. He enjoyed adventures, and he loved the outdoors!

A toy company named the teddy bear for Theodore "Teddy" Roosevelt after it was learned that Roosevelt refused to shoot a baby bear while hunting.

In 1900, at the age of 41, Roosevelt was elected Vice President. A year later, President McKinley was shot and killed. Roosevelt became our 26th President. At 42, he was the youngest leader the country had ever had.

1. **What is the main idea of the first paragraph?**

   A. Roosevelt had a natural history museum in his
   bedroom when he was a boy.

   B. The museum had 12 specimens.

   C. Roosevelt had two cousins.

   D. Roosevelt was a brave man.

2. **Which sentence best tells the main idea of the second paragraph?**

   A. Roosevelt loved the outdoors.

   B. Asthma makes it hard to run around and have fun.

   C. Roosevelt did not like to play.

   D. Roosevelt was a sickly child.

3. **Which detail does not tell about Roosevelt as a boy?**

   A. He opened his own natural history museum.

   B. He became President in 1901.

   C. He had asthma and often found it difficult to breathe.

   D. He once left a collection of dead mice in the icebox.

4. **From the selection, you can draw the conclusion that**

   A. Roosevelt's mother liked mice.

   B. Roosevelt respected his father's advice.

   C. everyone with asthma is small and frail.

   D. working out in a gym is a waste of time.

5. **In which book might you find this selection?**

   A. Small Nature Museums

   B. Living with Asthma

   C. The Childhoods of America's Presidents

   D. How the Teddy Bear Got Its Name

Honoring Heroes

> **Details** *in a story provide the reader with information about the main idea and help the reader better understand the story.*

Washington, D.C., is the capital of the United States. It is located between Virginia and Maryland on the Potomac River. Washington, D.C., is also the headquarters of the federal government. This incredible city is a symbol of our country's history and the home of many important historical landmarks.

Many of Washington, D.C.'s, famous landmarks are located in the National Mall. The Mall is a long, narrow, park-like area that provides large open spaces in the middle of the city's many huge buildings. In addition to being home to the U.S. Capitol, where Congress meets, and the White House, the Mall is also dedicated to honoring the history of our nation. Memorials for presidents George Washington, Abraham Lincoln, Thomas Jefferson, and Franklin D. Roosevelt can all be found in the Mall. There are also memorials honoring Americans who fought in the Korean and Vietnam Wars.

Near the Lincoln Memorial is another memorial. It is the National World War II Memorial. This memorial honors Americans who fought and supported the United States during World War II. The U. S. fought in this war from 1941 to 1945.

The memorial features a Rainbow Pool, two giant arches, a ring of stone columns, and a wall covered with gold stars. Each star represents 100 Americans who died while fighting in World War II.

Bob Dole, a former senator and World War II veteran, worked tirelessly to get this memorial built. He said that the memorial will remind Americans of the value of freedom. "Freedom is not free," said Dole. "It must be earned . . ."

More than $190 million was raised to build the memorial. Many businesses, private groups, and schools donated money to this cause. The memorial was completed in 2004.

1. Where is Washington, D.C., located? _____

   _____

2. Write three facts about Washington, D.C. _____

   _____

   _____

3. Which four presidents are memorialized in the National Mall? _____

   _____

4. Besides the four presidents, who else is honored in the Mall? _____

   _____

5. What is the name of the 2004 memorial? _____

   _____

6. Why was it built? _____

   _____

7. How long did the United States fight in World War II? _____

8. What are some features of the 2004 memorial? _____

   _____

9. Write what the stars represent. _____

   _____

10. What World War II veteran worked hard to get the memorial built? _____

    _____

11. What remembrance did Dole say the memorial will bring to the minds

    of people? _____

    _____

12. What were the sources of the over $190 million that was raised to build the

    memorial? _____

    _____

Read about another memorial in Washington, D.C. On another piece of paper, write five details about the memorial.

A Very Colorful House

➡️ **Context clues** *are words or sentences that can help determine the meaning of a new word.*

Jackson was excited! He and his family were on their way to the White House. Jackson could not wait to see the President's official **residence**. He had been reading all about it so that he might recognize some things he saw. After standing in a long line, Jackson, his sister, and their parents were allowed to enter the 132-room, six-floor **mansion**. They entered through the East **Wing**. Jackson knew that he and his family were only four of the 6,000 people who would visit this **incredible** house that day.

The first room they were shown by the **guide** was the State Dining Room. Jackson learned that 140 dinner guests could eat there at one time. "What a great place for a huge birthday party!" Jackson thought.

The Red Room was shown next. Red satin **adorned** its walls. The third room the **visitors** entered was the Blue Room. This room serves as the main **reception** room for the President's guests. Jackson wondered when the President would be out to greet him. After all, he was a guest, too.

The Green Room was the fourth room on the **tour**. Jackson and his family were not surprised to find green silk covering the walls in this room.

The last room was the biggest room in the White House. It is called the East Room. Here, guests are **entertained** after **formal** dinners. Jackson wondered if they could **vary** the entertainment by rolling in **huge** movie screens so they could all watch the latest movies. He wondered if kids were invited sometimes; maybe they had huge, bouncy boxes you could jump in. Perhaps they even set up huge ramps so all the kids could practice skateboarding and roller blading. How fun!

Jackson loved his tour of the White House. He was just sorry that he did not get to see the living quarters of the President's family. He wondered if the President had to make *his* bed every day!

© Scholastic Inc.

Write one of the bolded words from the story to match each definition below. Use context clues to help. Then write each numbered letter in the matching blank below to answer the question and learn an interesting fact.

1. following the usual rules or customs in an exact way __ __ __ __ __ __ __
   ₁

2. home __ __ __ __ __ __ __ __
   ₁₂   ₁₀

3. a gathering at which guests are received __ __ __ __ __ __ __ __ __ __
   ₉   ₁₇

4. kept interested with something enjoyable __ __ __ __ __ __ __ __ __ __ __
   ₁₅   ₁₆   ₈

5. decorated __ __ __ __ __ __ __
   ₁₃

6. a leader of a tour __ __ __ __ __
   ₄

7. a part that sticks out from a main part __ __ __ __
   ₂

8. a very large, stately house __ __ __ __ __ __ __
   ₇

9. a trip to inspect something __ __ __ __
   ₆

10. amazing __ __ __ __ __ __ __ __ __
    ₁₁

11. very large __ __ __ __
    ₅

12. guests __ __ __ __ __ __ __
    ₃

13. to change __ __ __ __
    ₁₄ ₁₈

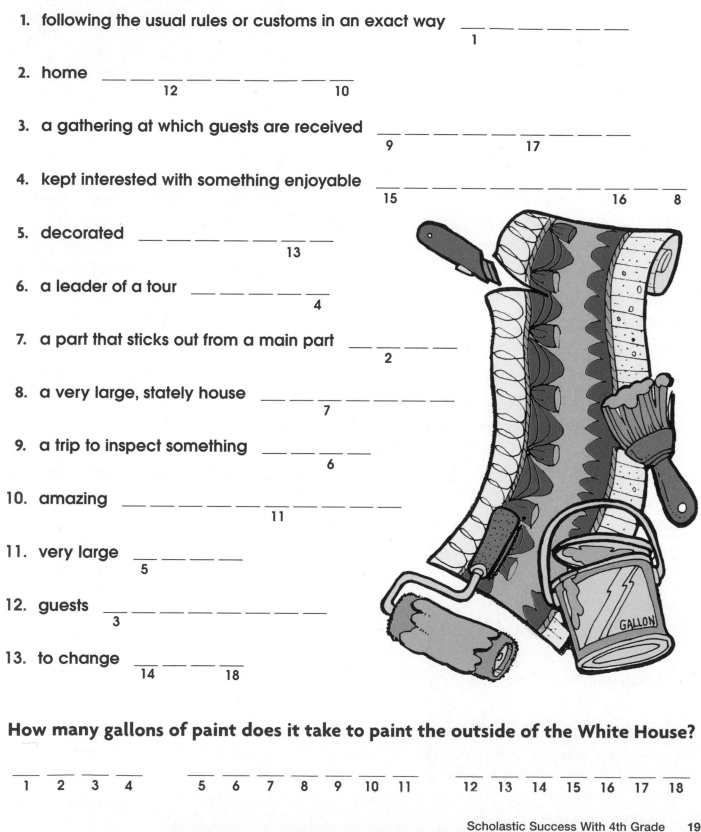

How many gallons of paint does it take to paint the outside of the White House?

__ __ __ __   __ __ __ __ __ __ __   __ __ __ __ __ __ __
 1 2 3 4   5 6 7 8 9 10 11   12 13 14 15 16 17 18

Rattle! Rattle!

Many kids think Cassidy is crazy! That is okay with her. Cassidy loves rattlesnakes, and that is that. She has every book there is about these fascinating creatures. She loves seeing these animals in the zoo.

Rattlesnakes are extremely poisonous. They often use the rattle in their tails to give a warning sound before they strike. They are classed as pit vipers.

Cassidy has decided her favorite kind of rattlesnake is a diamondback rattlesnake. These snakes can grow to be over seven and one-half feet long! These large rattlesnakes are among the most dangerous of all snakes, and they do not always rattle before striking. Like most rattlesnakes, diamondbacks like to eat birds and small mammals.

Part of the fun of being enamored with rattlesnakes is learning all kinds of interesting information about them. For example, Cassidy had always heard that you can tell the age of a rattler by the number of rattles in its tail. This, she learned, is not true. Two to four segments are added to the tail each year, one every time the rattler sheds its skin.

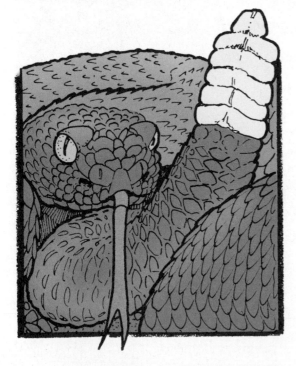

However, once about ten have accumulated, they begin to fall off! So you can never be quite sure just how old a rattlesnake is!

Sometimes Cassidy's mom wishes her daughter could love kittens or puppies or ponies instead of poisonous snakes. But actually, Cassidy's love for snakes is definitely what makes her unique.

Find a word in the snake to match each definition.

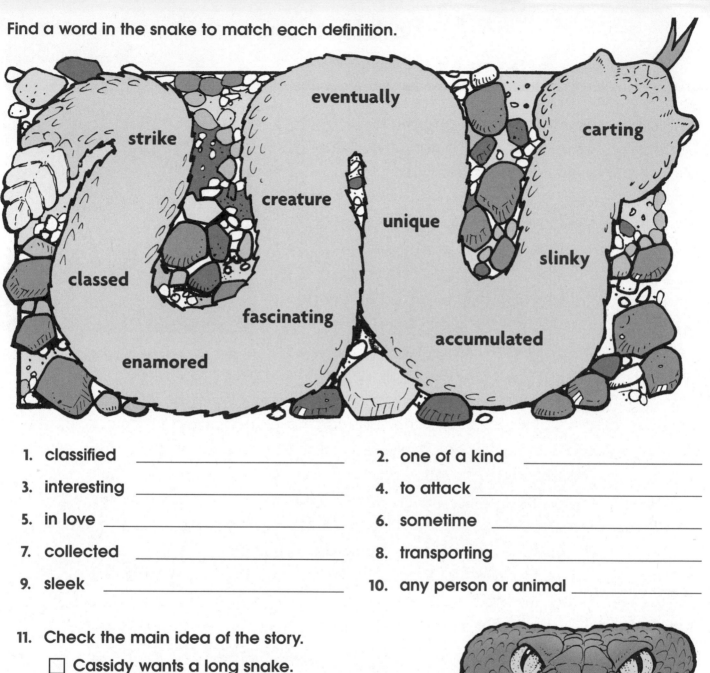

eventually

strike

carting

creature

unique

classed

slinky

fascinating

accumulated

enamored

1. classified _____

2. one of a kind _____

3. interesting _____

4. to attack _____

5. in love _____

6. sometime _____

7. collected _____

8. transporting _____

9. sleek _____

10. any person or animal _____

11. Check the main idea of the story.

☐ Cassidy wants a long snake.

☐ Cassidy loves large, dangerous rattlesnakes.

☐ Rattlesnakes do not always rattle before striking.

12. What kind of snake does Cassidy like best?

_____

Read an article about an animal that fascinates you. Choose five words from the article and write the definition of each on another piece of paper.

America's First People

To **compare** *and* **contrast** *ideas in a passage, determine how the ideas are alike and how they are different.*

Native Americans were the first people to live in America. They lived in many different areas of the United States including the Eastern Woodlands and the Southwest.

The Eastern Woodlands Native Americans had a much different lifestyle than those who lived in the Southwest. The Eastern Woodlands encompassed all of the area from what is now the Canadian border down to the Gulf Coast. The area also extended from the East Coast to the Mississippi River. The northern parts of this area had cold winters, and the whole region had warm summers.

The Southwest Native Americans lived in a large, warm, dry area. Today, Arizona, New Mexico, southern Colorado, and northern Mexico make up this area. In the northern part of this region, wind and water created steep-walled canyons, sandy areas, mesas, buttes, and other interesting landforms. In the southern part, the desert land was flat and dry.

The Iroquois, Wampanoag, Cherokee, and Chickasaw are just a few of the major Native American groups that made their home in the Eastern Woodlands. The Southwest was home to the Apache, Navajo, and Pueblo among others.

Housing was very different for the Native Americans who lived in these two different regions. The Eastern Woodlands natives built a variety of homes, depending on their location. Northern dwellers lived in dome-shaped wigwams covered with sheets of bark or in longhouses. A longhouse was a large, rectangular shelter that was home to a number of related families, each living in its own section. Those in the southeastern area often built villages around a central public square where community events took place.

Many of the Native Americans of the Southwest lived in cliff houses or large, many-storied homes built from rock and a mud-like substance called adobe. These adobe dwellings could house many families.

All of the Native Americans living in both regions ate a lot of corn, beans, and squash. Hunting was important in both regions, but fishing was more significant in the Eastern Woodlands.

The Native American groups living in both regions were excellent craftspeople. Those in the Eastern Woodlands made pottery, wicker baskets, and deerskin clothing. Many groups in the Southwest also made pottery and were very skilled at spinning cotton and weaving it into cloth. This cloth was made into breechcloths and cotton kilts for the men and a kind of dress for the women.

Learning about these fascinating people is important as they have played, and continue to play, a valuable role in our country's history.

1. **Fill in the Venn diagram using the descriptions below.**

wigwams and longhouses   excellent craftspeople
made pottery   cold winters, warm summers
hunting   buttes
many-storied homes   Arizona, New Mexico, and southern Colorado
steep-walled canyons   corn, beans, and squash
fishing   Iroquois and Cherokee
Apache and Navajo   bordered what is now Canada

Southwest   **Both**   **Eastern Woodlands**

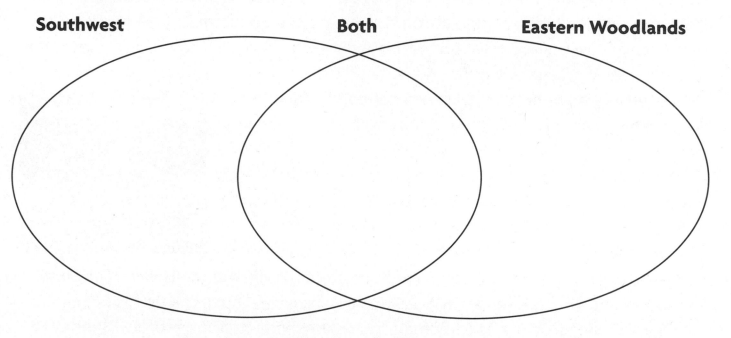

2. **Circle the ways longhouses and adobe houses were alike.**

   large   one-family dwellings   fairly small   multiple-family dwellings

3. **How was the climate in certain parts of the Eastern Woodlands different from other parts in the same region?** _____

_____

A Difficult Choice

Emily and Zach are confused! Their parents told them they could choose between Massachusetts and Arizona for their vacation this summer, and they think both states seem pretty awesome. Emily has always wanted to visit Boston, the capital of Massachusetts. Zach and she both agree that strolling along the Freedom Trail would be pretty neat. Walking the trail would enable them to see Boston's most famous historic landmarks, like the site of the school Ben Franklin attended and the Old State House. It was built in 1713 and served as the seat of the colonial government.

Emily and Zach both love the beach. If they went to Massachusetts, they could spend a few days at the beaches on Cape Cod. Emily loves boogie boarding, and Zach is great at body surfing. They both enjoy building sandcastles with their mom and dad.

Zach finds learning about Native Americans fascinating and has always wanted to travel along the Apache Trail in Arizona. This mountain highway passes Native American ruins in Tonto National Forest. Emily is not as interested in traveling along this trail as Zach, but they both would like to visit Phoenix, the capital, and then travel to Grand Canyon National Park and Meteor Crater. Zach learned in science class that Meteor Crater is a hole over 4,000 feet wide and 520 feet deep that was created when a huge object from space fell to Earth. The object has never been found. Zach would really like to try to locate it. Emily thinks he is crazy! If experienced scientists and researchers cannot find it, Zach might as well not even bother to try.

If Arizona is the chosen state, Emily and Zach would also like to stop at a few other places. Arizona is home to fifteen national monuments. That is more than any other state.

The only drawback for Zach if they choose Arizona would be the heat. It is very hot and dry in this southwestern state. Arizona has a lot of what Massachusetts does not—desert land. Once in June in Arizona, it got up to 128°F!

Massachusetts, on the other hand, is located in the northeastern United States. Here, Zach and Emily and their parents could enjoy mild temperatures of about 75° F. Their parents love hot weather, but Zach and Emily do not really like to sweat. Therefore, both know that they would prefer the climate of Massachusetts.

How will they ever decide to which state they should travel? If only they could take two trips!

1. "Pack" each suitcase to describe the two regions.

   Tonto National Forest

   Old State House

   Freedom Trail

   mild climate

   Phoenix

   Boston

   very hot

   Cape Cod

   Apache Trail

   Grand Canyon

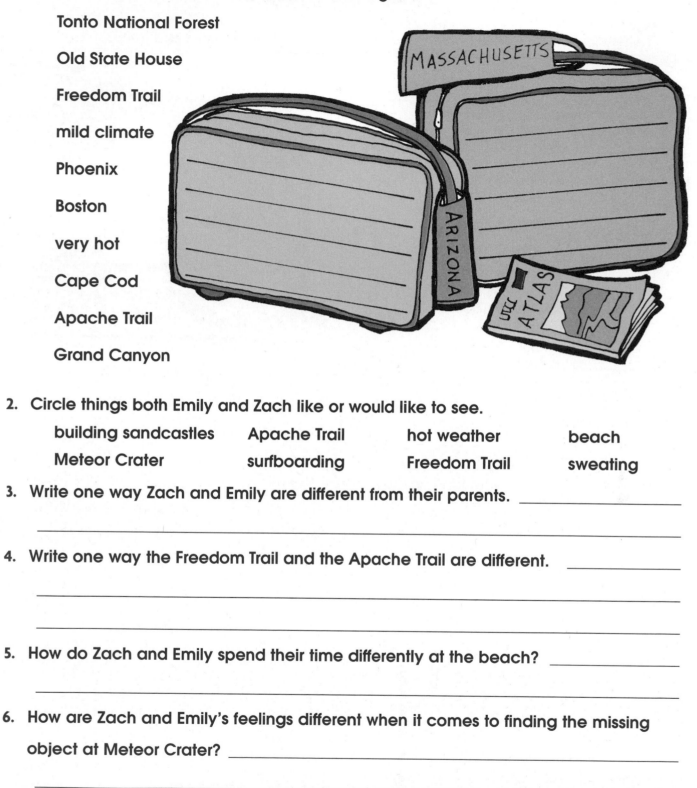

2. Circle things both Emily and Zach like or would like to see.

   | building sandcastles | Apache Trail | hot weather | beach |
   | Meteor Crater | surfboarding | Freedom Trail | sweating |

3. Write one way Zach and Emily are different from their parents. _____

   _____

4. Write one way the Freedom Trail and the Apache Trail are different. _____

   _____

   _____

5. How do Zach and Emily spend their time differently at the beach? _____

   _____

6. How are Zach and Emily's feelings different when it comes to finding the missing

   object at Meteor Crater? _____

   _____

Read about a state you would like to visit. On another piece of paper, write five differences between the state you chose and the state in which you live.

A Real Cool Cowboy

*The events in a story take place in a certain order. This is the **sequence** of events.*

Pecos Bill is a well-known character in American folklore. His legend developed from stories written by Edward O'Reilly in the early 1900's. This cowboy hero is often credited for being the creator of branding, roping, and other cowboy activities. It is also said that Pecos Bill taught broncos how to buck and cowboys how to ride.

Legend has it that Pecos Bill was born in the 1830s in Texas. He teethed on a bowie knife and had bears and other wild animals as friends. On a family trip to the West, little Bill fell out of the wagon near the Pecos River. He was found by coyotes that raised him.

Two famous natural landmarks are also amusingly traced back to Pecos Bill—the Grand Canyon and Death Valley. Supposedly, Pecos Bill once made a bet that he could ride an Oklahoma cyclone without a saddle. The cyclone was not able to throw him off, and it finally "rained out" under him in Arizona. This rain was so heavy that it created the Grand Canyon. When he reached California, Pecos Bill crashed. It was the force of his fall that is said to have created Death Valley. In actuality, some rocks in the deepest part of the Grand Canyon date back to about two billion years ago. The Colorado River began forming the Grand Canyon about six million years ago. Over centuries, the water eroded the layers of rock, and the walls of the canyon were created. More erosion occurred later as a result of wind, rain, and melting snow. Death Valley is a desert in California and Nevada. It contains the lowest point in the Western Hemisphere at 282 feet below sea level.

No one is quite sure how Pecos Bill died. One version says he laughed himself to death after listening to silly questions a man from Boston asked him about the West.

1. Look at each picture. Number the events in the order in which they happened in the story. Write a sentence for each.

2. Four words from the story are hidden in the puzzle. The definition of each word is given below. Shade in the letters for each word, reading left to right and top to bottom. The remaining letters will spell the name of a real cool cowboy two times.

a piece of writing

laughingly

attributed with

a particular form of something

a	p	r	t	e	i	c
c	o	l	e	s	a	b
m	u	s	i	i	n	l
g	l	y	l	c	p	r
e	d	e	i	t	c	e
o	d	v	s	e	b	r
i	s	l	l	i	o	n

Read a story about an imaginary character. On another piece of paper, write five events from the character's life in the order in which they happened.

Fooled You!

Maria decided to have a Prank Party for her friends on April Fools' Day. She invited five of her best friends to come over for the afternoon. Maria and her mom made some delicious "pranks" for her party. They made treats that looked like one food but tasted like another. For example, Maria and her mom made fried-egg sundaes. These sweet treats looked like a fried egg in a bowl, but they were really made of vanilla ice cream topped with marshmallow fluff and a round blob of yellow pudding.

Another treat looked like a thin-crust pizza with vegetables. However, it was really a tortilla with strawberry and apricot jam, a black licorice stick, a green fruit roll, white chocolate chips, and cashew halves. It was so easy to make that Maria's little brother, Juan, even helped.

To make a "pizza," Juan and Maria first stirred the two jams together. Then Maria spread the jam on a tortilla, being careful not to go all the way to the edge. Maria's mom sliced the licorice stick to resemble black olives and the fruit roll to look like green pepper strips. The cashew halves looked like mushrooms.

Next, Maria melted the white chocolate chips at half power in the microwave for one-minute intervals. Juan stirred the chips after each minute to see if they were completely melted. (Maria's mom made sure he had a dry spoon when he stirred because she said that water makes the chocolate lose its creaminess.) Once it was melted, Maria quickly spread the melted chocolate on the pizza. Then she and Juan topped the "pizza" with the "olives," "peppers," and "mushrooms."

Maria's friends loved the delicious pranks she had made. No one dared to play an April Fool's trick on Maria since her pranks were so tasty and fun!

1. **Number the steps in the order Maria and Juan made a Prank Pizza.**

___ **Juan and Maria topped the pizza.**

___ **Maria's mom created "olives" and "green peppers."**

___ **Maria melted the white chocolate chips.**

___ **Maria spread the jam on the tortillas.**

___ **Juan and Maria stirred the two jams together.**

___ **Juan stirred the chips with a dry spoon.**

___ **Maria spread the melted chocolate on the pizza.**

2. On the pizzas below, write one way a real pizza is similar to Maria's Prank Pizza and one way it is different from it.

Similar   **Different**

_____   _____

_____   _____

_____   _____

_____   _____

3. Write a synonym from the story for each word below.

trick _____

celebration _____

scrumptious _____

4. Why did Maria's mom make sure Juan used a dry spoon to stir the chocolate?

_____

5. Check the ingredients used in making the Prank Pizza.

___ crust   ___ strawberries   ___ tortilla

___ apricot jam   ___ red licorice   ___ green fruit roll

___ walnuts   ___ cashews   ___ chocolate chips

6. Circle the main idea of paragraph one.

Maria is a big prankster.

Maria "sweetly" tricked her friends on April Fools' Day.

Maria's mom had great prank ideas for April Fools' Day.

7. What ingredients were in the fried-egg sundaes?

_____

8. If the vegetables on Maria's pizza were real, what would they have been?

_____

Read the recipe of one of your favorite foods. Write each step on a strip of paper. Mix up the strips and then see if you can put them in the correct sequence.

A Happy Hero

*To better understand a character, a reader needs to carefully study, or **analyze**, a character's traits, personality, motivations, relationships, and strengths and weaknesses.*

One day, Lindsay and Erica were sitting at Lindsay's house working very diligently. Fourth grade was tough, and they were working on a science project about weather. Lindsay was a hard worker like Erica, so the two girls were happy to have each other as partners. They were currently writing about rain and were amazed to learn how much rain Hawaii gets. Lindsay found that Mount Waialeale, on the island of Kauai, gets about 420 inches of rain a year! In 1982, Mount Waialeale set a world record when it received 666 inches of rain. The girls knew that their classmates would find all these facts interesting.

The girls were enjoying the fun facts they were finding when all of a sudden, Lindsay saw Erica choking. Erica had been chewing on a pen cap and had accidentally swallowed it! Erica started pointing to her neck. Lindsay asked her if she was choking. When Erica nodded to say yes, Lindsay quickly got her mom to do the Heimlich maneuver to try to help Erica stop choking. (The Heimlich maneuver is a way to save someone from choking. This method is named after the doctor who invented it, Henry Heimlich.)

Lindsay's mom did not want to hurt Erica, so the first time she tried the Heimlich maneuver, she did not do it very hard. She tried a second time, and nothing happened. After trying it a third time, the pen cap flew out of Erica's mouth!

Erica was very grateful to Lindsay and her mom. She had been terrified when she realized she had swallowed the pen cap and could not breathe. Lindsay's quick thinking saved her friend. This was one science project that both girls would never forget!

1. Circle each word that describes Lindsay.

   hard worker   boring   brave   fast-thinking

   quick-acting   selfish   timid   lazy

2. Circle each word that tells how Erica might have been feeling when she realized she was choking.

   scared   thankful   enthusiastic   helpless

   courageous   sick   alarmed   friendly

3. What do you think Lindsay might be when she grows up? _____

   _____

4. Write *L* for Lindsay, *E* for Erica, or *B* for both.

   _____ good students   _____ frightened   _____ persistent

   _____ dependable   _____ grateful   _____ appreciative

5. What is the name of the doctor who invented the lifesaving maneuver?

   _____

6. What place gets about 420 inches of rain a year? _____

7. Circle the average amount of rain Mount Waialeale received each day in 1982.

   almost 3"   just under 2"   just over 4"   about 1"

8. Why do you think this project will be one neither girl will ever forget? _____

   _____

   _____

   _____

Choose a character from a book. On another piece of paper, make a list of ten words that describe this character.

A New Team for Juan

Juan was angry! His mom had signed him up late for baseball, and now he was not on his old team. He would not get to play with Tyler, Joe, and Brad. They had played together for four years! And they all loved Coach Dave—he was one of the best coaches in the league. Juan was not even sure if he wanted to play at all. He just knew it would not be any fun.

At the first practice, Juan walked slowly to the field. He saw one guy pitching and one hitting. The guy hitting struck out. "Great!" thought Juan. "I will be on a team with no hitters!" Juan continued on to the field. He saw some guys playing catch. One guy missed an easy ball. "Perfect!" thought Juan. "I will also have to teach them how to catch!"

Juan thought about calling it quits when he suddenly realized that Eric, a friend from school, was on the team. Eric was a great pitcher! "Well, maybe I will stay for a bit," Juan said to himself.

Juan started looking around some more. He recognized two other kids he had watched when he had been on the other team. One was a fast runner, and one never missed a pop fly. "Hey! This team might be okay after all!" thought Juan.

Eric was excited to see Juan. "Hey, Juan! I'm glad you are on our team. We are going to have a great team. Do you know who our coach is?"

Juan was sure the coach would not be as good as Coach Dave, but Eric was excited. "So, who is the coach, Eric?" Juan asked, somewhat indifferently.

"It's Home Run Harvey!" Eric replied excitedly.

"Home Run Harvey!" exclaimed Juan. "The one and only Home Run Harvey from the university team?"

"That is right," said Eric. "His little brother is on our team, and he wants to coach." Juan could not believe how lucky he was to get on Home Run Harvey's team!

"So who is his brother?" Juan asked.

"Tim is over there," said Eric, pointing to the guy who had not caught what Juan had called an "easy ball."

Juan felt badly for thinking negatively about Tim's missed catch. Everyone misses a ball now and then. Juan could not wait to tell his friends about his new team and coach!

1. Check how Juan felt in each situation.

	positive	negative
He could not play baseball with his friends.		
He sees a player on his new team strike out.		
He sees his friend, Eric.		
He learns Home Run Harvey is the coach.		

2. Why was Juan angry that he could not play on his old team? _____

_____

3. Underline when Juan first started feeling more positive about the new team.

   when he saw a player who was a fast runner

   when he saw a player who never missed a pop fly

   when he saw Eric

4. Why do you think Juan felt badly about what he thought when he saw Tim miss

   a catch? _____

5. Circle the words that describe Juan at the end of the story.

   angry   scared   excited   pessimistic   remorseful   timid

6. Circle the main idea of the story.

   Juan's mom made a terrible mistake, and now Juan had to suffer.

   What Juan thought was going to be a negative experience soon looked
   like it could be a positive one.

   Juan is going to get awesome coaching from a very talented ball player.

7. What kind of season do you think Juan's team will have? _____

_____

_____

**Choose three characters from a book. On another piece of paper, write two different
words to describe each character.**

Such Choices

Making predictions *is using information from a story to determine what will happen next.*

Hurray! Spring break is here! Tommy's mom and dad are also on vaction from work all week. They want to plan all kinds of fun things to do, like biking, hiking, fishing, swimming, and tennis. They are hoping for some warm, enjoyable weather. However, they just cannot decide which day to do each activity. So, they decided to check the weather forecast in the newspaper before making some final plans.

THE FIVE-DAY FORECAST

Monday	Tuesday	Wednesday	Thursday	Friday
a beauty with no clouds; high of 82	partly cloudy with a 40% chance of afternoon thunderstorms; high of 80	lingering showers until noon; then clearing and cooler with a high of 70	partly sunny with a high of 60	partly cloudy with a high of 65

1. Tommy and his dad want to spend one whole day fishing. On which day(s) might they not want to go fishing? _____

2. What day would be the best day for swimming? _____

3. What other activities could Tommy and his family do on Tuesday and Wednesday?

   _____

   _____

4. On what days do you think the family might wear jeans and jackets? _____

   _____

5. Do you think Tommy and his family are pleased with the forecast? Why or why not?

   _____

   _____

6. To do the kinds of activities Tommy and his family want to do, which forecast do you think they would like to see every day of spring break? Why?

   _____

   _____

7. Write the word from the forecast that means "staying." _____

8. Circle the words that describe Tommy's family.

   incompetent   athletic   energetic   listless

9. Circle the things Tommy and his family might want to take with them if they go swimming on Monday.

   jacket   goggles   sunglasses

   cooler with drinks   rain umbrella   sunscreen

10. Write a paragraph about what Tuesday might be like for Tommy.

    _____

    _____

    _____

    _____

Read the weather forecast in the newspaper. Choose four different cities in the country. On another piece of paper, make a list of the activities you could do in each city, based on the forecast. What other information did you use to make your list?

A New Start

*Every story has certain **story elements**. These elements include the characters, the setting, the problem, and the solution.*

In the 1500s, brave men and women and their children sailed from Europe across the Atlantic Ocean to America, looking for a better way of life. These people wanted better jobs than they had in their homelands, and many wanted the freedom to choose their own religion. Still others wanted the opportunity to be able to own land.

This period of time in America is known as the colonial period. It lasted about 170 years. During this time, many colonists worked very hard creating a new nation. The first English colony, Jamestown, was established in 1607. Between 1607 and 1733, 13 permanent colonies were established on the east coast of America. These colonies started to grow and prosper as more and more people from other countries began to immigrate. As the population of the colonies grew, trade and manufacturing developed quickly, especially in towns that had good harbors.

Despite the growth and the many successes of the colonies, the colonists also faced their fair share of problems. One very big problem was the friction between the colonies and Britain. The colonists wanted very much to control themselves and have more say in making decisions that affected them. However, the British Parliament would not allow it. This angered the colonists, so they often ignored British laws.

As Britain imposed more and more taxes on the colonists, the colonists grew angrier and angrier. Acts passed by Parliament, such as the Sugar Act and the Stamp Act, forced the colonists to take action against Britain.

In 1774, delegates from all the colonies except Georgia met to decide how to gain some independence from Britain. They met again in 1775. The delegates helped organize an army and a navy to fight the British soldiers. The colonists wanted freedom from Britain. They outlined this freedom on July 4, 1776, in the Declaration of Independence.

© Scholastic Inc.

List each story element.

main characters: _____

setting: _____

problem: _____

solution: _____

Use words from the story to complete the puzzle.

Across

1. Britain _____ many taxes on the colonists, which greatly angered them.

7. People from other countries, looking for better jobs or religious freedom, would _____ to America.

8. The colonies decided they wanted to gain _____ from Britain.

Down

2. Thirteen _____ colonies were established in America between 1607 and 1733.

3. _____ from almost all of the colonies met to discuss how to gain independence from Britain.

4. The colonists tried to organize an army and a navy to fight the British _____ .

5. The men, women, and children who left their countries to come to America were very _____ .

6. There was _____ between the American colonies and Britain.

9. As people from other countries moved to America, the colonies started to grow and _____.

On another piece of paper, list the story elements from your favorite movie.

A "Peachy" Beach Day

*The **cause** is what makes something happen.*
*The **effect** is what happens as a result of the cause.*

The day was beautiful! Janie and Jake's mom decided to take them to the beach. She even told them that since they had finshed their chores without complaining, they could each bring a friend. Janie and Jake were excited! They loved the beach.

Janie decided to ask Hayley to go since Hayley had just had her over to play last week. Jake asked his friend Charlie— they went everywhere together. Once both friends had arrived, it was time to load up the van. The kids packed some beach toys they might want—shovels, buckets, beach balls, and flippers. Mom packed a cooler with sandwiches and drinks, towels, sunscreen, and a chair for herself.

On the way to the beach, Jake and Charlie groaned. They had forgotten their boogie boards. Oh well! At least they had buckets and shovels they could use to build a huge sandcastle. Jake and Charlie loved to see how big they could make a sandcastle. They even liked to add roads and moats and lots of other details.

Once they reached the beach, everyone helped unload and set up. Then Mom put sunscreen on everyone. It was going to be a hot one—91° with no clouds! Everyone even put on hats.

Right away, the kids started playing. Jake and Charlie started working on their sandcastle, and Janie and Hayley went looking for shells. What a great day!

1. **By each cause, write the letter of the effect.**

   Cause:

   ____ **It was a beautiful, hot day.**

   ____ **They forgot their boogie boards.**

   ____ **Jake and Charlie go everywhere together.**

   Effect:

   A. **Jake asked Charlie to go to the beach.**

   B. **Mom put sunscreen on all the kids.**

   C. **Jake and Charlie were disappointed.**

2. Write *C* for cause or *E* for effect for each pair of sentences.

a. _____ Mom decided to take the kids to the beach.

   _____ The day was beautiful.

b. _____ They forgot their boogie boards.

   _____ Jake and Charlie would be building sandcastles instead of
   boogie boarding.

c. _____ Janie and Jake each got to take a friend to the beach.

   _____ The children finished their chores without complaining.

d. _____ Janie asked Hayley to go with her to the beach.

   _____ Hayley had just had Janie over to play.

3. Circle the main idea of the first paragraph.

   Janie and Jake loved to go to the beach.

   Janie and Jake finished their chores without complaining.

   Since it was a beautiful day, Janie and Jake's mom was taking them to
   the beach.

4. Janie and Jake each asked a friend to go to the beach for a different reason. Write
   each child's reason on the correct sandcastle.

Janie

Jake

5. What might Hayley or Charlie have thought on the way home from the beach?

_____

_____

Simon had to miss baseball practice last night. On another piece of paper, write three
possible causes for this effect.

Planet Particulars

*To make an **inference** is to figure out what is happening in a story from clues the author provides.*

There are eight planets that travel around the sun. They are much smaller than the sun and stars which are shining balls of hot gases. The sun and stars produce their own heat and light. The planets do not produce heat or light. They get almost all of their heat and light from the sun. Each planet has features that make it unique.

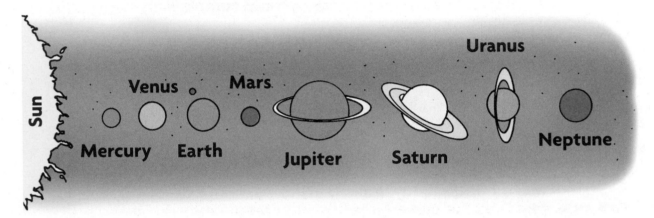

1. The largest planet, _____, is the fifth planet from the sun. It is about 1,000 times bigger than Earth. Saturn is next to this planet.

2. _____ rotates while lying on its side. It takes about 84 Earth years to orbit the sun. It is the seventh planet from the sun.

3. _____ 's surface temperature is about 370° F below zero! Brrrrr! It is the eighth planet from the sun.

4. We live on _____, the third planet from the sun. It takes this planet 365 days to orbit the sun. It is often called the "living planet."

5. Many rings surround _____. It takes 10,759 Earth days to orbit the sun. It is located between Uranus and Jupiter.

6. _____ is the closest planet to the sun. It is next to Venus, the second planet from the sun. This planet only takes 88 Earth days to orbit the sun.

7. _____ is often called the "red planet." It lies between Earth and Jupiter, the largest planet. This planet has the largest volcano in the solar system—much higher than Mount Everest!

8. _____ was called the "mystery planet" for a long time because it is covered by thick clouds. It is the second planet from the sun.

Guess the State

Spencer, Jack, Grant, and Kara are new in Mrs. Steen's fourth-grade class. Each of these students came from one of the following states: Pennsylvania, Arizona, Washington, and Massachusetts. They are taking turns giving the class clues about the state from which they moved. The other children are trying to guess the state from the clues.

Use the following clues to help you determine which state was the home of each new student. Write each new student's name on the correct state outline below. Label the state in which all the students now live.

1. Spencer is not from the Keystone State.

2. Grant is not from the south or the east.

3. Kara is not from the south or the west.

4. Jack is not from the south or the west.

5. Grant and Spencer are both from states that border another country.

6. Jack and Kara lived the closest to each other before they moved.

7. Grant used to be able to visit the Space Needle.

8. Many of Spencer's old friends speak Spanish very well.

9. Kara used to live in "the birthplace of the United States."

10. Jack used to vacation on Cape Cod. He also loved strolling along the Freedom Trail.

11. All four children love their new state. It is located in the northeastern corner of the United States. It is the largest New England state. Its nickname is the Pine Tree State. Canada forms its northern boundary.

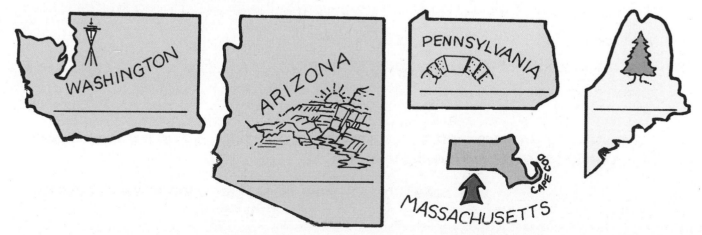

Off to the City

Maura and her grandmother are going into the city today to run some errands and do some shopping. Maura loves spending time with her grandmother. The two of them always have so much to talk about. Maura loves to hear about all the funny things her grandmother did when she was Maura's age. They did some really interesting things way back then when there were no TV's. For example, Maura's grandmother used to play jacks. She and her best friend, Sue, were the best jacks players in their school.

At 10:00 A.M. sharp, Grandma pulled in the driveway to pick up Maura. She honked the horn as she always did on their big shopping days. This was the signal that they had a busy day ahead and could not waste any time.

Maura ran out to the car, dressed in the new jeans and top Grandma bought her on their last trip. Maura knew that Grandma loved to see Maura wearing the clothes she had bought her.

As expected, Grandma told Maura some more funny things she did when she was Maura's age. Today, she told Maura how she and Sue were so hungry for candy one day in July that they decided to put on a performance and charge admission. The two girls dressed up like clowns. Grandma said people laughed so hard that the two girls were able to buy all kinds of fun treats that day. Maura made a note to herself to definitely try that some day.

Before they knew it, Maura and Grandma were in the city. Grandma found a parking spot, and away they went to begin their big day!

1. **Why are Maura and Grandma going to the city?** _____

_____

2. **List something Grandma did for fun when she was a girl. Compare it with something Maura might spend her time doing for fun.**

_____

_____

Help Maura and Grandma find their way around the city. Follow the directions to complete the map.

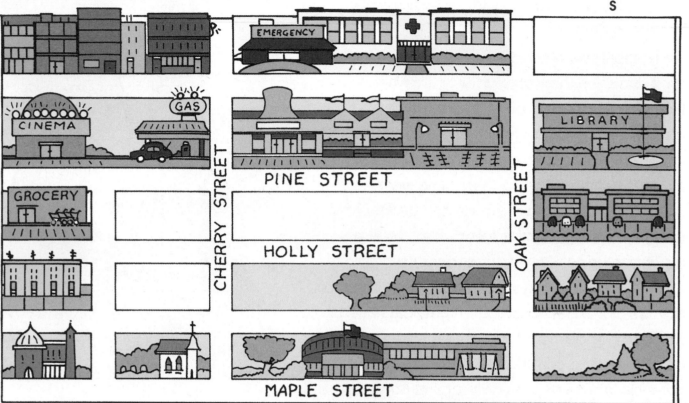

1. Maura wants to go to the mall first. It is just south of the hospital. Cherry Street runs along the western side of the mall. Label the mall.

2. On the southern side of Pine Street and the western side of Oak Street is Grandma's eye doctor. Draw a pair of eye glasses here.

3. There are five houses on Elm Street east of the hospital. Elm Street is south of the hospital. Label Elm Street and draw five houses across from the library.

4. The supermarket is located on the corner of Holly Street and Evergreen Street. Grandma needs some groceries. Label Evergreen Street.

5. There is a great park where Maura wants to play that is located between Maple and Pear streets. Oak Street runs north/south along the western side of the park. Label Pear Street, and draw three trees in the park.

6. The fire station is located on the western side of Cherry Street, north of Holly Street. Draw and label it.

7. The police station is located to the south of the fire department. Draw and label it.

 Draw a map that shows how to get from your house to your favorite fast-food restaurant.

Food for Fitness

➡️ **Classifying** *means putting things into categories with other similar things.*

Katie knows that it is very important to eat right and to exercise in order to stay healthy. That is why she gets up every morning and has **oatmeal**, a **banana**, and a glass of **milk** for breakfast. Then Katie goes to play kickball.

Katie, Jimmy, Toni, and Anna always organize a two-on-two game of kickball. After playing all morning, the foursome usually sits down for lunch. Katie knows Toni's lunch by heart— **chicken nuggets**, **carrots** and dip, an **apple**, and two **chocolate chip cookies**. Jimmy's lunch varies a little. Some days it is **ham** on **wheat bread**, **grapes**, **yogurt**, and a **candy bar**. Other days his mom will make him come home to eat a good, hot meal of **peas** and **corn**, **rice**, a **hamburger**, **strawberries**, and homemade **ice cream**. Usually on those days, Jimmy has eaten **doughnuts** for breakfast.

The only meat Anna eats is fish, so she often has **fish sticks**, crunchy **broccoli**, a **pear**, **cheese** and **crackers** and occasionally a piece of her mom's delicious **chocolate cake**. Katie always wants a bite of the cake. Sometimes Anna shares, and sometimes she does not.

To finish off her day of trying to eat healthy, Katie usually goes home to one of her dad's magnificent meals. Tonight they are having **pork chops**, **pasta**, **cauliflower** with cheese sauce, and her choice of turtle **cheesecake** or a **vanilla milk shake**. Although Katie and her friends eat some sweets, they try not to eat a lot of them, and they exercise each day.

© Scholastic Inc.

Write each bolded word from the story in the chart under the correct category.

Dairy	Vegetables	Grains	Fruits	Meat & Fish	Fats/Sweets

1. What does Katie do to stay healthy? _____

2. Circle the foods Anna would NOT eat.

    hamburger   broccoli   apple   chicken   cheese   ribs   salmon

3. List four foods Katie might have had for a healthy lunch. _____

    _____

4. Write *C* for Cause and *E* for Effect

    ___ Jimmy goes home to eat a good, hot meal.

    ___ Jimmy has probably eaten doughnuts for breakfast.

5. Write *K* for Katie, *J* for Jimmy, *T* for Toni, or *A* for Anna.

    ____ chocolate chip cookies   ____ fish sticks

    ____ candy bar   ____ chicken nuggets

    ____ banana   ____ ham

    ____ pear   ____ corn

    ____ carrots   ____ oatmeal

On another piece of paper, list all the foods you eat in one day. Classify the foods.

Flower Fun

To **draw conclusions** *is to use the information in a story to make a logical assumption.*

Aaaaaahhhhh! It was that time of year again—time to plant flowers. Christina and her dad were trying to decide what kind of flowers to plant this year. Her dad showed her an ad in the morning paper. He wanted Christina to check it out so she could help him determine what they should buy. The two always like to surprise Christina's mom with beautiful flowers before her "big day" in May. Christina was surprised to see Flower Power was having a sale. She knew they had better hurry to the store.

FLOWER POWER SALE
Beautiful flowers of all kinds
— annuals and perennials—
are all on sale — 25% OFF!
All pots and hanging baskets
are on sale, too
Buy one, get one FREE!
Reg. $3.99 to $49.99
Hurry! Sale ends Tuesday!
Flower Power
2418 Harbor Ave.

1. What time of year is it? _____

2. Circle the day in May on which Christina and her dad want her mother to enjoy beautiful flowers.

    Father's Day   **Earth Day**   **Mother's Day**   **Easter**

3. Circle why Christina and her dad will probably go to Flower Power today.

    because they are having a sale

    because they want to plant today

    because the two always plant flowers together

4. Why was Christina surprised that Flower Power was having a sale? _____

    _____

5. Why might Christina and her dad want to buy new pots or hanging baskets? _____

    _____

6. Why does the ad say to hurry? _____

    _____

On the Move

Sam and Danny cannot believe that they have to move away from Florida. Florida is so awesome! They can play outside all day long—every day. It is almost always warm and sunny, and all of their friends live there. What will they do without Brendan, Bailey, John, Alexis, and Brian? They will never have such great friends again. Never!

However, Sam and Danny are very excited for their dad. He has a great new job. The only problem is that the job is in New Hampshire. Danny was not even sure where this state was located. After learning that it is way up north near Canada, both boys did get a little excited about playing in the snow. Danny has always wanted to learn to ski, and Sam thinks playing ice hockey sounds like fun.

Sam and Danny also like the location of New Hampshire. It is between Maine and Vermont and not far from Boston, Massachusetts. Quebec, Canada, borders this state on the north. Neither of the boys has ever visited this part of the country, so they are now looking forward to exploring a new area. If only their friends could come with them! Their parents have promised that they can visit their old friends over spring break and even go to Disney World. The boys think that moving to New Hampshire will not be so bad after all.

1. **How do Sam and Danny feel about Florida?** _____

    _____

2. **Circle how Sam and Danny feel about leaving their friends.**

    They are sad.

    They do not know what they will do without their good friends.

    They know they will make a lot of new friends.

3. **Circle how the boys feel about moving to New Hampshire.**

    They think it sounds like a fun, interesting part of the country.

    They are excited about visiting their old friends on spring break.

    They are disappointed that it is next to Vermont.

4. **On the map above, label New Hampshire and the country and states that border it.**

The Wonderful Whale

A **summary** tells the most important parts of a story.

For each paragraph, circle the sentence that tells the most important part.

1. The largest animal that has ever lived is the blue whale. It can grow up to 100 feet long and weigh up to 200 tons. Whales, for the most part, are enormous creatures. However, some kinds only grow to be 10 to 15 feet long.

The blue whale is the largest animal.

Most whales are enormous creatures.

Some whales are only 10 to 15 feet long.

2. Whales look a lot like fish. However, whales differ from fish in many ways. For example, the tail fin of a fish is up and down; the tail fin of a whale is sideways. Fish breathe through gills. Whales have lungs and must come to the surface from time to time to breathe. Whales can hold their breath for a very long time. The sperm whale can hold its breath for longer than an hour.

Whales and fish do not share similar breathing patterns.

Whales can hold their breath for about an hour.

Whales might look a lot like fish, but the two are very different.

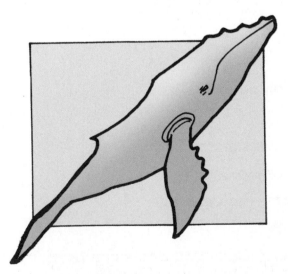

3. Baleen whales have no teeth. Toothed whales have teeth. Baleen whales have hundreds of thin plates in their mouth. They use these plates to strain out food from the water. Their diet consists of tiny animals. Toothed whales eat such foods as other fish, cuttlefish, and squid.

Whales can be divided into two groups— baleen and toothed.

Baleen whales have plates in their mouths; toothed whales do not.

Toothed whales use their teeth to chew their food.

© Scholastic Inc.

4. Whales have a layer of fat called blubber. Blubber keeps them warm. Whales can live off their blubber for a long time if food is scarce. Blubber also helps whales float.

Layers of fat are called blubber.

Blubber is very important to whales and has many purposes.

Blubber is what makes whales float.

5. Write the main idea of each paragraph to complete a summary about whales.

_____

_____

_____

_____

_____

6. Fill in the whale and the fish with the following descriptions. Write what the two have in common in the shared space. Write the descriptions that are specific to each on the spaces that don't overlap.

can hold breath for long time   people love to watch

gills   tail fin sideways

live in ponds   tail fin up and down

live in oceans   lungs

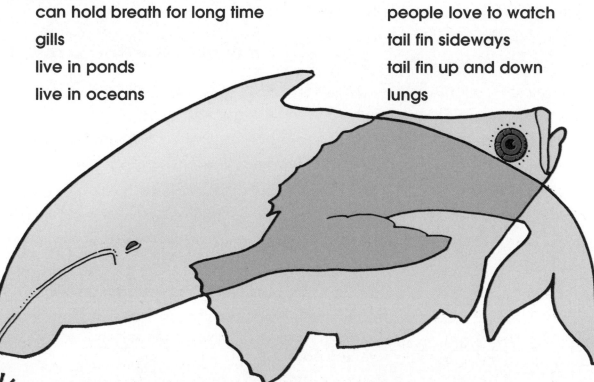

 Read information about another animal. On another piece of paper, write a summary of the information.

Climbing Blindly

A **fact** is information that can be proven.
(Example: Asia is a continent.)

An **opinion** is information that tells what someone thinks.
(Example: Asia is the most interesting continent in the world.)

Mount Everest is the highest mountain in the world.
This mountain is located in Asia. Asia is home to all
five of the world's highest mountains. Mount
Everest's peak is five and one-half miles above sea
level. That is very high!

Many climbers have tried to climb to the top
of Mount Everest's approximately 29,028-foot
peak. The first people to reach the peak were Sir
Edmund Hillary and Tenzing Norgay. Since then,
thousands of people have survived the climb to
Mount Everest's top.

One of the successful climbers is Erik
Weihenmayer. Like all who try to climb this huge
mountain, Erik faced strong winds, snow, and
avalanches. However, what really made Erik's
climb unbelievable is the fact that he is blind. After losing his vision at age 13, Erik
began climbing at age 16. He has climbed the tallest mountains on all seven
continents. Erik became the first blind person to reach the peak of Mount Everest.

At the age of 32, Erik began his climb as part of a 19-member team. His team wore
bells that he could follow during his climb, and fellow climbers were quick to warn him
of such things as a big drop on the right or a boulder to the left. Erik also used long
climbing poles and an ice ax to feel his way across the ice, rock, and snow on the
mountain.

During his climb, Erik encountered many dangers. He struggled through 100 m.p.h.
winds and sliding masses of snow, ice, and rock. Because the air became thinner the
higher Erik climbed, he wore an oxygen mask, as do many who climb high mountains.
This helped him breathe as he climbed higher and higher. It took Erik about two-and-a
half months to reach the top of this incredible mountain.

© Scholastic Inc.

1. Write *F* for fact or *O* for opinion.

    ___ Erik is very courageous.

    ___ The bells made Erik's climb a lot easier.

    ___ Erik is blind.

    ___ All climbers should use climbing poles and ice axes.

    ___ Mount Everest is the world's tallest mountain.

    ___ Erik's oxygen mask helped him breathe.

    ___ Erik used tools to help him climb.

    ___ Erik is proud of his achievement.

2. List three interesting facts from the story. _____

    _____

    _____

3. Write your opinion of Erik's accomplishment. _____

    _____

    _____

4. Circle words that describe Erik.

    brave   foolish   cautious   strong   daring   athletic

5. What are some climbing tools many climbers use? _____

    _____

6. Do you think bells are a good idea for all teams of climbers to use? Why or

    why not? _____

    _____

    _____

7. Why do you think Erik attempted this dangerous climb? _____

    _____

    _____

Read about another adventurous person. On another piece of paper, write three facts and three opinions about this person.

Don't Worry, Be Happy

*Understanding an author's purpose when writing will make appreciating literature easier for the reader. Authors have a purpose when writing such as to **inform** (give readers facts), to **persuade** (convince readers to do or believe something), or to **entertain** (tell an interesting story).*

If I were a bird, I'd fly up high,
Above the clouds, up in the sky.
I'd float and sing and soar and play,
Without any worries to ruin my day.

If I were a dolphin, I'd splash in the sea,
And dive and flip—what fun for me!
I'd play with friends under the sea so blue.
There'd be no chores or homework to do.

If I were a bear, I'd sleep all day,
And then wake up at night to play.
I'd fish and run and jump and climb,
With no one around to ruin my good time.

If I were a dog, during the day I'd rest,
So when my master came home, I'd be at my best—
Ready to run or play ball or catch,
Ready to jump, roll over, or fetch.

But I'm not a dog or a bird or a bear.
I'm not a dolphin who can swim everywhere.
I'm just a kid who wants to have fun,
But I know I can't till my work's all done!

1. Circle why you think the author wrote this poem.

   to persuade   to inform   to entertain

2. Circle what you think the author is trying to tell you.

   The author wants to fly or swim or play all day.

   Working is not what the author would choose to do.

   The author wants to be an animal.

3. Circle why you think the author thinks about being something else.

   The author wants to escape from worries and work and be free like animals.

   The author wants a pet.

   The author would love to be an animal.

4. List three things the author wants to leave behind. _____

   _____

5. Write the following words on the matching animal. Some words will be used more than once.

fly	play ball	splash	jump	climb	float	sing
sleep	run	play	flip	roll over	dive	fetch
soar	rest	fish	catch			

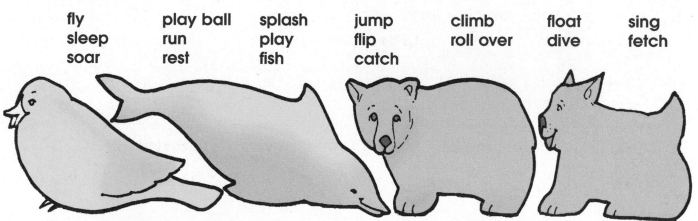

6. Write *F* for Fact or *O* for Opinion.

   ___ The author would like to escape worries and work like a bird or a dolphin.

   ___ The author is unhappy as a human and wants to be an animal.

   ___ The author knows work needs to be finished before playing.

   ___ The author just wants to have fun.

   ___ The author feels sorry for all kids who have to do work.

   Find three articles in a newspaper or magazine that are written for different purposes. Share the articles with a friend.

Improve Learning by Skating

I believe that all students should be able to roller blade during school. Roller blading would allow students to get around the school more quickly. This would leave more class time, and thus, students would learn more. It would also get the students outside quicker, so they could enjoy a longer recess. Because everyone would be moving quickly in the hallways, there would be no time for talking or messing around. The teachers would really like that!

Roller blading is a very good form of exercise. Just think of how physically fit every student would be! Being physically fit often leads to better health. Consequently, students would be absent less and would be learning more.

Finally, roller blading is fun. More learning, better physical fitness, and fun, I believe, are the keys to a successful school.

1. **Circle the author's purpose for writing this passage.**

   to persuade   to inform   to entertain

2. **Why do you think the author wrote this article?**_____

   _____

3. **List three reasons students should be allowed to roller blade during school.**

   _____

   _____

   _____

4. **List three reasons students should not be allowed to roller blade during school.**

   _____

   _____

   _____

 On another piece of paper, write an article about a change you would like to see take place. Read the article to a friend.

Scholastic Success With

GRAMMAR

Types of Sentences

A. What kind of sentence is each of the following? Write *declarative*, *interrogative*, *exclamatory*, or *imperative* on the line.

> **RETEACHING:** A **declarative sentence** makes a statement. An **interrogative sentence** asks a question. An **exclamatory sentence** shows strong feeling. An **imperative sentence** states a command.

1. Merlin carried the baby to safety. _____

2. Why did traitors poison the town's wells? _____

3. Go back and fetch the missing sword. _____

4. Slip the sword into the groove, and pull it out. _____

5. The king was England's bravest ruler! _____

6. Who will follow Selene? _____

B. Identify which groups of words are incomplete sentences and which are complete sentences. Write *incomplete* or *complete* on the line.

1. Sarah at the edge of the square. _____

2. The knights fought so bravely! _____

3. How did Kay treat her dog? _____

4. The sword out of the stone. _____

5. Natalie was trained to be a pilot. _____

C. Correct the incomplete sentences in part B. Add an action word to each one. Then rewrite the complete sentence on the line.

1. _____

2. _____

Types of Sentences

A. Add the correct end punctuation mark
to each sentence. Then write *declarative,*
interrogative, exclamatory, or *imperative*
to tell what kind of sentence it is.

> **RETEACHING:** A **declarative sentence**
> makes a statement. An **interrogative
> sentence** asks a question. An **exclamato-
> ry sentence** shows strong feeling. An
> **imperative sentence** states a command.

1. How do turtles protect themselves_   _____

2. What heavy, hot suits of steel they wore_   _____

3. Pretend that you are an acrobat or juggler_   _____

4. The students sang songs, told stories, and recited poems_   _____

B. Use one of the words below to complete each sentence.
Then identify each sentence by writing *declarative, interrogative,*
exclamatory, or *imperative.*

pass   won   listened   play

1. The audience _____ to the bagpipes.   _____

2. What kind of games did pioneers like
   to _____?   _____

3. Please _____ me the pepper.   _____

4. I've _____ three chess games in a row!   _____

C. Write an example of a declarative, interrogative, exclamatory, and
imperative sentence. Be sure to use the correct end punctuation.

1. Declarative: _____

2. Interrogative: _____

3. Exclamatory: _____

4. Imperative: _____

Types of Sentences

Decide if there is an error in the underlined part of each sentence.
Fill in the bubble next to the correct answer.

1. <u>you do like</u> to see movies about knights and castles?

   ⓐ You do like
   ⓑ Do you like
   ⓒ correct as is

2. Please hand me that mystery book about the <u>Middle Ages?</u>

   ⓐ the Middle Ages!
   ⓑ the Middle Ages.
   ⓒ correct as is

3. Grandfather described life in the early part <u>of the century.</u>

   ⓐ of the century?
   ⓑ of the century!
   ⓒ correct as is

4. Why don't you write about <u>your life!</u>

   ⓐ your life?
   ⓑ your life.
   ⓒ correct as is

5. <u>Begin by describing</u> your very first memory.

   ⓐ begin by describing
   ⓑ By describing
   ⓒ correct as is

6. I had such fun swimming <u>in the ocean?</u>

   ⓐ in the ocean
   ⓑ in the ocean!
   ⓒ correct as is

7. What do you remember about your first day <u>in school?</u>

   ⓐ in school!
   ⓑ in school.
   ⓒ correct as is

8. <u>another story</u> about our relatives in Mexico.

   ⓐ Tell me another story
   ⓑ Another story
   ⓒ correct as is

9. The fish looked so colorful swimming in <u>the Caribbean Sea</u>

   ⓐ the Caribbean Sea!
   ⓑ the Caribbean Sea?
   ⓒ correct as is

10. He told us about <u>his trip?</u>

    ⓐ his trip
    ⓑ his trip.
    ⓒ correct as is

Simple and Complete Subjects and Predicates

A. Draw a line between the complete subject and the complete predicate. Underline the complete subject once and the simple subject twice.

RETEACHING: The **simple subject** is the main noun or pronoun that tells whom or what the sentence is about. The **complete subject** is the simple subject and all of the words that go with it. The **simple predicate** is the verb that tells what the subject does or is. The **complete predicate** is the verb and all the words that tell what the subject does or is.

1. A small family lived on a faraway planet.

2. The family's two children played near the space launch.

3. The little girl dreamed about life on Earth.

4. Huge spaceships landed daily on the planet.

5. The spaceship mechanics repaired huge cargo ships.

6. Twinkling stars appeared in the black sky.

B. Draw a line between the complete subject and the complete predicate. Underline the complete predicate once and the simple predicate twice.

1. The planet's inhabitants lived in underground homes.

2. A special machine manufactures air inside the family's home.

3. The athletic girl jumped high into the air.

4. Many toys and games cluttered the children's playroom.

5. The children's father described weather on Earth.

C. Circle the complete subject in each sentence. Underline the complete predicate.

1. The underground home contained large, comfortable rooms.

2. The playful child rolled his clay into a ball.

Simple and Complete Subjects and Predicates

A. Read each sentence. Circle the complete subject. Underline the simple subject.

1. My whole family had a picnic on Saturday.

2. The warm, sunny day was perfect for an outing in the park.

3. My cousin Fred brought his guitar and harmonica.

4. Everyone sang favorite folk songs.

5. The people in the park applauded us.

B. Read each sentence. Circle the complete predicate. Underline the simple predicate.

1. We watched the space shuttle on TV this morning.

2. The huge spaceship rocketed into space at 6:00 A.M.

3. During the flight, the six astronauts released a satellite into space.

4. The space shuttle *Columbia* circled Earth for three days.

5. The spacecraft landed smoothly on Monday at noon.

C. Write three sentences. Circle the complete subject and underline the complete predicate in each sentence.

1. _____

2. _____

3. _____

Simple and Complete Subjects and Predicates

What part of each sentence is underlined? Fill in the bubble next to the correct answer.

1. My cousin lives on a big ranch in Montana.
   - ⓐ simple subject
   - ⓑ complete subject
   - ⓒ simple predicate

2. Her family raises cattle on the ranch.
   - ⓐ complete subject
   - ⓑ simple predicate
   - ⓒ complete predicate

3. Rosa's job is feeding the chickens before school.
   - ⓐ simple subject
   - ⓑ complete subject
   - ⓒ simple predicate

4. Her brother John feeds the horses.
   - ⓐ complete subject
   - ⓑ simple predicate
   - ⓒ complete predicate

5. My cousin Rosa rides her horse across the range.
   - ⓐ simple subject
   - ⓑ complete subject
   - ⓒ complete predicate

6. John spreads fresh hay in the pasture.
   - ⓐ simple subject
   - ⓑ simple predicate
   - ⓒ complete predicate

7. Their nearest neighbors often go into town with them.
   - ⓐ simple subject
   - ⓑ complete subject
   - ⓒ simple predicate

8. The dinner bell rings at 6:30 every evening.
   - ⓐ simple subject
   - ⓑ complete subject
   - ⓒ simple predicate

9. The whole family sits on the porch and reads about space.
   - ⓐ simple subject
   - ⓑ complete subject
   - ⓒ complete predicate

10. Rosa searches the Internet for sites about animals.
    - ⓐ complete subject
    - ⓑ simple predicate
    - ⓒ complete predicate

Compound Subjects and Predicates

> **RETEACHING:** A **compound subject** is two or more subjects in the same sentence, usually joined by a connecting word such as *and* or *or*. A **compound predicate** is two or more verbs in the same sentence, usually joined by a connecting word such as *and* or *or*.

A. Underline the compound subject in each sentence.

1. Pig One, Pig Two, and Pig Three wrote Goldilocks a letter.

2. The bears, rabbits, and pigs attended a party.

3. Carrots, beets, and squash grow in the garden.

4. Later this month Teddy and Osito will visit Baby Bear.

5. My brothers and sisters really enjoyed the housewarming.

B. Circle the compound predicate in each sentence.

1. Peter's mother cleaned and peeled the crispy carrots.

2. The guests laughed and giggled at June's funny jokes.

3. The sly wolves waited and watched for the passing animals.

4. Goldilocks weeds and waters her garden every day.

5. The author writes and edits her amusing fairy tales.

C. Write the compound subject or compound predicate that completes each sentence. Then write *CS* for compound subject or *CP* for compound predicate.

> authors and illustrators   buys and reads

1. My friend _____ all of that author's books. _____

2. Many _____ visit our school. _____

Compound Subjects and Predicates

A. Underline the simple subject in each sentence. Then rewrite the two sentences as one sentence with a compound subject.

1. The teacher visited the ocean. Her students visited the ocean.

   _____

2. Seagulls flew overhead. Pelicans flew overhead.

   _____

3. Seashells littered the sand. Seaweed littered the sand.

   _____

4. Carlos ran on the beach. Tanya ran on the beach.

   _____

B. Circle the simple predicate in each sentence. Then rewrite the two sentences as one sentence with a compound predicate.

1. The artist paints sea life. The artist draws sea life.

   _____

2. I collect driftwood. I decorate driftwood.

   _____

3. Seals swim near the pier. Seals dive near the pier.

   _____

Compound Subjects and Predicates

A. Fill in the bubble next to the compound subject.

1. The deer and bison grazed in the high mountain meadow.
   - ⓐ deer and bison
   - ⓑ grazed in
   - ⓒ high mountain meadow

2. Last weekend Rosa and Kay camped by the lake.
   - ⓐ Last weekend
   - ⓑ Rosa and Kay
   - ⓒ camped by

3. On Friday Alice and I saw a movie about gray wolves.
   - ⓐ Alice and I
   - ⓑ saw a movie
   - ⓒ about gray wolves

4. Last year students and teachers created a wildlife mural.
   - ⓐ Last year
   - ⓑ wildlife mural
   - ⓒ students and teachers

5. My friends and I were hiking in the White Mountains.
   - ⓐ were hiking
   - ⓑ friends and I
   - ⓒ the White Mountains

B. Fill in the bubble next to the compound predicate.

1. All night long the chilly wind moaned and howled.
   - ⓐ All night long
   - ⓑ chilly wind
   - ⓒ moaned and howled

2. Joan picked and peeled the apples in the morning.
   - ⓐ picked and peeled
   - ⓑ the apples
   - ⓒ in the morning

3. Last night Ed and Cody washed and dried the dishes.
   - ⓐ Last night
   - ⓑ Ed and Cody
   - ⓒ washed and dried

4. Many students wrote and revised their book reports.
   - ⓐ Many students
   - ⓑ wrote and revised
   - ⓒ their book reports

5. The famous sculptor cut and polished the cold, gray granite.
   - ⓐ famous sculptor
   - ⓑ cut and polished
   - ⓒ cold, gray granite

Compound Sentences

A. Read each sentence. Decide if it is a simple sentence or a compound sentence. Write *simple* or *compound* on the line.

1. Dad had been horseback riding before. _____

2. Paul felt a little nervous on a horse, but he would never admit it. _____

3. He discovered that riding was a lot of fun, and he couldn't wait to tell his friends about it. _____

4. There don't seem to be many bears in the national park this year. _____

5. Suddenly Mom pointed out the car window toward some trees. _____

6. We all looked out the window, but the bears turned out to be people in brown coats. _____

B. Underline the simple sentences that make up each compound sentence.

1. Connor had seen many parks in his life, but he never had seen a park like this one.

2. Dad brought a pair of binoculars, and Nate used them to look for animals.

3. He saw his first live bear, and the hair stood up on his arms.

4. It was an exciting moment, but it only lasted a second.

5. The bear was no bear at all, and Felicia was embarrassed.

6. He hadn't seen a bear, but he kept looking.

Compound Sentences

A. Read each sentence. Underline the simple sentences that make up the compound sentence. Circle the coordinating conjunction in each sentence.

> **RETEACHING:** A compound sentence joins two simple sentences with a comma and a **coordinating conjunction.** *And, but,* and *or* are commonly used coordinating conjunctions.

1. One day we were in the park, and we saw two ducks swimming by.

2. We watched the ducks for a while, but they disappeared into the tall grass.

3. The ducks might have gone to a nest, or they could have swum to the shore.

4. We walked along the grassy bank, but we could not find them anywhere.

5. We sat down on the dock, and out came the ducks again.

6. One adult duck led six ducklings around the pond, and the other adult followed behind the babies.

B. Read each compound sentence. Choose the coordinating conjunction that makes sense and write it on the line.

1. The ducklings are brown, _____ the adult ducks are white. (but, or)

2. The ducklings were playing, _____ they were learning, too. (but, or)

3. The ducklings ate a lot, _____ they grew quickly. (but, and)

4. We brought bread with us, _____ we fed the ducks. (and, but)

5. Maybe they knew us, _____ maybe they just liked the food we fed them. (and, or)

C. Write a compound sentence. Underline the simple sentences, and circle the coordinating conjunction you used.

_____

_____

© Scholastic Inc.

Compound Sentences

A. Fill in the bubble that tells whether the sentence is a simple sentence or a compound sentence.

1. There are many planets in our solar system, but there is only one sun.
   - (a) simple
   - (b) compound

2. The sun is a star, and a star is a giant ball of burning gases.
   - (a) simple
   - (b) compound

3. A moon is a satellite that moves around a planet.
   - (a) simple
   - (b) compound

4. Earth has only one moon, but the planet Mars has two moons.
   - (a) simple
   - (b) compound

5. The word *orbit* means "to travel around something."
   - (a) simple
   - (b) compound

B. Is the underlined part correct? Fill in the bubble next to the right answer.

1. The sun is <u>a star, but It is not</u> the biggest star.
   - (a) a star, but it is not
   - (b) a star but, it is not
   - (c) correct as is

2. Some stars are bigger than <u>the sun and, some stars</u> are smaller.
   - (a) the sun and some stars
   - (b) the sun, and some stars
   - (c) correct as is

3. Other stars seem smaller than <u>the sun, they are</u> just farther away.
   - (a) the sun, but they are
   - (b) the sun, They are
   - (c) correct as is

4. Do hot stars give off <u>blue light or do they</u> give off red light?
   - (a) blue light or, do they
   - (b) blue light, or do they
   - (c) correct as is

5. Our sun is not the <u>hottest star, but it</u> is not the coolest star either.
   - (a) hottest star but it
   - (b) hottest star but, it
   - (c) correct as is

Common and Proper Nouns

A. Circle the common nouns in each sentence.

1. The farmer lives in the green house down the road.

2. The farmer grows wheat, soybeans, and corn.

3. The fields are plowed before he plants the crop.

4. Crops are planted in rows so that they can be watered easily.

5. As the plants grow, the farmer removes weeds and looks for bugs.

B. Underline the proper nouns in each sentence.

1. John Vasquez grows soybeans and alfalfa on a 30-acre farm near Tulsa, Oklahoma.

2. The Vasquez Farm is next to the Rising J Horse Ranch.

3. Mr. Vasquez and his daughter Sally sell alfalfa to the owner of the ranch.

4. Sometimes Joker, a quarter horse, knocks down the fence to get the alfalfa.

5. Every October people come to the Vasquez Farm for the annual
   Harvest Celebration.

**C. Rewrite each sentence. Replace each underlined common noun with a
   proper noun.**

1. We walked down the street to the park.

_____

2. My aunt lives in the city.

_____

Common and Proper Nouns

RETEACHING: A **common noun** names a person, place, thing, or idea. A **proper noun** names a specific person, place, thing, or idea. A proper noun begins with a capital letter.

A. Circle the common nouns in each sentence. Underline the proper nouns.

1. The *Atlanta Constitution* published a story about celebrations.
2. *Three Dogs on a Summer Night* is a movie about poodles.
3. We like to sing "She'll Be Comin' 'Round the Mountain" at the campfire.
4. Last August my friend John went to Germany with his grandparents.
5. My family always goes to the beach for Memorial Day.

B. Complete the chart below by writing each common and proper noun in the correct column. Then add three common nouns and three proper nouns to the chart.

newspaper	The Sun News
city	Cobblestone
day	book
magazine	month
Chicago	July
park	Tuesday
Young Arthur	
Yellowstone National Park	

Common Nouns	Proper Nouns
newspaper	*The Sun News*

Common and Proper Nouns

**Read each sentence. Are the nouns underlined written correctly?
Fill in the bubble next to the right answer.**

1. I go to <u>abraham lincoln school</u>.
   - (a) abraham lincoln School
   - (b) Abraham Lincoln School
   - (c) correct as is

2. I brought <u>a peanut butter sandwich</u>.
   - (a) a Peanut Butter sandwich
   - (b) a peanut butter Sandwich
   - (c) correct as is

3. I sang <u>row, row, row your boat</u> today.
   - (a) Row, Row, Row Your Boat today.
   - (b) "Row, Row, Row Your Boat" today.
   - (c) correct as is

4. My school is located on the <u>corner of Maple Avenue and Elm Street</u>.
   - (a) Corner of Maple Avenue and Elm Street
   - (b) corner of Maple avenue and Elm street
   - (c) correct as is

5. I wrote a book report on *<u>cherokee summer</u>* for reading class.
   - (a) *Cherokee Summer*
   - (b) *Cherokee summer*
   - (c) correct as is

6. <u>My best friend John</u> sits in the third row.
   - (a) My Best Friend John
   - (b) My best Friend John
   - (c) correct as is

7. My <u>spanish class begins at noon</u>.
   - (a) Spanish class begins at Noon
   - (b) Spanish class begins at noon
   - (c) correct as is

8. That painting <u>is called "Sunflowers."</u>
   - (a) is Called sunflowers.
   - (b) is called <u>Sunflowers</u>.
   - (c) correct as is

9. I wrote <u>about washington, d.c.</u>
   - (a) about Washington, D.C.
   - (b) about Washington, d.c.
   - (c) correct as is

10. Later I'll go to <u>austin's better books</u>.
    - (a) Austin's Better Books
    - (b) austin's Better Books
    - (c) correct as is

Singular and Plural Nouns

> **RETEACHING:** A **singular noun** names one person, place, thing, or idea. A **plural noun** names more than one person, place, thing, or idea. Add –s to form the plural of most nouns. Some plural nouns are irregular, and their spellings need to be memorized.

A. Underline the singular nouns in each sentence.

1. I opened the door and found the shoes, cap, and bat I needed for the game.

2. I headed down to the fields with my bat on my shoulder.

3. My friends were standing by the fence near the dugout.

4. We were playing on the same team.

5. That day I hit two grounders, a foul, and a homer.

B. Underline the plural nouns in each sentence.

1. My uncles taught me to stand with my feet closer together.

2. The first time I hit a home run, I danced on each of the bases.

3. In the third game, all the players hit the ball.

4. My brothers, sisters, and cousins came to every game.

5. Four teams were in the playoffs, but our team won the championship.

C. Circle the singular nouns in each sentence. Underline the plural nouns.

1. The teams and players received awards when the season ended.

2. In the games to come, I will try to be a better hitter, catcher, and teammate.

3. My mother and father were the proudest parents at the assembly.

4. They gave me a new glove for my achievements.

Singular and Plural Nouns

**A. Circle the singular nouns in each sentence.
Underline the plural nouns in each sentence.**

> **RETEACHING:** A **singular noun** names one person, place, thing, or idea. A **plural noun** names more than one person, place, thing, or idea. Add -s to form the plural of most nouns. Some plural nouns are irregular, and their spellings need to be memorized.

1. My homework last night was to write a story about friends.

2. At home I thought about the people who are my friends.

3. My three dogs, one cat, and four birds are also my pals.

4. I wrote about adventures with my pets and my buddies.

5. My teacher liked my story so much that he read it to his classes.

B. Write each noun in the box in the correct column on the chart. Remember that some nouns keep the same form in the singular and plural.

chair	mice
mouse	chairs
teeth	tooth
sheep	men
foot	feet
man	

Singular Nouns	Plural Nouns
1. _____	_____
2. _____	_____
3. _____	_____
4. _____	_____
5. _____	_____
6. _____	_____

C. Write two sentences. Use one singular noun and one plural noun from the chart in each sentence.

1. _____

2. _____

Singular and Plural Nouns

Decide if the underlined part of the sentence has an error.
Fill in the bubble next to the correct answer.

1. I read seven <u>chapter in my book</u> last night.

   ⓐ chapter in my books
   ⓑ chapters in my book
   ⓒ correct as is

2. In chapter one, <u>a father and a son</u> went to the mountains.

   ⓐ a fathers and a son
   ⓑ a father and a sons
   ⓒ correct as is

3. They built their campsite under some <u>trees near a creeks</u>.

   ⓐ tree near a creeks
   ⓑ trees near a creek
   ⓒ correct as is

4. The first night the father saw <u>a bear eating nut</u>.

   ⓐ a bear eating nuts
   ⓑ a bears eating nuts
   ⓒ correct as is

5. Two <u>bear cubs</u> were in the bushes hiding.

   ⓐ bear cub
   ⓑ bears cub
   ⓒ correct as is

6. The <u>bear cubs' mother</u> helped them find berries to eat.

   ⓐ bear cub's mother
   ⓑ bear cubs mother
   ⓒ correct as is

7. In the morning, there were four <u>deers and a sheep</u> nearby.

   ⓐ deers and a sheeps
   ⓑ deer and a sheep
   ⓒ correct as is

8. The <u>son's teeths</u> were red after eating berries.

   ⓐ son's teeth
   ⓑ son's tooths
   ⓒ correct as is

9. A bird flew <u>by Dads head</u> and into the tent.

   ⓐ by Dad's head
   ⓑ by Dads' head
   ⓒ correct as is

10. It took almost an hour to get that <u>bird out of the tent's</u>.

    ⓐ birds out of the tents
    ⓑ bird out of the tent
    ⓒ correct as is

Subject and Object Pronouns

A. Read the sentences. Circle the subject pronoun in the second sentence that replaces the underlined word or words.

1. The fourth graders read a book about the rain forest.

   They read a book about the rain forest.

2. Then Ada wrote a poem about a huge Kapok tree.

   Then she wrote a poem about a huge Kapok tree.

3. Juan, Jill, and I painted a mural of rain forest mammals.

   We painted a mural of rain forest mammals.

B. Read the sentences. Draw two lines under the object pronoun in the second sentence that replaces the underlined word or words.

1. Mr. Patel's class sent a fan letter to the author.

   Mr. Patel's class sent a letter to her.

2. Ms. Torres, a rain forest expert, visited the fourth graders last week.

   Ms. Torres, a rain forest expert, visited them last week.

3. She said, "You can find information in the library.

   She said, "You can find it in the library."

C. Circle the subject pronoun and underline the object pronoun in each sentence.

1. I saw you at the library yesterday.

2. You can call me tonight about our class project.

3. Will he make an informative poster for us?

Subject and Object Pronouns

A. Choose the pronoun in parentheses ( ) that completes each sentence, and write it on the line. Then identify the kind of pronoun in the sentence by writing *S* for *subject* or *O* for *object*.

1. _____ took a boat trip through the Everglades. (We, Us) _____

2. The boat's captain gave _____ a special tour. (we, us) _____

3. The captain said, "_____ will love the wildlife here!" (You, Us) _____

4. _____ brought a camera in my backpack. (I, Me) _____

5. I used _____ to photograph birds, turtles, and alligators. (he, it) _____

6. My sister Kit carried paper and pencils with _____. (she, her) _____

7. Kit used _____ to sketch scenes of the Everglades. (they, them) _____

8. _____ is an excellent artist. (She, Her) _____

B. Rewrite each sentence. Replace the underlined words with the correct subject or object pronoun.

1. <u>Our grandparents</u> sent a postcard to <u>my sister, my brother, and me</u>.

_____

2. <u>The postcard</u> was addressed to <u>my older brother</u>.

_____

C. Write two sentences. In the first, use a subject pronoun. In the second, use an object pronoun.

1. _____

2. _____

Subject and Object Pronouns

A. Fill in the bubble next to the pronoun that can replace the underlined words.

1. <u>Carlos and Sue</u> have a very popular pet-care service.
   - ⓐ They
   - ⓑ Them
   - ⓒ He

2. Many people hire <u>Carlos and Sue</u> to feed their cats.
   - ⓐ her
   - ⓑ they
   - ⓒ them

3. Carlos asked <u>Jenna and me</u> to help out for a day.
   - ⓐ we
   - ⓑ us
   - ⓒ me

4. <u>Jenna and I</u> were delighted to help.
   - ⓐ We
   - ⓑ Us
   - ⓒ They

5. I agreed to meet <u>Sue</u> at the Chan's house this afternoon.
   - ⓐ she
   - ⓑ her
   - ⓒ them

B. Fill in the bubble next to the pronoun that correctly completes each sentence.

1. Dot, Ed, and _____ visited the Air and Space Museum recently.
   - ⓐ I
   - ⓑ me
   - ⓒ us

2. Fortunately, _____ knew his way around the huge exhibition hall.
   - ⓐ her
   - ⓑ he
   - ⓒ him

3. _____ really wanted to see the biplanes.
   - ⓐ She
   - ⓑ Them
   - ⓒ Her

4. Then Ed told Dot and _____ about the Wright Brothers' flight.
   - ⓐ I
   - ⓑ me
   - ⓒ she

5. I persuaded Dot and _____ to visit the museum again soon.
   - ⓐ he
   - ⓑ him
   - ⓒ we

Possessive Pronouns

A. Underline the possessive pronoun in each sentence.

> **RETEACHING:** A **possessive pronoun** is a pronoun that shows ownership or belonging.

1. I miss my best friend, Carlos, because he is spending the summer in Seattle, Washington.

2. He is staying with his favorite cousins, Blanca and Eduardo, during July and August.

3. The cousins have been showing Carlos around their city.

4. When I opened my e-mail this morning, I read about the ferry ride they took across Puget Sound.

5. Blanca also showed Carlos her favorite beach for clam digging.

6. Eduardo said, "Carlos, this will be your best vacation ever!"

7. Then Blanca added, "Our next stop will be the Space Needle."

B. Write the possessive pronoun from the box that completes each sentence. Use the underlined word or words to help you.

my	her	his	their	our

1. _____ grandparents sent <u>me</u> a long letter in Spanish.

2. <u>They</u> said that _____ goal was to help me learn the language.

3. <u>Grandmother</u> included the words to _____ favorite Spanish song.

4. <u>Grandfather</u> wrote a list of _____ special tips for learning a language.

5. During _____ next visit, <u>we</u> will try to speak as much Spanish as possible.

6. <u>I</u> know that _____ speaking ability will improve with this kind of help.

Possessive Pronouns

A. **Write the possessive pronoun in parentheses ( )**
that correctly completes each sentence.

1. The sports magazine and newspaper are _____. (my, mine)

2. Where is _____ atlas of the United States? (your, yours)

3. Which of the mysteries on the shelf is _____? (your, yours)

4. These new dictionaries will soon be _____. (our, ours)

5. Where is _____ copy of *Charlotte's Web*? (her, hers)

B. **Write the possessive pronoun that completes each sentence.**

1. My brother and I really enjoy visiting _____ neighborhood library.

2. Every year Ms. Lee, the librarian, displays _____ choices for the year's best reading.

3. Then all the library users vote for _____ favorite books, too.

4. For _____ favorite, I chose a photo biography about Babe Ruth.

5. Luke said that _____ first choice was Jerry Spinelli's new novel.

6. _____ friends Sue and Ed told me that they voted for the same book.

7. I asked them, "What is _____ reason for choosing this book?"

8. They replied, "It's because _____ taste in books is the best."

C. **Write three sentences about something you treasure.**
Use a possessive pronoun in each sentence.

1. _____

2. _____

3. _____

Possessive Pronouns

Look at the underlined words in each sentence. Fill in the bubble next to the possessive pronoun that refers back to the underlined word or words.

1. <u>I</u> love baseball, and _____ hobby is collecting baseball cards.

   (a) his   (c) your

   (b) our   (d) my

2. Many <u>baseball-card collectors</u> buy _____ cards from special dealers.

   (a) your   (c) their

   (b) his   (d) her

3. A <u>classmate named Ralph</u> keeps _____ cards in an album.

   (a) my   (c) our

   (b) his   (d) your

4. <u>Sue</u> treasures that rare Jackie Robinson card of _____.

   (a) ours   (c) hers

   (b) mine   (d) his

5. On Saturday <u>Mom and I</u> packed _____ lunch and ate it at the ballpark.

   (a) his   (c) your

   (b) their   (d) our

6. Once <u>all the players</u> signed _____ names on a baseball for me.

   (a) his   (c) my

   (b) their   (d) her

7. "<u>I</u> exclaimed, "This signed baseball is _____ greatest treasure!"

   (a) theirs   (c) ours

   (b) my   (d) yours

8. Grandfather asked <u>me</u> whether this new baseball cap was _____.

   (a) her   (c) you

   (b) your   (d) mine

9. When the players scored, <u>people in the audience</u> waved _____ baseball caps.

   (a) his   (c) their

   (b) my   (d) her

10. I just read a book about <u>Roberto Clemente</u> and _____ amazing career.

    (a) his   (c) their

    (b) my   (d) your

Action Verbs

A. Underline the action verb in each sentence, and then write it on the line.

> **RETEACHING:** An **action verb** is a word that shows action. Some action verbs, such as *jump,* name actions you can see. Others, such as *think,* name actions you can't see.

1. Judy Hindley wrote a book about the history of string. _____

2. An illustrator painted funny pictures about string. _____

3. Long ago people twisted vines into long, strong ropes. _____

4. People still weave long, thin fibers into cloth. _____

5. My sister knits sweaters from thick wool yarn. _____

6. We stretched the rope hammock from tree to tree. _____

7. I always tie a ribbon around a birthday package. _____

8. We learned about different kinds of knots. _____

9. He made a belt from three different colors of string. _____

10. We wished for another book by Judy Hindley. _____

B. Underline the action verb that is more vivid.

1. The rabbit quickly (moved, hopped) across the lawn.

2. I (pounded, touched) the nail with my hammer.

3. The thirsty dog (drank, slurped) the water noisily.

4. I (made, sewed) a quilt from scraps of fabric.

C. Write two sentences about how someone did something. Include a vivid action verb in each sentence.

1. _____

2. _____

Action Verbs

A. Circle the action verb in each sentence.

> **RETEACHING:** An **action verb** is a word that shows action. Some action verbs name actions you can see, such as *jump*. Others name actions you can't see, such as *think*.

1. People use string in many different ways.

2. Fran and I tie the packages with string.

3. We imagine people from earlier times.

4. These people invented rope, string, and cord.

5. The lively, happy tone of this story amazes me.

B. For each sentence, underline the action verb in parentheses that creates a more vivid picture.

6. We (sit, lounge) on the big chairs near the pool.

7. The horses (go, gallop) across the field.

8. Minna and Max (gulp, eat) their sandwiches in a hurry.

9. The workers (drag, move) the heavy load across the yard.

10. Rosa and I (put, staple) the parts together.

 Use each of these action verbs in a sentence: follow, shout, rush, slip, pound. Write your sentences on another sheet of paper.

Action Verbs

A. Fill in the bubble next to the action verb in each sentence.

1. The space shuttle circled Earth twenty times.
   - (a) space
   - (b) circled
   - (c) twenty

2. Yesterday morning my class watched the newscast on TV.
   - (a) morning
   - (b) class
   - (c) watched

3. I think about space exploration all the time.
   - (a) think
   - (b) exploration
   - (c) time

4. Before a mission, astronauts train for months.
   - (a) mission
   - (b) train
   - (c) months

5. She read a biography about the first woman in space.
   - (a) read
   - (b) about
   - (c) space

B. For each sentence, fill in the bubble next to the more vivid action verb.

1. At the beach, we _____ for pieces of driftwood.
   - (a) looked
   - (b) hunted

2. We _____ into the foamy waves.
   - (a) walked
   - (b) plunged

3. Several artists _____ a huge castle out of sand.
   - (a) sculpted
   - (b) made

4. I _____ my beach towel under a large umbrella.
   - (a) put
   - (b) spread

5. The wild horses _____ along the sandy seashore.
   - (a) galloped
   - (b) ran

© Scholastic Inc.

Verb Tenses

A. Write *present* if the underlined word is a
present tense verb, *past* if the underlined
word is a past tense verb, and *future* if it
is future tense.

1. The story of sneakers <u>started</u> with the
   development of rubber. _____

2. People in Central and South America <u>melted</u> gum from trees. _____

3. On Friday she <u>will celebrate</u> her tenth birthday. _____

4. Rubber <u>protected</u> the wearer's feet. _____

5. Gum <u>acts</u> as an eraser. _____

6. Everyone <u>will carry</u> a small backpack. _____

7. Unfortunately, pure rubber <u>cracks</u> in cold weather. _____

8. Charles Goodyear <u>believed</u> in a solution. _____

9. We <u>will visit</u> two museums. _____

10. Goodyear <u>licenses</u> the process to shoe companies. _____

11. The shoe companies <u>manufactured</u> shoes with rubber soles. _____

B. Look at the sentences with present tense verbs in part A.
Then rewrite each one with the past tense form of the verb.

1. _____

2. _____

3. _____

Verb Tenses

A. Underline each subject. Decide whether it is singular or plural. Then circle the present tense verb that correctly completes the sentence, and write it on the line.

1. Anna _____ dark-purple sneakers.   wear   wears

2. The sneakers _____ a squeaky sound on the floor.   make   makes

3. The girl _____ her sister how to tie her sneakers.   teach   teaches

4. Tight sneakers _____ your feet.   hurt   hurts

5. Loose sneakers _____ blisters.   cause   causes

6. Joe _____ his new sneakers under his bed.   place   places

7. Rachel _____ new sneakers before the race.   buy   buys

8. The students _____ comfortable sneakers.   want   wants

B. Look at the present tense verbs in the box. Decide whether they agree in number with a singular or a plural subject. Then write each word in the correct column on the chart. An example is given.

lace	laces
design	designs
reach	reaches
erase	erases

Present-Tense Verbs	
With Most Singular Subjects and *he, she, it*	With Plural Subjects and *I, we,* and *you*
laces	lace
_____	_____
_____	_____
_____	_____

Verb Tenses

A. Look at the underlined verb or verbs. Fill in the bubble next to the correct tense.

1. Tomorrow we <u>will march</u> in the Independence Day parade.

   a) past
   b) present
   c) future

2. Last week my sister and I <u>sewed</u> our old-fashioned costumes.

   a) past
   b) present
   c) future

3. Many townspeople <u>will dress</u> as Western pioneers.

   a) past
   b) present
   c) future

4. Everyone <u>participates</u> in the celebration.

   a) past
   b) present
   c) future

5. <u>Will</u> local cowhands <u>ride</u> their horses?

   a) past
   b) present
   c) future

B. Decide if the underlined verbs are correct. Fill in the bubble next to the right answer.

1. The parade <u>will began</u> at 10:00 tomorrow morning.

   a) will begin
   b) will begins
   c) correct as is

2. The marching bands <u>will arrive</u> in town this afternoon.

   a) will arrives
   b) will arrived
   c) correct as is

3. One parade float <u>will shows</u> an old-time newspaper office.

   a) will showed
   b) will show
   c) correct as is

4. When <u>will</u> the square dancers <u>performed</u>?

   a) will perform
   b) will performs
   c) correct as is

5. Later we <u>will celebrate</u> with a picnic.

   a) will celebrates
   b) will celebrated
   c) correct as is

Main and Helping Verbs

A. Read each sentence. Underline the helping verb once and the main verb twice.

1. What will happen to the doughnuts?

2. Uncle Ulysses has equipped the lunchroom with labor-saving devices.

3. Homer was polishing the metal trimmings.

4. Uncle Ulysses had tinkered with the inside workings.

5. The Ladies' Club was gathering.

6. Homer will handle everything.

7. Mr. Gabby was talking to Homer about his job.

8. A chauffeur had helped a woman out of a black car.

9. Now she is wearing an apron.

10. She will need some nutmeg.

B. In each sentence, circle the main verb and underline the helping verb. Then identify when the action occurs by writing *past, present,* or *future.*

1. The lady had asked for baking powder. _____

2. The rings of batter will drop into the hot fat. _____

3. Homer is learning about the doughnut machine. _____

4. People will enjoy the doughnuts later. _____

5. Everyone has eaten Homer's doughnuts. _____

6. We are taking doughnuts for friends. _____

Main and Helping Verbs

A. Read each incomplete sentence. Underline the main verb. Then circle the helping verb that correctly completes the sentence, and write it on the line.

> **RETEACHING: Main verbs** show the main action in a sentence. **Helping verbs** help the main verb show tense. Helping verbs, such as *am, is, are, was, were, has, have, had,* or *will,* work with main verbs to tell when an action occurs.

1. Justin _____ cooking seafood stew. (will, was)

2. He _____ added spices and lemon juice. (had, is)

3. Sally and Mick _____ prepared stew before. (will, have)

4. Justin _____ tasting the broth. (is, had)

5. "I _____ add a little more pepper," Justin says. (will, has)

6. His friends _____ just arrived for dinner. (are, have)

B. Underline the main verbs, and write the helping verbs on the lines.

1. On Saturday Betty will bake rye bread. _____

2. Henry has pickled some fresh cucumbers. _____

3. Gertrude is picking raspberries and blackberries. _____

4. Alison had planted an herb garden. _____

5. Marie and Harry have tossed the salad. _____

6. They are planning another picnic. _____

C. Write sentences using the main and helping verbs below.

1. will meet _____

2. had arrived _____

3. is listening _____

Main and Helping Verbs

Decide if the underlined verbs in each sentence are correct.
Then fill in the bubble next to the correct answer.

1. Today Francesca <u>will traveled</u> to Peru by plane.

   ⓐ is traveling
   ⓑ am traveling
   ⓒ correct as is

2. She is <u>photograph</u> the stone ruins of Machu Picchu next week.

   ⓐ will photograph
   ⓑ had photographed
   ⓒ correct as is

3. An American explorer <u>had discovered</u> the ancient Incan city in 1911.

   ⓐ has discovered
   ⓑ is discovering
   ⓒ correct as is

4. Since then, many people <u>will visited</u> the ruins of the city.

   ⓐ have visited
   ⓑ have visiting
   ⓒ correct as is

5. Yesterday Francesca's brothers <u>had looking</u> at pictures of Machu Picchu.

   ⓐ have looking
   ⓑ were looking
   ⓒ correct as is

6. They <u>were wondering</u> about the Incan civilization.

   ⓐ had wondering
   ⓑ has wonder
   ⓒ correct as is

7. Centuries ago the Inca <u>had creating</u> a great empire.

   ⓐ have creating
   ⓑ had created
   ⓒ correct as is

8. What <u>had happening</u> to them?

   ⓐ has happening
   ⓑ had happened
   ⓒ correct as is

9. The Spanish explorers <u>will conquered</u> the Inca in 1532.

   ⓐ had conquered
   ⓑ are conquered
   ⓒ correct as is

10. Francesca <u>will discover</u> Incan culture in present-day Peru.

   ⓐ has discovering
   ⓑ was discover
   ⓒ correct as is

Linking Verbs

A. Underline the linking verb in each sentence, and circle the words it links.

RETEACHING: A **linking verb** links the subject of a sentence to other words in the sentence. A linking verb does not show action. It tells what the subject is, was, or will be.

1. I am an enthusiastic reader.

2. My favorite books are nonfiction.

3. This bookstore is the best one in town.

4. The nonfiction books here are always interesting.

5. The store's owner is very knowledgeable.

6. His name is Terry Baldes.

7. Mr. Baldes was once an inventor and a scientist.

8. The bookstore's windows were very attractive last month.

9. Last Saturday's main event was an appearance by my favorite author.

10. My friends are big admirers of Mr. Baldes.

B. Write the linking verb in each sentence on the line.

1. An important invention is the telephone. _____

2. The telephone's inventor was Alexander Graham Bell. _____

3. At one time, most telephones were black. _____

4. Today cellular phones are very popular. _____

5. Cell phones were uncommon 25 years ago. _____

C. Write two sentences. Include a linking verb in each one.

1. _____

2. _____

© Scholastic Inc.

Linking Verbs

A. Underline the correct linking verb in ( ). Write *S* if the subject is singular and *P* if it is plural.

1. The natural history museum (was, were) very busy last weekend. _____

2. Many visitors (was, were) tourists. _____

3. The new displays of rocks and gems (is, are) very popular. _____

4. One amazing rock (is, are) bright blue. _____

5. My favorite gems (was, were) the purple amethysts. _____

6. The gold nuggets (is, are) bright yellow. _____

7. The museum's first floor (is, are) full of Native American artifacts. _____

8. The carved wooden canoes (is, are) enormous. _____

9. The Tlingit woodcarvers (was, were) true artists. _____

10. This canoe (was, were) hand painted over a hundred years ago. _____

11. I (am, is) a big supporter of the museum. _____

B. Complete each sentence. Write *is* or *are* on the line.

1. The apatasaurus skeleton _____ gigantic.

2. These saber-tooth tigers _____ very impressive.

3. The exhibit cards _____ most informative.

4. The tiny dinosaur _____ really cute.

C. Write a sentence with a singular subject and a sentence with a plural subject. Include a linking verb in each sentence.

1. _____

2. _____

Linking Verbs

Read each incomplete sentence below. Then fill in the bubble next to the linking verb that correctly completes the sentence.

1. Denver, Colorado, _____ a large city.

   ⓐ were

   ⓑ are

   ⓒ is

2. This growing metropolis _____ a mile high.

   ⓐ are

   ⓑ is

   ⓒ were

3. Gold prospectors _____ the city's founders in 1858.

   ⓐ is

   ⓑ was

   ⓒ were

4. From 1860 to 1945, Denver _____ a mining and agricultural community.

   ⓐ were

   ⓑ was

   ⓒ will be

5. Today many local residents _____ government workers.

   ⓐ are

   ⓑ is

   ⓒ was

6. Now the automobile _____ the quickest way to travel.

   ⓐ were

   ⓑ is

   ⓒ are

7. In earlier times, horses and buggies _____ popular modes of transportation.

   ⓐ were

   ⓑ is

   ⓒ was

8. I _____ a student in a Denver public school.

   ⓐ were

   ⓑ am

   ⓒ is

9. Last year my school's sports teams _____ very successful.

   ⓐ was

   ⓑ were

   ⓒ is

10. I _____ a spectator at the local games.

   ⓐ was

   ⓑ were

   ⓒ is

Irregular Verbs

A. Underline the irregular verb in each sentence.

1. This morning Mom bought a red and a green toothbrush.

2. Pat made a tuna sandwich in the kitchen.

3. Mom quickly came into the dining room.

4. Deever rode her bicycle over to Pat's house.

5. Deever shook her head in great amusement.

6. They heard a great deal of noise in the kitchen.

7. Deever took a close look at the bright red toothbrush.

8. Pat carefully thought about the green and red toothbrushes.

9. Deever broke the silence with a sly laugh.

B. Circle the irregular past tense verb in parentheses ( ). Then write it on the line to complete the sentence.

1. We _____ a funny story about two toothbrushes. (hear, heard)

2. Pat _____ his decision after fifteen long minutes. (made, make)

3. Mom finally _____ E.J. an orange toothbrush. (buy, bought)

4. E.J. _____ into a song with a big smile on his face. (broke, break)

5. We all _____ to the nearest supermarket on our bikes. (ride, rode)

6. Deever _____ to the store with us. (came, come)

7. E.J. _____ with laughter at Pat's joke. (shook, shake)

Irregular Verbs

A. Underline the helping verb and the irregular past participle in each sentence.

> **RETEACHING:** An **irregular verb** does not form the past tense by adding -ed. The past participle is the form of the verb used with *has*, *have*, *had*, or *will have*.

1. We have chosen a fantastic day for our school picnic.

2. Mr. Torres has brought all the food and beverages in his van.

3. We have eaten all of the carrots on the table.

4. Ms. Chang has hidden the prizes for the treasure hunt.

5. By noon our teacher had taken over forty photographs.

6. All the fourth graders have gone on a short walk to the lake.

7. They had heard about the great paddleboats there.

8. Some of my friends have ridden in the boats.

9. The school has bought new sports equipment for our afternoon game.

B. Circle the irregular past participle in parentheses ( ). Then write it on the line to complete the sentence.

1. By May I had _____ about an amazing automobile. (hear, heard)

2. Test drivers have _____ it on experimental runs. (taken, took)

3. My friend's family has _____ to Utah to see it. (went, gone)

4. My friend has _____ in the automobile, too. (ridden, rode)

5. I have _____ this car as a research topic. (chose, chosen)

6. My mom has _____ photos of the car, too. (bought, buy)

7. I have also _____ home articles and books about the car. (bring, brought)

Irregular Verbs

A. Complete each sentence. Fill in the bubble next to the irregular past-tense verb.

1. Last week, we _____ the news about our baseball team's victory.
   - ⓐ hear
   - ⓑ heard
   - ⓒ hears

2. Yesterday morning, Mom and I _____ the bus downtown.
   - ⓐ rode
   - ⓑ rides
   - ⓒ ride

3. Then we _____ in line for an hour.
   - ⓐ stand
   - ⓑ stands
   - ⓒ stood

4. We finally _____ four tickets to the first game in the playoffs.
   - ⓐ bought
   - ⓑ buys
   - ⓒ buying

5. Then we _____ lunch to celebrate.
   - ⓐ eat
   - ⓑ ate
   - ⓒ eats

B. Complete each sentence. Fill in the bubble next to the correct helping verb and past participle.

1. That old adobe house _____ on top of the mesa for a century.
   - ⓐ has stood
   - ⓑ has stand
   - ⓒ has stands

2. We _____ up there many times.
   - ⓐ have rode
   - ⓑ have ride
   - ⓒ have ridden

3. Our great-grandfather _____ pictures of the house long ago.
   - ⓐ had drawn
   - ⓑ had draw
   - ⓒ had drew

4. We _____ the sketches for many years.
   - ⓐ have keep
   - ⓑ have kept
   - ⓒ have keeps

5. Fortunately, my family _____ very good care of the drawings.
   - ⓐ has took
   - ⓑ has take
   - ⓒ has taken

Adjectives

A. In the following sentences, circle the adjectives that tell what kind. Underline the adjectives that tell how many.

> **RETEACHING:** An **adjective** is a word that tells more about a person, place, or thing.

1. We watched many colorful creatures swim through the dark water.

2. A few tilefish were building small burrows.

3. Suddenly one strange and unusual fish swam by us.

4. Eugenie swam over to the mysterious fish.

5. It looked like a jawfish with a big head and four dark patches on its back.

6. Was this rare fish a new species?

7. We put the tiny fish in a large bucket of cold seawater.

8. Eugenie has made several amazing discoveries.

B. Complete each sentence with an adjective that tells what kind or how many.

1. The _____ fish was named after David.

2. The fish had a _____ head.

3. The fish lived in a _____ burrow at the bottom of the ocean.

4. The tiny fish turned out to be a _____ species.

5. David took _____ photographs that appeared in magazines.

C. Write two sentences. Use adjectives that tell what kind and how many in each sentence.

1. _____

2. _____

Adjectives

A. Write an adjective to complete each sentence.

> **RETEACHING:** An **adjective** is a word that tells more about a person, place, or thing.

1. The _____ dog ate most of the cat's food.

2. The _____ cat found a nearly empty bowl.

3. The cat ate what remained of her _____ meal.

4. The cat pushed the _____ dish over to where a _____ girl was sitting.

5. The girl refilled the dish with _____ food.

B. Read each sentence. Circle the adjective that describes each underlined noun.

1. The gray <u>cat</u> saw the shaggy <u>dog</u> sitting in the dark <u>corner</u>.

2. The cat saw some <u>cat food</u> on the dog's droopy <u>mouth</u>.

3. The cat slipped out of the little <u>kitchen</u> and went into the quiet <u>backyard</u>.

4. She started digging in the soft <u>dirt</u> under a shady <u>tree</u>.

5. The dog looked out the enormous <u>window</u> and saw the cat with a large <u>bone</u>.

C. Write two sentences that tell what happened next. Use vivid adjectives in your writing.

1. _____

_____

2. _____

_____

Adjectives

Add an adjective to each line to describe the noun.
Use the example on the right as a guide.

1. winter

_____, winter

_____, _____, winter

_____, _____, _____, winter

mud
brown mud
gooey, brown mud
wet, gooey, brown mud

2. lemon

_____, lemon

_____, _____, lemon

_____, _____, _____, lemon

3. worm

_____, worm

_____, _____, worm

_____, _____, _____, worm

4. tree

_____, tree

_____, _____, tree

_____, _____, _____, tree

Adjectives

Fill in the bubble next to the word in each sentence that is an adjective.

1. I had an important decision to make this morning.

   - (a) important
   - (b) decision
   - (c) morning

2. I wanted to buy an appropriate pet for my sister.

   - (a) wanted
   - (b) buy
   - (c) appropriate

3. First, I looked at a striped lizard.

   - (a) First
   - (b) striped
   - (c) lizard

4. Then, I considered getting two hamsters.

   - (a) considered
   - (b) two
   - (c) hamsters

5. The white hamster was named George.

   - (a) white
   - (b) hamster
   - (c) George

6. I admired the noisy parrot.

   - (a) I
   - (b) noisy
   - (c) parrot

7. I watched a gigantic turtle on a rock.

   - (a) gigantic
   - (b) turtle
   - (c) rock

8. Several gerbils ran on a wheel.

   - (a) Several
   - (b) gerbils
   - (c) wheel

9. I finally decided to get a saltwater aquarium.

   - (a) decided
   - (b) saltwater
   - (c) aquarium

10. I'm sure my family will enjoy the colorful fish.

    - (a) sure
    - (b) family
    - (c) colorful

Adjectives That Compare

**A. In each sentence, underline the adjective
that compares.**

1. Anna is older than her brother Caleb.

2. That was the loudest thunderstorm of the entire summer.

3. Seal is the biggest cat that I have ever seen.

4. Papa is quieter than Sarah.

5. The roof of the barn is higher than the top of the haystack.

6. The kitten's fur was softer than lamb's wool.

7. Sarah pointed to the brightest star in the sky.

8. What is the saddest moment in the story?

**B. Underline the adjective in parentheses ( ) that completes each
sentence correctly. On the line write *two* or *more than two* to show
how many things are being compared.**

1. On the (hotter, hottest) day in July, we went swimming. _____

2. Today is (warmer, warmest) than last Tuesday. _____

3. Is winter (colder, coldest) on the prairie or by the sea? _____

4. This is the (taller, tallest) tree in the entire state. _____

5. Sarah's hair is (longer, longest) than Maggie's. _____

6. Of the three dogs, Nick was the (friendlier, friendliest). _____

7. Caleb's horse is (younger, youngest) than Anna's pony. _____

8. The new foal is the (livelier, liveliest) animal on the farm. _____

Adjectives That Compare

Choose the adjective that completes each sentence and write it on the line.

> **RETEACHING: Comparative adjectives** compare two things by adding -er to the adjective or by using the word *more*. **Superlative adjectives** compare three or more things by adding -est or by using the word *most.*

funnier   funniest

1. The _____ book I've ever read is about a family of mice.

2. The book is much _____ than the movie.

busier   busiest

3. The book department is _____ than the shoe department.

4. The _____ bookstore in the city is on King Street.

more exciting   most exciting

5. Hiking in the woods is _____ than watching TV.

6. This is the _____ ride at the amusement park.

more challenging   most challenging

7. Is a game of checkers _____ than a game of chess?

8. I think that soccer is the _____ of all the field games.

more tiring   most tiring

9. We found that swimming was _____ than walking.

10. Of all the afternoon's activities, tennis was the _____.

more delicious   most delicious

11. The strawberries are _____ than the green grapes.

12. This is the _____ apple that I have ever eaten.

Adjectives That Compare

Fill in the bubble next to the correct comparative or superlative adjective.

1. I believe that a dog is much _____ than a cat.

   ⓐ friendlier

   ⓑ friendliest

2. My poodle is the _____ dog of all the dogs in the dog-training class.

   ⓐ more intelligent

   ⓑ most intelligent

3. The gazelle is the _____ animal in the animal park.

   ⓐ more graceful

   ⓑ most graceful

4. The movie about turtles is _____ than the book about frogs.

   ⓐ more fascinating

   ⓑ most fascinating

5. The diamondback rattler is _____ than a bull snake.

   ⓐ more dangerous

   ⓑ most dangerous

6. I think that the jaguar is the _____ of all the big cats.

   ⓐ more beautiful

   ⓑ most beautiful

7. Did you know that a cheetah is _____ than a lion?

   ⓐ swifter

   ⓑ swiftest

8. Your parrot is _____ than my cockatoo.

   ⓐ noisier

   ⓑ noisiest

9. This chimpanzee is _____ than that gorilla.

   ⓐ more playful

   ⓑ most playful

10. That polar bear is the _____ mammal I've ever seen.

    ⓐ larger

    ⓑ largest

Prepositions

A. Read each sentence. Underline each group of words that begins with a preposition, and circle the preposition. Some sentences have more than one prepositional phrase.

> **RETEACHING: Prepositions** show the relationship between a noun or pronoun and another word or group of words in a sentence such as *in, on, of, for,* or *at.* Groups of words introduced by a preposition are called **prepositional phrases.**

1. The boy cut out pictures of mountains, rivers, and lakes.
2. He enjoyed pasting them on the walls of his room.
3. His father responded to the scenes in the pictures.
4. He decided that he would take his son on a camping trip.
5. They carried supplies in a backpack and knapsack.
6. The boy drank a hot drink from his father's mug.
7. That afternoon they hiked in the mountains for hours.
8. They were disappointed when they found many campers at the Lost Lake.
9. The boy and his father continued on their journey.
10. Finally, they stopped at a quiet place for the night.
11. The boy and his father ate and slept in a tent.
12. The tent kept them safe from the wind and rain.
13. Will this trip make the boy feel closer to his father?
14. What else will they see on their camping trip?

B. Complete each sentence with a prepositional phrase.

1. Let's go to the store _____
2. I just received a letter _____
3. Eduardo found his missing sneaker _____
4. Tanya always plays soccer _____

© Scholastic Inc.

Prepositions

A. Circle the preposition in each sentence.

1. Herb often goes hiking in the Rocky Mountains.

2. He always carries a water jug and a compass with him.

3. Today he saw wild columbines growing on the mountainsides.

4. Then he passed a doe and her fawn searching for food.

5. The deer stood very still and stared at him.

6. Then the two creatures disappeared into the woods.

B. Complete each sentence with a prepositional phrase. You may wish to use some of the prepositions from part A or the prepositions *from, over, under, to,* or *by*.

1. Each summer Suzanne goes camping _____

2. Usually they camp _____

3. They pitch their small, green tent _____

4. Her mother cooks _____

5. Suzanne sometimes hears ravens cawing _____

6. Once she saw a black bear running very quickly _____

C. Use the prepositions *of, with,* and *at* in three sentences of your own.

1. _____

2. _____

3. _____

Prepositions

Fill in the bubble next to the word from the sentence that is a preposition.

1. Last summer the Camachos took a trip to three national parks.
   - (a) to
   - (b) trip
   - (c) Last

2. The family was from San Antonio, Texas.
   - (a) family
   - (b) was
   - (c) from

3. The family left their home on a Saturday morning.
   - (a) family
   - (b) on
   - (c) left

4. First they headed for Carlsbad Caverns, New Mexico.
   - (a) for
   - (b) First
   - (c) Caverns

5. Rita saw bats fly over her head.
   - (a) saw
   - (b) bats
   - (c) over

6. Next the family visited cliff dwellings left by the Anasazi people.
   - (a) Next
   - (b) cliff
   - (c) by

7. Then they camped at Arches National Park.
   - (a) at
   - (b) they
   - (c) Then

8. Edwin sat under a sandstone formation called Delicate Arch.
   - (a) sat
   - (b) under
   - (c) called

9. Rita and Edwin took photographs of their favorite sites.
   - (a) took
   - (b) their
   - (c) of

10. They talked with their friends the next week.
    - (a) talked
    - (b) with
    - (c) their

Subject-Verb Agreement

A. Underline the subject once and the verb twice. Write *present* if the verb is in the present tense and *past* if the verb is in the past tense.

1. Tucker lives in a drain pipe. _____

2. It opens into a pocket. _____

3. Tucker collected stuffing for the pocket. _____

4. The mouse filled the pocket with paper and cloth. _____

5. Tucker sits at the opening of the drain pipe. _____

6. He watches the people in the subway station. _____

7. The young boy worked at his father's newsstand. _____

8. They sell papers there on weekdays. _____

B. Underline the subject once and the verb twice. Then write *singular* if the subject and verb are singular and *plural* if the subject and verb are plural.

1. The nighttime crowd passes by quickly. _____

2. Trains run less often at that time. _____

3. Papa waits for business. _____

4. The station feels quiet and lonely. _____

5. People rush home at the end of the day. _____

6. Mama and Papa make very little money. _____

Subject-Verb Agreement

A. Underline the subject. Then circle the verb in parentheses ( ) that agrees with the subject.

1. Crickets _____ a musical sound. (make, makes)

2. Actually, only the males _____ sounds. (produce, produces)

3. I _____ for the sound of crickets on a summer night. (listen, listens)

4. You _____ them in places outside the city. (hear, hears)

5. Mario _____ a cricket in the subway station. (find, finds)

6. His mother _____ the cricket a "bug." (call, calls)

B. Underline the subject and verb in each sentence. Then rewrite each sentence in the present tense. Be sure your subjects and verbs agree.

1. Mario wanted the cricket for a pet.

   _____

2. He wished for a pet of his own.

   _____

3. Crickets seemed like unusual pets to his mother.

   _____

4. Maybe insects scared her!

   _____

Subject-Verb Agreement

A. Fill in the bubble next to the verb that agrees with the subject of the sentence.

1. Chester _____ tall buildings for the first time.
   - ⓐ see
   - ⓑ sees

2. The city _____ him.
   - ⓐ surprise
   - ⓑ surprises

3. The stars _____ Chester's attention.
   - ⓐ catch
   - ⓑ catches

4. Maybe he _____ for his home in Connecticut.
   - ⓐ wish
   - ⓑ wishes

5. One star _____ familiar to Chester.
   - ⓐ is
   - ⓑ are

B. Is the underlined verb correct? Fill in the bubble next to the right answer.

1. Now the animals <u>crouch</u> against the cement.
   - ⓐ crouches
   - ⓑ crouched
   - ⓒ correct as is

2. At this moment, their eyes <u>is</u> on the sky.
   - ⓐ are
   - ⓑ were
   - ⓒ correct as is

3. The sky <u>looks</u> so beautiful right now.
   - ⓐ look
   - ⓑ looked
   - ⓒ correct as is

4. Last night the cricket <u>view</u> Times Square for the first time.
   - ⓐ views
   - ⓑ viewed
   - ⓒ correct as is

5. One week ago, Chester <u>experiences</u> a much different world.
   - ⓐ experience
   - ⓑ experienced
   - ⓒ correct as is

Punctuating Dialogue

A. Underline the exact words of the speaker. Circle the quotation marks.

> **RETEACHING: Quotation marks** show the beginning and end of a speaker's exact words. When the speaker comes first, place a comma between it and the beginning quotation mark. When a quotation comes first, use a comma, question mark, or exclamation point before the end quotation mark. Use a period at the end of the sentence.

1. Eva exclaimed, "I really like tall tales!"

2. "Davy Crockett is my favorite character," said Juan.

3. I asked, "Who likes Sally Ann Thunder Ann Whirlwind?"

B. Add the missing quotation marks to each sentence.

1. __I am a big fan of hers,__ replied Shavon.

2. I added, __Sally can even sing a wolf to sleep.__

3. __How did Sally tame King Bear?__ asked our teacher.

4. __Sally really ought to be in the movies,__ said Don.

C. Write the missing punctuation marks in each sentence.

1. __What kind of person is Sally __ __ asked Davy Crockett__

2. The schoolmarm replied__ __Sally is a special friend__ __

3. __She can laugh the bark off a pine tree__ __ added Lucy__

4. The preacher said__ __She can dance a rock to pieces__ __

5. __I'm very impressed__ __ exclaimed Davy__

D. Write two sentences of dialogue between Davy Crockett and Sally.

1. _____

2. _____

© Scholastic Inc.

Punctuating Dialogue

A. Add the missing commas to the sentences.

1. "Well__ we are having a canned-food drive next week."

2. "Oh__ Ed__ can you bring some containers to school?"

3. "Yes__ I have several at home, Jody."

4. "Thank you__ Mr. Poole, for all your suggestions."

B. Add the missing quotation marks and/or commas to each sentence.

1. __Kim, your posters for the talent contest are terrific!__ I exclaimed.

2. She replied, __Thank you, Doug, for your kind words.__

3. Our teacher asked, __Meg__ will you play your guitar or sing?__

4. "Oh__ I plan to do both,__ said Meg.

5. __Will you perform your juggling act this year Roberto?__ Jay asked.

6. __No__ I want to do a comedy routine,__ he replied.

C. Add the missing punctuation to each sentence.

1. __Kit__ which act did you like best__ __ asked Mina__

2. He replied__ __Oh__ I enjoyed the singing pumpkins and the tap dancing elephants__ __

3. __Well__ I liked the guitar player__ __ said Mina__

D. Write two more sentences of dialogue about a school talent show.

1. _____

2. _____

Punctuating Dialogue

Read what each child says. Then rewrite the dialogue for each set of speech balloons. Use correct punctuation and capitalization for writing quotations.

© Scholastic Inc.

Punctuating Dialogue

**Decide if there is an error in the underlined part of each sentence.
Fill in the bubble next to the correct answer.**

1. "Rosa, tell me one of your <u>favorite
   jokes</u>" said Ken.

   (a) favorite jokes."
   (b) favorite jokes,"
   (c) correct as is

2. "What do <u>sharks eat?</u> she asked.

   (a) sharks eat?"
   (b) sharks eat"
   (c) correct as is

3. <u>Ken replied "tell</u> me. I don't know.

   (a) Ken replied. "Tell
   (b) Ken replied, "Tell
   (c) correct as is

4. "They eat peanut butter and jellyfish
   <u>sandwiches," replied</u> Rosa.

   (a) sandwiches" replied
   (b) sandwiches." replied
   (c) correct as is

5. <u>Oh, that</u> was funny!" exclaimed
   Ken.

   (a) "Oh, that
   (b) Oh that
   (c) correct as is

6. <u>"Rosa? tell</u> me another one," he
   said.

   (a) "Rosa tell
   (b) "Rosa, tell
   (c) correct as is

7. "What years do frogs <u>like best</u>
   asked Rosa smugly.

   (a) like best?"
   (b) like best,"
   (c) correct as is

8. "Frogs like Hoppy New <u>Years,"
   laughed</u> Ken.

   (a) Years" laughed
   (b) Years, laughed
   (c) correct as is

9. <u>"No frogs</u> like leap years," insisted
   Rosa.

   (a) "No, frogs
   (b) No frogs
   (c) correct as is

10. "Ken said. <u>"my</u> joke is funnier."

    (a) said "My
    (b) said, "My
    (c) correct as is

Adverbs

A. Underline the verb. Then circle the adverb that tells when.

1. Later, newsboys shouted the weekend forecast.

2. Yesterday, a huge snowstorm hit New York City.

3. It got very cold soon.

4. A train tried to plow through the snow earlier.

5. Then the train went off the track.

B. Underline the verb. Then circle the adverb that tells where.

1. Snow fell everywhere.

2. Drifts of snow piled up.

3. People were trapped inside.

4. Some people tunneled out from their homes.

5. People there traveled by sled.

C. Underline the adverb in each sentence. Write *when* if the adverb tells when or *where* if it tells where.

1. People had never seen a storm so bad.   _____

2. Pipes burst underground.   _____

3. The water inside had frozen.   _____

4. Soon people started to freeze, too.   _____

© Scholastic Inc.

Adverbs

A. Underline the verb once. Then circle the adverb that describes the verb and tells how.

1. Grandma talked happily to the frolicking sea lions.

2. The sea birds squawked sharply as they dived.

3. Andy greeted the girl and Grandma warmly.

4. He guided them expertly through the Galápagos Islands.

5. Grandma wrote about the islands regularly in her diary.

6. The girl recorded the trip faithfully in her diary.

7. She responded personally to everything she saw.

8. Andy and the girl looked eagerly at the creatures on the shore.

9. Grandma and the girl jumped quickly off the boat.

10. They snorkeled easily with their breathing tubes and fins.

11. The girl saw sea creatures clearly through her face mask.

12. She gazed intently at the yellow-tailed surgeonfish.

13. Swiftly the sea lions surrounded Grandma and the girl.

14. The sea lion pups chased and nipped one another playfully.

B. Complete each sentence with an action verb and an adverb that describes it and tells how.

1. The big male sea lion _____

2. The girl and her grandmother _____

© Scholastic Inc.

Adverbs

A. Fill in the bubble next to the adverb that tells how.

1. Carolina and Gabriella dove rapidly under a big wave.

    ⓐ rapidly
    ⓑ under
    ⓒ big

2. Then a wave crashed loudly against the shore.

    ⓐ crashed
    ⓑ loudly
    ⓒ against

3. Both Carolina and Gabriella were very strong swimmers.

    ⓐ Both
    ⓑ very
    ⓒ strong

4. At the beach, the tide was somewhat low.

    ⓐ At
    ⓑ low
    ⓒ somewhat

5. Carolina quickly spotted a group of bottle-nose dolphins.

    ⓐ quickly
    ⓑ spotted
    ⓒ bottle-nose

B. Fill in the bubble next to the word that is <u>not</u> an adverb.

1. Gabriella and Carolina swam very slowly toward the playful mammals.

    ⓐ very
    ⓑ slowly
    ⓒ playful

2. "They are so curious!" Carolina exclaimed excitedly.

    ⓐ so
    ⓑ curious
    ⓒ excitedly

3. One baby dolphin came very close.

    ⓐ One
    ⓑ very
    ⓒ close

4. The mother dolphin nudged Carolina so gently.

    ⓐ nudged
    ⓑ so
    ⓒ gently

5. Then swiftly and mysteriously, the dolphins disappeared.

    ⓐ swiftly
    ⓑ disappeared
    ⓒ mysteriously

Sassy Sentences

A **sentence** is a group of words that expresses a complete thought. When you write a sentence, you put your thoughts into words. If the sentence is complete, the meaning is clear. It contains a subject (the naming part) and a predicate (an action or state of being part).

These are sentences.
Sally sells seashells at the seashore.
Betty Botter bought a bit of better butter.

These are not sentences.
Peck of pickled peppers.
Flying up a flue.

Make complete sentences by adding words to each group of words. Try to create tongue twisters like the sentences above.

1. _____ flips fine flapjacks.

2. Sixty slippery seals _____.

3. _____ fed Ted _____.

4. Ruby Rugby's baby brother _____.

5. _____ managing an imaginary magazine.

6. Sam's sandwich shop _____.

7. _____ back blue balloons.

8. _____ pink peacock pompously _____.

9. Pete's pop Pete _____.

10. _____ sawed Mr. Saw's _____.

11. A flea and a fly _____.

12. _____ black-backed bumblebee.

💡 **Create your own tongue twisters to share with friends. Make sure each one expresses a complete thought.**

Link It Together

A sentence needs two parts, a subject and a predicate, to express a complete thought.
The **subject part** tells whom or what the sentence is about.
The **predicate part** tells what the subject is or does.

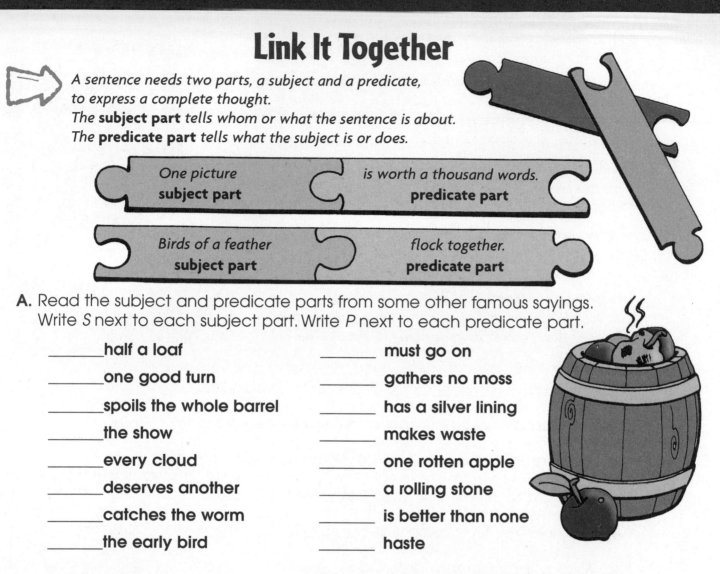

| One picture **subject part** | is worth a thousand words. **predicate part** |
| Birds of a feather **subject part** | flock together. **predicate part** |

A. Read the subject and predicate parts from some other famous sayings.
Write *S* next to each subject part. Write *P* next to each predicate part.

_____half a loaf

_____one good turn

_____spoils the whole barrel

_____the show

_____every cloud

_____deserves another

_____catches the worm

_____the early bird

_____ must go on

_____ gathers no moss

_____ has a silver lining

_____ makes waste

_____ one rotten apple

_____ a rolling stone

_____ is better than none

_____ haste

B. Now combine the subject and predicate parts to create these famous sayings.

1. _____

2. _____

3. _____

4. _____

5. _____

6. _____

7. _____

8. _____

Make up some sayings of your own. Then circle the subject part and underline the predicate part of each sentence.

That's Groovy!

There are four kinds of sentences. Each one does something different.

A **declarative sentence** *tells something.*
It is a **statement** *and ends with a period.*
My grandparents grew up during the 1960s.

An **interrogative sentence** *asks something.*
It is a **question** *and ends with a question mark.*
Do you know who the hippies were?

An **imperative sentence** *tells someone to do something.*
It is a **command** *and ends with a period.*
Check out this photo of my grandmother.

An **exclamatory sentence** *shows strong feeling.*
It is an **exclamation** *and ends with an exclamation mark.*
Now that's one strange-looking outfit she has on!

Read the following sentences. Identify what kind of sentence each one is. Write *S* for statement, *Q* for question, *C* for command, and *E* for exclamation.

_____ **1.** Grandma says there was a fashion revolution in the 1960s.

_____ **2.** What an amazing time it must have been!

_____ **3.** Here's a photo of my grandfather in his teens.

_____ **4.** How do you like those sideburns and the long hair?

_____ **5.** Take a look at what he's wearing.

_____ **6.** I don't believe those bellbottoms and sandals!

_____ **7.** Please tell me he's not wearing beads.

_____ **8.** I'm glad these fashions are no longer in style!

_____ **9.** Have you ever seen anything so funny?

_____ **10.** Try not to laugh too hard.

_____ **11.** One day our grandchildren may laugh at us.

_____ **12.** What's so funny about what we're wearing?

Now, look at other "photos" from the sixties and write a statement (S), a question (Q), a command (C), and an exclamation (E) about each one. Make sure to begin and end your sentences correctly.

S _____

Q _____

C _____

E _____

S _____

Q _____

C _____

E _____

S _____

Q _____

C _____

E _____

Invite someone to listen as you expressively read aloud the sentences that you wrote, showing what kind of sentences they are by the way that you read them.

A Whale of a Fish

When you write, the words and phrases in your sentences must be in an order that makes sense. Compare the sentences in each pair. Which ones make more sense?

An enormous fish what the whale shark is!
What an enormous fish the whale shark is!

The largest fish in the world the whale shark is.
The whale shark is the largest fish in the world.

Use each group of words to write a sentence that makes sense.

1. of 60 feet?   that the whale shark   Did you know   to a length   can grow

_____

2. two school buses   end to end!   That's about   parked   as long as

_____

3. are not a threat   These huge creatures   like some other sharks are.   to humans

_____

4. to look for   float near the surface   plankton and tiny fish.   Whale sharks

_____

5. it must be   alongside a whale shark.   Imagine   to swim   how amazing

_____

Now rewrite the following sentences so that the words and phrases are in an order that makes better sense.

6. An estimated 27,000 known species of fish there are in the world.

_____

7. Of all these species one of the smallest is the dwarf pygmy goby?

_____

8. When it is fully grown is less than a half-inch long this species of goby!

_____

9. In the seas and rivers of Asia makes its home this tiny fish.

_____

Number Sentences

Words such as who, what, where, why, when, *and* how, *and helping verbs such as* is, are, was, were, do, did, *and* can *at the beginning of sentences, signal interrogative sentences, or questions.*

What *is an odd number?*
Do *you know what an even number is?*
Is *2 an odd number or an even number?*

Change each statement below into a question. Remember to begin and end each sentence correctly.

1. Numbers that cannot be divided evenly by 2 are called odd numbers.

_____

2. All even numbers can be divided evenly by 2.

_____

3. Zero is considered an even number.

_____

4. Numbers that have 0, 2, 4, 6, or 8 in the ones place are even numbers.

_____

5. Odd numbers end in 1, 3, 5, 7, or 9.

_____

6. The number 317,592 is an even number because it ends in 2.

_____

7. The sum is always an even number when you add two even numbers.

_____

8. The sum of two odd numbers is also an even number.

_____

9. The same rule applies if you subtract an odd number from an odd number.

_____

10. You can figure out all the rules for working with odd and even numbers.

_____

© Scholastic Inc.

Proofing Pays

Capitalization and end punctuation help show where one sentence ends and the next one begins. Whenever you write, proofread to make sure each sentence begins with a capital letter and ends correctly. Here's an example of how to mark the letters that should be capitalized.

have you ever heard of a Goliath birdeater? it is
the world's largest spider. this giant tarantula can grow
to 11 inches in length and weigh about 6 ounces. now that's
a big spider! although it is called a birdeater, it usually
eats small reptiles and insects. these spiders are
mostly found in rain forests .

Read the passage below. It is about another amazing animal, but it is not so easy to read because the writer forgot to add end punctuation and to use capital letters at the beginning of sentences. Proofread the passage. Mark the letters that should be capitals with the capital letter symbol. Put the correct punctuation marks at the ends of sentences. Then reread the passage.

think about the fastest car you've ever seen in the Indianapolis 500 race

that's about how fast a peregrine falcon dives it actually reaches speeds over

200 miles an hour how incredibly fast they are peregrine falcons are also very

powerful birds did you know that they can catch and kill their prey in the air

using their sharp claws what's really amazing is that peregrine falcons live in

both the country and in the city keep on the lookout if you're ever in New York

City believe it or not, it is home to several falcons

What do you know about the bee hummingbird, atlas moth, or capybara? Choose one, do some research, and write several sentences about it on a piece of paper. Then proofread your writing. Does every sentence begin and end correctly? Are all the words spelled correctly?

Spout Some Specifics

To be a good writer, it is important to know what you are writing about, to be specific, and to include details. All this helps to create a picture for your readers and will make your writing more interesting and informative. Compare the two phrases below. Which one is more specific, interesting, and informative? Which one creates a more vivid picture?

a vehicle   or   *an old, rusty, dilapidated pick-up truck with flat tires and a shattered windshield*

For each general word or phrase, write a more specific word. Then add details to describe each specific word.

	Specific Word	Details
1. a body of water		
2. a piece of furniture		
3. an article of clothing		
4. a child's toy		
5. a noise or sound		
6. a tool		
7. a group of people		
8. a reptile		
9. garden plants		
10. a kind of fruit		
11. a kind of vegetable		
12. a drink		
13. footwear		
14. musical instrument		
15. a holiday		

Look at yourself in the mirror. Then write on a piece of paper as many words and phrases as you can to describe yourself so that someone who does not know you would get a clear, vivid picture of what you look like.

Make It Interesting

A sentence can be very simple. This sentence tells who did what.
The crew worked.

As you write and revise your writing, add details about people, places, or things, or about where, when, and what happens. This will make your writing more interesting. Here's how the sentence above was revised several times. Each sentence gives a little more information.

The construction crew worked.
The construction crew worked quickly.
The construction crew worked quickly to clear the rubble.
The construction crew worked quickly to clear the rubble at the building site.
The construction crew worked quickly yesterday to clear the rubble at the building site.

Rewrite each sentence four times. Add new details each time to tell more about whom or what, how, where, and when.

The children played.

1. _____

_____

2. _____

_____

3. _____

_____

4. _____

_____

A package arrived.

1. _____

_____

2. _____

_____

3. _____

_____

4. _____

_____

Rewrite the following sentence several times on a piece of paper. Remove a detail each time until you are left with a very simple sentence.

The excited team cheered wildly after winning the championship basketball game.

© Scholastic Inc.

Order the Combination

Have you ever noticed how short sentences can make your writing sound choppy? When two sentences have different subjects and the same predicate, you can use the conjunction and to combine them into one sentence with a compound subject.

My friends ordered a pepperoni pizza. I ordered a pepperoni pizza.
My friends and I ordered a pepperoni pizza.

When two sentences have the same subject and different predicates, you can use and to combine them into one sentence with a compound predicate.

My mom ordered. She had pasta instead.
My mom ordered and had pasta instead.

When two sentences have the same subject and predicate and different objects, you can combine them into one sentence with a compound object using and.

My dad wanted anchovies on his pizza. He also wanted onions.
My dad wanted anchovies and onions on his pizza.

Fill in the missing subject, object, or predicate in each set of shorter sentences. Then combine the sentences by making compound subjects, objects, or predicates using and.

1. _____ are sweet and juicy.

   _____ are sweet and juicy.

   _____

2. I _____ about the history of basketball for homework.

   I _____ about the history of basketball for homework.

   _____

3. _____ is so much fun!

   _____ is also so much fun! (Change is to are.)

   _____

4. I like _____ more than broccoli or cauliflower.

   I like _____ more than broccoli or cauliflower.

   _____

5. I'd like to have _____ for breakfast.

   I'd also like to have _____ for breakfast.

   _____

A New Challenge

When you write, you may want to show how the ideas in two simple sentences are related. You can combine the two sentences by using a comma and the conjunctions and, but, *or* or *to show the connection.* And *shows a link between the ideas,* but *shows a contrast, and* or *shows a choice. The new sentence is called a* **compound sentence***.*

> **My sister wants to join a football team. My parents aren't so happy about it.**
> **My sister wants to join a football team,** but **my parents aren't so happy about it.**
>
> **Annie is determined. Her friends think she'd make a great place kicker.**
> **Annie is determined,** and **her friends think she'd make a great place kicker.**
>
> **Should Annie play football? Should she try something else?**
> **Should Annie play football,** or **should she try something else?**

Combine each pair of sentences. Use *and, but,* or *or* to show the connection between the ideas and make a compound sentence.

1. My sister Annie has always participated in sports. Many say she's a natural athlete.

_____

_____

2. Soccer, basketball, and softball are fun. She wanted a new challenge.

_____

_____

3. My sister talked to my brother and me. We were honest with her.

_____

_____

4. I told Annie to go for it. My brother told her to stick with soccer or basketball.

_____

_____

5. Will Dad convince her to try skiing? Will he suggest ice skating?

_____

_____

 Continue the story about Annie's choice on another piece of paper. Include some compound sentences to tell what happens. Make sure your sentences begin and end correctly. Remember to check for spelling errors.

© Scholastic Inc.

Hot Subjects

If two sentences share the same subject, information about the subject can be written as a phrase after the subject in the new sentence. Be sure to use commas to set apart the phrase from the rest of the sentence.

Sentence 1: **The Gateway Arch is America's tallest human-made monument.**

Sentence 2: **The monument rises 630 feet above the ground.**

Combined: **The Gateway Arch, America's tallest human-made monument, rises 630 feet above the ground.**

Read the sentences. Combine the ideas in each pair into one sentence by including information in a phrase after the subject in the sentence.

1. The Caspian Sea is the world's largest lake.
The lake covers an area about the same size as Montana.

_____

2. The Komodo dragon is a member of the monitor family.
It can grow to a length of 10 feet.

_____

3. Our closest star is the sun.
It is estimated to be more than 27,000,000°F.

_____

4. Ronald W. Reagan was our nation's 40th president.
He worked as a Hollywood actor for almost 30 years.

_____

5. Georgia is the state that grows the most peanuts.
It harvests over 2 billion pounds each year.

_____

6. Jackie Robinson was the first African American to play in the major leagues.
He played for the Brooklyn Dodgers.

_____

Sentence Building

When you write about something, try to include interesting details. Sometimes you can take the important details from several related sentences and add them to the main sentence.

Kyle and Jim had a great plan.
They're my brothers.
The plan was for a tree house.

Now here's a sentence that combines all the important details.
My brothers Kyle and Jim had a great plan for a tree house.

Read each group of sentences. Take the important details from the two related sentences and add them to the main sentence to make one sentence.

1. My brothers built a tree house. They built it in the old oak tree. It's in our backyard.

_____

2. Jim made a ladder for the tree house. He made it out of rope. It is sturdy.

_____

3. Kyle bought paint. The paint was brown. He bought a gallon.

_____

4. Kyle and Jim finished painting. They painted the walls. It took an hour.

_____

5. Jim painted a sign. He painted "no trespassing." The sign is on the tree house door.

_____

6. A squirrel leaped into their tree house. It leaped from a branch. It was curious.

_____

7. The visitor startled my brothers. It was unexpected. My brothers were unsuspecting.

_____

8. The squirrel leaped out of the tree house. It was frightened. It was in a big hurry.

_____

© Scholastic Inc.

Write three short sentences on a piece of paper about a funny experience. Then try to combine them into one sentence. Which sounds better, one sentence with lots of details or two or three shorter sentences each with one detail? Why?

Applause for the Clause

Sometimes you can use words such as when, because, while, *and* before *to combine two sentences with related ideas into one sentence with a main clause and a dependent clause. A* **clause** *is a group of words with a subject and a predicate. A* **dependent clause** *cannot stand alone. An* **independent clause** *can stand alone.*

Lee woke up late today. He realized he hadn't set the alarm last night.
<u>**When Lee woke up late today,** **he realized he hadn't set his alarm last night.**</u>

↑   ↑

This is a dependent clause.   *This is an independent clause.*

When the dependent clause comes before the main clause as in the above sentence, add a comma after the dependent clause. If the dependent clause follows the main clause, you do not need a comma. Here's an example.

Lee was upset. He was going to be late for school.
Lee was upset because **he was going to be late for school.**

Use the word inside the parentheses to combine each pair of sentences into one.

1. I waited for my parents to get home. I watched a movie. (while)

_____

2. My brother was in his room. He had homework to do. (because)

_____

3. The movie was over. The power went out. (before)

_____

4. This happens all the time. I wasn't concerned. (since)

_____

5. I didn't mind the dark at first. I heard a scratching sound. (until)

_____

6. I found my flashlight. I started to look around. (when)

_____

7. I was checking the living room. I caught Alex trying to hide. (when)

_____

Triple the Fun

When you write, you may want to list three or more items or ideas in a series in a single sentence. Be sure to use a comma after each item in a series except after the last item.

Max dressed quickly, ate breakfast, and raced out the door.
Luis, Jamie, Leroy, and Sam met Max at the baseball field.
They were hopeful, excited, and nervous about their first game.

Answer each question below in a complete sentence. Use commas where they are needed. Make sure each sentence begins and ends correctly. Remember to check your spelling.

1. What are the titles of three books you've read recently or would like to read? Remember to underline the title of each book.

_____

2. What are four of the planets in our solar system closer to the sun than Neptune?

_____

3. What are three green, leafy vegetables?

_____

4. What countries would you like to visit? Include at least three in your answer.

_____

5. What months fall between January and July?

_____

6. What three things have you done today to help out at home?

_____

7. What states or bodies of water border your state?

_____

8. What activities do you and your friends enjoy in the summer?

_____

9. Who are some of the most important people in your life?

_____

Make up some questions like the ones above and challenge someone you know to answer them on a piece of paper. Correct the sentences.

Comma Capers

You know that you must use commas in a series of three or more items.
Max, Sam, and Alex ordered burgers, fries, and milkshakes for lunch.

Here are some additional rules you need to know about commas.
Use commas

— *to set off the name of the person or group you are addressing.*
Here's your order, boys.

— *after words like* yes, no, *and* well.
Well, what do you want to do now?

— *before a conjunction that joins two sentences.*
The boys finished lunch, and then they went to a movie.

Read the sentences below. Decide which ones need commas and which ones do not.
Use this symbol ⋏ to show where commas belong.

1. I'd like a bike a pair of in-line skates and a snowboard for my birthday.
2. Well my friend you can't always have what you want when you want it.
3. No but I can always hope!
4. My friends and I skate all year long and snowboard during the winter.
5. I used to like skateboarding but now I prefer snowboarding and in-line skating.
6. What sports games or hobbies do you enjoy most Jody?
7. I learned to ski last year and now I'm taking ice-skating lessons.
8. Skiing ice skating and skateboarding are all fun things to do.

Review the four rules above for using commas. Then write an original sentence for each
rule. Begin and end each sentence correctly. Remember to check your spelling.

9. _____

10. _____

11. _____

12. _____

**Writers use commas for other reasons. As you read a newspaper, an article in your favorite
magazine, a letter, or a book, look for examples of commas in sentences and jot them down
on a piece of paper. Then see if you can figure out the rules.**

Show Time

 Sometimes a writer can change the order of the words in a sentence to make it more interesting.

**The telephone rang just as the girls were about to leave.
Just as the girls were about to leave, the phone rang.**

**Gina decided to answer it in spite of the time.
In spite of the time, Gina decided to answer it.**

*Do not forget to add a comma when you begin a sentence with a clause
or a phrase that cannot stand alone, as in the second and last sentences.*

Rewrite each sentence by changing the order of the words.

1. Marta watched for the bus while Gina answered the phone.

_____

2. The caller hung up just as Gina said, "Hello."

_____

3. The girls were going to miss the one o'clock show unless they hurried.

_____

4. The bus had already come and gone by the time they got to the corner.

_____

5. The next bus to town finally showed up after the girls had waited a half hour.

_____

6. The girls decided to catch the four o'clock show since they missed the earlier show.

_____

7. They wouldn't have to stand in line later since Gina bought the tickets first.

_____

8. Gina and Marta were at the theater by three o'clock even though it was early.

_____

9. They bought a tub of popcorn and drinks once they were inside.

_____

© Scholastic Inc.

Keeps On Going

*Writers sometimes make the mistake of running together two or more
sentences without telling how the ideas are related. This kind of sentence
is called a* **run-on sentence***.*

**Kansas holds the record for having the largest ball of twine
in the United States can you believe it weighs over 17,000
pounds in fact, the giant ball is 40 feet in circumference,
11 feet tall, and made up of more than 1,100 miles of twine!**

*To fix a run-on sentence, identify each complete thought or idea and break it into
shorter sentences.*

**Kansas holds the record for having the largest ball of twine in the United States.
Can you believe it weighs over 17,000 pounds? In fact, the giant ball is 40 feet
in circumference, 11 feet tall, and made up of more than 1,100 miles of twine!**

Rewrite each run-on sentence correctly. Remember to begin and end each
sentence correctly.

1. Did you know that the United States is the top meat-eating country in the world
each person consumes about 260 pounds of meat each year beef is the most
commonly eaten meat.

    _____

    _____

    _____

2. Have you ever noticed that Abraham Lincoln faces right on a penny he is not the
only president on a U.S. coin who does Thomas Jefferson faces right on newer
nickels too?

    _____

    _____

    _____

3. It would be fantastic to have a robot to do all my chores, help do my homework,
and play games I really think the day will come unfortunately, it won't come soon
enough for me.

    _____

    _____

    _____

A Long School Year

Have you ever accidentally left out words when you write? Whenever you write, it is always a good idea to proofread for words that may be missing. Here is an example of what to do when you want to add a missing word as you proofread.

I got an _{e-mail} from my friend last night.
∧

We _{met} last summer when my family was in Japan.
∧

Read the passage below about school in Japan. Twenty words are missing. Figure out what they are and add them to the sentences. Use the ∧ symbol to show where each missing word belongs. Then write each missing word above the sentence.
Hint: Every sentence has at least one missing word.

How would like to go to school on Saturdays? If you lived in the of Japan,

that's just where you'd be each Saturday morning. I have a who lives in Japan.

Yuichi explained that attend classes five and one-half a week. The day is on

Saturday. I was also surprised to that the Japanese school is one of the longest

in the world–over 240 days. It begins in the of April. While we have over two

months off each, students in Japan get their in late July and August. School

then again in fall and ends in March. The people of believe that a good is very

important. Children are required to attend school from the age of six to the of

fifteen. They have elementary and middle just like we do. Then most go on to

school for another three years. Yuichi says that students work very because the

standards are so high. He and some of his friends even extra classes after

school. They all want to get into a good someday.

 Write several sentences about something that interests you on a piece of paper. Rewrite the sentences on another piece of paper, this time leaving out a key word in each one. Challenge someone you know to add the missing words. Then compare the two sets of sentences.

Parts of a Paragraph

A **paragraph** is a group of sentences that tells about one main
idea. The **topic sentence** tells the main idea and is usually the
first sentence. **Supporting sentences** tell more about the main idea.
The **closing sentence** of a paragraph often retells the main idea
in a different way. Here are the parts for one paragraph.

Paragraph Title: **Starting Over**

Topic Sentence: **Today started off badly and only got worse.**

Supporting Sentences: 1. **Everyone in my family woke up late this morning.**

2. **I had only 15 minutes to get ready and catch the bus.**

3. **I dressed as fast as I could, grabbed an apple and my
backpack, and raced to get to the bus stop on time.**

4. **Fortunately, I just made it.**

5. **Unfortunately, the bus was pulling away when several
kids pointed out that I had on two different shoes.**

Closing Sentence: **At that moment, I wanted to start the day over.**

When you write a paragraph, remember these rules:

• **Indent** the first line to let readers know that you are beginning a paragraph.
• **Capitalize** the first word of each sentence.
• **Punctuate** each sentence correctly (? ! . ,).

Use all the information above to write the paragraph. Be sure to follow the rules.

_____

paragraph title

_____

_____

_____

_____

_____

_____

_____

What's the Topic?

*Every paragraph has a topic sentence that tells the main idea of the paragraph,
or what it is about. It usually answers several of these questions:*

Who? What? Where? When? Why? How?

Here are some examples.

**The doe and her fawn faced many dangers in the forest.
We were amazed by our guest's rude behavior.
Baking bread from scratch is really not so difficult, or so I thought.
Getting up in the morning is the hardest thing to do.**

Did these topic sentences grab your attention? A good topic sentence should.

Here are some topics. Write a topic sentence for each one.

1. convincing someone to try octopus soup

_____

2. an important person in your life

_____

3. an embarrassing moment

_____

4. the importance of Independence Day

_____

5. lunchtime at the school cafeteria

_____

Now list some topics of your own. Then write a topic sentence for each one.

_____
Topic #1

_____   _____
Topic #2   **Topic #3**

_____
Topic sentence #1

_____
Topic sentence #2

_____
Topic sentence #3

Topic Talk

Most paragraphs begin with a topic sentence, but it can appear elsewhere in a paragraph. Sometimes a topic sentence is located at the end of a paragraph or even in the middle.

A boiling mass of clouds was almost overhead. A bolt of lightning streaked across the darkened sky. Thunder boomed, and it began to rain and hail. <u>We had to find a safe place quickly!</u> There wasn't a moment to spare because early summer storms sometimes turn into tornadoes.

Read the paragraph again. This time try the topic sentence elsewhere in the paragraph.

Read each paragraph. Notice that each one is missing a topic sentence. Think about the supporting sentences. What main idea do you think they support? Write a topic sentence to tell the main idea of each paragraph. Remember that a topic sentence is not always the first sentence of a paragraph.

1.   **The days are growing longer. The winter snows are melting as the temperatures rise. Colorful crocuses are popping up here and there. Robins have begun to return north, and creatures are beginning to come out of their winter burrows. _____**

_____

2.   _____

It was fun and easy. Students, parents, and teachers began saving the box tops from all Healthful Foods products. After we collected 100,000 box tops, we mailed them to Healthful Foods headquarters. We earned 10 cents for each box top for a total of $10,000. Our school will use the money to buy computers.

3.   **The last weekend in June is quickly approaching. You know what that means.**

_____

This year the festivities will begin at 10:00 A.M. at Twin Lakes Picnic Grove, pavilion 12. As always, there will be music, dancing, lots of great food, games, and some new surprises! We look forward to seeing you.

A Lot of Details

 When you are ready to write a topic sentence, think about the main topic or idea of the paragraph you will be writing and the details you plan to include. Then jot down several possible sentences and choose the best one. Remember that a topic sentence can answer several questions: Who? What? Where? When? Why? How?

> *Tony Hawk*
> *– skateboarder*
> *– retired*
> *– turned professional at age 14*
> *– made history at Summer X Games in 1999—landed a "900"*
> *(a complete somersault done 2 1/2 times in midair)*

Possible topic sentences: **There is no other skateboarder like Tony Hawk.**
Tony Hawk was an extraordinary skateboarder.
Tony Hawk is a legend in skateboarding.

Here are some topics with details. Write two topic sentences for each one on the lines below.

1. **Pet Rocks**	2. **Komodo Dragon**	3. **A Great Dessert**
— fad in the 1970s — idea came from Gary Dahl, a salesman — sold rocks as pets — came with a manual — manual had tips on how to teach a pet rock tricks	— member of monitor family — grows to 10 feet and weighs 300 pounds — meat eater — dangerous to humans — largest lizard in the world — long neck and tail, strong legs — found on Komodo Island	— slice a banana — add vanilla ice cream — sprinkle on some walnuts — cover with lots of hot fudge sauce — top with mounds of whipped cream and a cherry

1. _____

_____

2. _____

_____

3. _____

_____

Remember that the supporting sentences you write support or tell more about the main idea in your topic sentence. Read the paragraph below. Draw one line under the topic sentence. Draw two lines under the supporting sentences. Check (√) the closing sentence.

Tony Hawk

Tony Hawk was an extraordinary skateboarder. He turned professional when he was only 14 years old. Now retired, Tony made history in 1999 by landing a trick called the "900" at the Summer X Games. Tony Hawk may just be the greatest skateboarder ever.

Now, review the topics on the previous page. Choose one. Then review the details listed about the topic in the box. Next, use the information to write at least three supporting sentences to support the topic sentence you wrote. Include a closing sentence and a title. Write the paragraph below.

_____

_____

_____

_____

_____

_____

_____

Make a list of topics you would like to write about. Choose one. Then list on a piece of paper details you know about the topic. Do some research if necessary. Then write a topic sentence and several supporting sentences.

© Scholastic Inc.

Drizzle With Details

A good paragraph needs supporting sentences that tell more about the main idea of the topic sentence. Supporting sentences are sometimes called detail sentences. Every detail sentence in a paragraph must relate to the main idea. In the following paragraph, the one supporting sentence that does not relate to the main idea has been underlined.

My first day of softball practice was a total disaster! Not only was I ten minutes late, but I also forgot my glove. Then during batting practice, I missed the ball every time I took a swing. <u>I definitely have improved on my catching skills.</u> To make matters even worse, I tripped in the outfield and twisted my ankle. I was definitely not off to a very good start.

Read the following paragraph. Underline the topic sentence. Then cross out any supporting sentences that do not relate to the main idea.

Yesterday our science class went on a field trip to a pond. Next month we're going to the ocean. That will be fun. We've been studying the pond as an ecosystem in class. Our teacher wanted us to observe firsthand all the different habitats in and around the pond. She had us keep a checklist of the different kinds of plants and animals in each pond habitat. One of the boys accidentally fell in. He was really embarrassed. Along the water's edge I saw several kinds of plants partly underwater, two salamanders, snails, and water bugs. I observed many different habitats.

© Scholastic Inc.

Read the title and topic sentence for each of the following paragraph plans. Then write four supporting sentences that relate to and support each one.

1. **Paragraph Title:**   Uniforms—To Wear or Not to Wear?
   Topic Sentence: Our school should require all students to wear uniforms.

   Supporting Sentences:

   1. _____

   2. _____

   3. _____

   4. _____

2. **Paragraph Title:**   An Adventure in Dreamland
   Topic Sentence: Last night I had the most incredible dream.

   Supporting Sentences:

   1. _____

   2. _____

   3. _____

   4. _____

3. **Paragraph Title:**   A Sad Day
   Topic Sentence: I will always remember how sad I was that day.

   Supporting Sentences:

   1. _____

   2. _____

   3. _____

   4. _____

© Scholastic Inc.

Choose one of the titles and topic sentences above. On a piece of paper, write a paragraph using the supporting sentences you wrote above. Include more supporting sentences that relate to the topic sentence if you want. Then add a closing sentence. Remember to indent, begin and end sentences correctly, punctuate correctly, and check your spelling.

A Musical Lesson

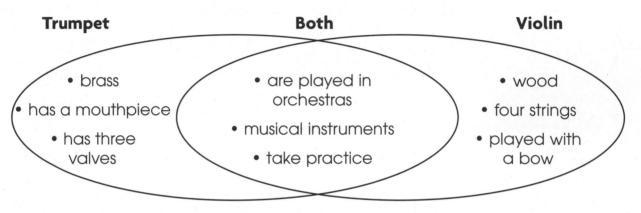

*There are many kinds of paragraphs. When you write a **comparison paragraph**, you compare by telling how things are similar and contrast by telling how things are different. You can use a Venn diagram to help organize your ideas. Here is an example.*

Trumpet   **Both**   **Violin**

- brass
- has a mouthpiece
- has three valves

- are played in orchestras
- musical instruments
- take practice

- wood
- four strings
- played with a bow

Complete the paragraph using details to compare and contrast the trumpet and violin. Remember to capitalize and punctuate correctly.

Trumpet Versus Violin

The trumpet and violin are both musical instruments that are _____

_____. However, there are some

important differences. The trumpet _____

_____

_____

_____

On the other hand, the violin _____

_____

_____

_____

Both instruments_____

_____

Make a list on a piece of paper of things to compare and contrast such as a house and an apartment building, ice skating and skateboarding, or spinach and broccoli. Choose one pair. Make and complete a Venn diagram like the one above. Then write a paragraph to tell how they are similar and different.

© Scholastic Inc.

Is That a Fact?

What is the difference between a fact and an opinion? A **fact** can be checked or proven. An opinion is what someone believes or feels about something. An **opinion** cannot be proven.

Fact → **Cocoa beans are used to make chocolate.**
Opinion → **Chocolate pudding is better than chocolate ice cream.**

Read each sentence. Write *F* next to each fact. Write *O* next to each opinion.

_____ **1.** Everyone in the world thinks chocolate makes the best candy.

_____ **2.** In Switzerland, the average person eats about 22 pounds of chocolate in a year.

_____ **3.** That means the Swiss eat about 160 million pounds of chocolate annually.

_____ **4.** I think Americans eat more chocolate than that.

_____ **5.** People also use chocolate to make drinks and to flavor recipes.

_____ **6.** There's nothing better than a chocolate donut with chocolate glaze.

Look at the pictures. Then write two facts and two opinions about each snack food. Use clue words such as *think, best, believe, like,* and *dislike* to signal an opinion.

1. Fact: _____

_____

_____

Opinion: _____

_____

_____

2. Fact: _____

_____

_____

Opinion: _____

_____

_____

3. Fact: _____

_____

_____

Opinion: _____

_____

_____

As you listen to a conversation among your friends about an issue that is important to them, try to identify the facts and opinions you hear and write them down on a piece of paper. Then ask, "Can this statement be proven?" If the answer is yes, then it is a fact. If not, then it is an opinion. Circle any clue words or phrases that signal opinions.

I'm Convinced!

In a **persuasive paragraph,** *you give an opinion about something and try to convince readers to think or feel the way you do. A convincing persuasive paragraph includes*

— **a topic sentence that clearly states your opinion.**
— **reasons that support your opinion.**
— **facts to back up your opinion.**
— **a strong closing sentence that summarizes your opinion.**

Pretend you are a world famous chef who prepares dishes that include edible insects—insects that you can eat. You want to persuade people to include insects in their diet. Here is a topic sentence for a persuasive paragraph.

Everyone should try cooking with insects.

Here are some reasons and facts.
• Many insects like mealworms, crickets, and weevils are edible.
• People in many cultures around the world eat insects.
• Many insects are low in fat and rich in vitamins.
• Lots of tasty recipes include insects.
• Insects are really quite delicious.

Now put it all together. Write a persuasive paragraph that includes a title and a strong closing sentence. Remember the rules for writing a paragraph.

Paragraph Title: _____

Topic Sentence: _____

_____

Reasons/Facts: _____

_____

_____

_____

_____

_____

_____

Closing Sentence: _____

_____

Step by Step

When you write an **expository paragraph**, *you give facts and information, explain ideas, or give directions. An expository paragraph can also include opinions. Here are some topic ideas for an expository paragraph.*

Explain how to play the flute.
Tell why you do not like brussels sprouts.
Give facts about yourself.

Explain how to bathe a dog.
Tell what skills you need to skateboard.
Give the facts about your favorite band.

Here is an example of an expository paragraph. It explains how to fry an egg.

Frying an egg is not all that difficult. After melting a little bit of butter in a frying pan, just crack the eggshell along the rim of the pan and let the egg drop into the pan. Do it gently so the yolk does not break. Let the egg fry over a low heat for about a minute or so. That is all it takes.

Complete the following topics for expository paragraphs with your own ideas.

Explain how to	Give facts about	Tell why
_____	_____	_____
_____	_____	_____
_____	_____	_____

Use the form below to develop one of your ideas for an expository paragraph.

Paragraph Title: _____

Topic Sentence: _____

_____

Details/Facts/Steps: _____

_____

_____

_____

_____

Closing Sentence: _____

_____

Now, use the plan above to write a paragraph on a piece of paper. If you are giving directions for doing or making something, include words such as *first, next, after that,* and *finally* to make the steps clear for your readers.

A Sentence Relationship

*You can write sentences about cause and effect relationships. A **cause** is the reason something happens. An **effect** is the result of the cause, or what actually happens. Words such as* so, because, *and* since *are used in cause and effect sentences.*

        effect   *cause*

School was cancelled today because **the storm dumped two feet of snow.**

        cause   *effect*

The snow and wind knocked out power lines, so **many homes were without electricity.**

        cause   *effect*

Since **there was no school today, I went back to bed and slept another hour.**

Add a cause to each of the following sentences about the day that school was cancelled because of snow.

1. Many shops, stores, and offices were closed _____

_____

2. My friends and I love snow days _____

_____

3. It took several minutes to open the back door _____

_____

4. Our snow blower would not start _____

_____

Add an effect to each of the following sentences.

5. I shoveled snow for two hours, _____

_____

6. My sister could not find her boots, _____

_____

7. Since our street was finally plowed by noon, _____

_____

8. By late afternoon it began snowing again, _____

_____

What a Mess!

*You can write a paragraph using a cause and effect
relationship. One way to begin is to state a cause. Then you
write about the effects that happen as a result of that cause.*

**The piercing sound of the smoke alarm
reminded Max that he had forgotten to check
the pot of stew heating up on the stove. The
stew had boiled over, the bottom of the pot was
scorched, and smoke was filling the kitchen.
Dinner was obviously ruined, and Max was in big
trouble. What a mess!**

Answer each question about the paragraph above.

1. **What is the cause?** _____

_____

2. **What were the effects? List them.** _____

_____

_____

Read the first sentence of the following paragraph. It states a cause. What might happen
as a result? Continue the paragraph. Write what you think the effects will be.

I walked into my room just as Sebastian, our very inquisitive cat, managed to

tip over the goldfish bowl that had been on my desk. _____

_____

_____

_____

_____

_____

_____

**Brainstorm a list of causes on a piece of paper. Here are some to get you started:
eating too many cookies   staying up too late   not studying for a test
Then list some possible effects. Develop your ideas into a paragraph.**

A Vivid Picture

A **descriptive paragraph** creates a vivid image or picture for readers. By choosing just the right adjectives, you can reveal how something looks, sounds, smells, tastes, and feels. Compare the sentences from two different paragraphs. Which one creates a more vivid picture?

The pizza with sausage and onions tasted so good.

The smooth, sweet sauce and bubbly mozzarella topped with bite-sized chunks of extra hot sausage and thin slivers of sweet onion on a perfectly baked, thin crust delighted my taste buds.

Cut out a picture of something interesting and paste it in the box. Then brainstorm a list adjectives and descriptive phrases to tell about it.

_____   _____

_____   _____

_____   _____

_____   _____

_____   _____

_____   _____

Now, write a paragraph about the picture. Begin your paragraph with a topic sentence that will grab readers. Add supporting sentences that include the adjectives and descriptive phrases listed to create a vivid picture.

_____

_____

_____

_____

_____

_____

Here is a set of adjectives: bumpy, dusty, narrow, steep, curvy, unpaved, well-worn. Think about what they might describe. Then, on a piece of paper use the words to write a descriptive paragraph that paints a picture.

© Scholastic Inc.

Numerous, Spectacular Words

When you write, do you sometimes overuse descriptive words like good, bad, nice, *or* wonderful?
Overused words can make your writing boring.

> The weather was **good** for our first camping trip. *(fair)*
> A ranger gave us some really **good** tips about the park. *(useful)*
> Mom thought the campsite near the stream was **good**. *(lovely)*
> My older brother is a **good** fly fisherman. *(skilled)*
> He said his equipment is too **good** for me to use, though! *(valuable)*

Now reread the sentences. This time use the words in parentheses in place of the word good.
*You can use a thesaurus to help find words. A thesaurus is a reference book that gives synonyms
and antonyms for words.*

Identify eight frequently overused descriptive words in the passage below and list them
in the answer spaces. Next, use a thesaurus to write three synonyms for each word, or
write three synonyms you know. Then revise the passage. Use editing symbols to cross out
the overused words and add the more effective synonyms to replace them.

> **Our family has a dog named Scooter. He's normally very good until it's time
> to bathe him. That's when our nice, little terrier turns into a big, furry monster.
> Scooter isn't really bad. He's just hard to handle when he doesn't want to do
> something. I think he's afraid of water. You should see how sad he looks once we
> manage to get him into the tub.**

1. _____   _____
2. _____   _____
3. _____   _____
4. _____   _____
5. _____   _____
6. _____   _____
7. _____   _____
8. _____   _____

**Reread a composition you have recently written. Look for overused words and then
use a thesaurus to find other words that you could use instead to make your writing
more interesting.**

Action Alert

When you write, think about the verbs that you choose to express action in your sentences. Are they as exact as they can be? Do they tell your readers exactly what you want to say?

The child **broke** the plastic toy.
The child **smashed** the plastic toy.
The child **cracked** the plastic toy.

Each verb creates a different picture of what happened.

Read each sentence. Underline the verb. Then rewrite each sentence using a more exact verb. You may want to use a thesaurus.

1. Three young hikers went up the steep hill.

_____

2. A lone runner ran around the track.

_____

3. The wind blew through the treetops.

_____

4. The janitor cleaned the scuff marks off the floor.

_____

5. The audience laughed at the hilarious scene.

_____

6. The diners ate the delicious meal.

_____

7. The young tourists liked the castle most of all.

_____

8. The children slept for about an hour.

_____

9. The biologist looked at the unusual specimen.

_____

 Here are some commonly used verbs: make, tell, say, speak, ride. On a piece of paper, list as many exact verbs as you can think of for each one. Use a thesaurus for additional words. Then write several sentences using the exact words on your list.

© Scholastic Inc.

Colorful Clues

You can compare two things that are not alike in order to give your readers a clearer and more colorful picture. When you use like or as to make a comparison, it is called a **simile**.

Max is as slow as molasses when he doesn't want to do something.
My sister leaped over the puddles like a frog to avoid getting her shoes wet.
The angry man erupted like a volcano.

When you make a comparison without like or as, it is called a **metaphor**. You compare things directly, saying the subject is something else.

The disturbed anthill was a whirlwind of activity.
The oak trees, silent sentries around the cabin, stood guard.
Jenny and I were all ears as we listened to the latest gossip.

Finish the metaphors and similes.

1. Crowds of commuters piled into the subway cars like _____

   _____

2. Chirping crickets on warm summer night are _____

   _____

3. After rolling in the mud, our dog looked like _____

4. Happiness is _____

5. Just learning to walk, the toddler was as wobbly as _____

   _____

6. After scoring the winning point, I felt as _____

   _____

7. Having a tooth filled is about as much fun as _____

   _____

8. A summer thunderstorm is _____

   _____

9. _____ is _____

10. _____ is like _____

Adding Spice

Sometimes you can spice up your writing by giving human characteristics and qualities to non-human things such as animals and objects. This is called **personification**.

**The sagging roof groaned under the weight of all the snow.
The falling leaves danced in the wind.**

You can also use **hyperbole**, or deliberate exaggeration, to make a point clearer or to add drama to your writing.

**The lost hiker is so hungry he could eat a bear.
Yesterday was so hot, we could have fried eggs on the sidewalk.**

Personify the animal or object in each sentence by giving it human qualities.

1. The rusted hinges on the old wooden door _____

   _____

2. As several birds began feasting on the farmer's corn, the scarecrow _____

   _____

3. A gentle summer breeze _____

   _____

4. Just as I walked past the statue of Ben Franklin, it _____

   _____

Complete each sentence with an example of a hyperbole.

5. The salsa was so spicy hot _____

   _____

6. The pumpkin grew so large _____

   _____

7. If we placed all the books in the library end to end, they _____

   _____

8. My room was so cold last night that by morning _____

   _____

Listen for examples of hyperbole in the conversations that you hear throughout the day. Jot them down in a notebook. Then make up some of your own.

Daily Notes

When you keep a journal, you can record the facts and details about events that happen in your life and your feelings or opinions about them. Your journal entries can be a valuable resource when you are looking for writing ideas.

3/9 We had to take Fuzzer to his new home today. Our new landlord said he could not stay with us at our apartment anymore. I know Fuzzer will be much happier at the farm where he can run and play, but I still felt so sad. I tried not to cry, but I could not help it. Fuzzer has been part of our family for nine years. We grew up together. I will miss him very much!

3/15 I had to go to my sister's dance recital at the Palace Theater last night. She performed in three numbers. At first I didn't want to go because I thought it would be boring, but it wasn't. I actually felt really proud of my sister! She was fantastic. I guess I really should tell her.

3/19 Today, the entire fourth grade went on a field trip to the state capital. It was incredible! We met a state senator. She showed us around the capitol building. We even got to listen to the senators discuss a new law. Later, we toured the governor's mansion. Boy, is that a big house!

Think about the events that have happened in your life over the last several days. Did anything of special importance happen at home, on the way to or from school, or in your community, the country, or the world? Record the facts, details, and your feelings or opinions about two events on the journal page below. Write the date for each entry.

_____/_____/_____

_____

_____

_____

_____

_____/_____/_____

_____

_____

_____

_____

Story Time

A story has **characters**, *a* **setting** *(where and when the story takes place), and a* **plot** *(the events that happen in a story). The main story character often faces a problem which is introduced at the* **beginning** *of a story, developed in the* **middle**, *and solved at the* **end**.

Develop your own story about the picture. First, answer the questions.

1. **What or who is the story about?** _____

_____

_____

_____

2. **Where and when does it take place?** _____

_____

_____

_____

3. **How will the story begin?** _____

_____

_____

_____

_____

_____

4. **What happens in the middle?** _____

_____

_____

5. **How will the story end?** _____

_____

_____

Use your answers to write a story on another sheet of paper. Include a title. Be sure to tell the events in the order they happen. Remember the rules for writing a paragraph.

Compile magazine pictures that spark story ideas. From time to time choose one of the pictures and make up an oral story about it. You can record your story and save it. Use it to write a story at another time.

What Did You Say?

Some stories may include dialogue, or the exact words of story characters. Dialogue lets readers know something about the characters, plot, setting, and problem or conflict in a story. Use quotation marks around a speaker's exact words and commas to set off quotations. Remember to put periods, question marks, exclamation points, and commas inside the quotation marks.

"Get away from my bowl!" yelled Little Miss Muffet when she saw the approaching spider.

"Please don't get so excited," replied the startled spider. "I just wanted a little taste. I've never tried curds and whey before."

Use your imagination to complete the dialogue between the fairy tale or nursery rhyme characters. Include quotation marks and commas where they belong and the correct end punctuation.

1. When Baby Bear saw the strange girl asleep in his bed, he asked his parents, _____

   _____

   His mother replied, _____

2. Humpty Dumpty was sitting on the wall when he suddenly fell off. On the way down

   he shouted, _____

   Two of the king's men approached. One whispered nervously to the other, _____

   _____

3. When Jack realized he was about to fall down the hill with a pail of water, he yelled,

   _____

   _____cried Jill,

   as she went tumbling down the hill after Jack.

4. The wolf knocked on the door of the third little pig's house. When there was no

   answer, the wolf bellowed, _____

   Knowing that he and his brother were safe inside his sturdy brick house, the third

   little pig replied, _____

   _____

Let's Get Organized

When you write a report or story, it helps to review your notes and organize them into an outline to show the order in which you want to discuss them.

Chester Greenwood → **subject of the report**

  I. Who was Chester Greenwood? → **main idea becomes topic sentence**
    A. born in 1858 → **supporting details become supporting sentences**
    B. grew up in Farmington, Maine
    C. as a child had ear problems in winter

  II. His first invention—earmuffs
    A. needed a way to protect ears from cold
    B. 1873 at age 15 began testing his ideas
    C. idea for fur-covered earflaps worked
    D. people saw and also wanted earflaps
    E. grandmother helped produce them

  III. His later accomplishments
    A. founded a telephone company
    B. manufactured steam heaters
    C. over 100 inventions

Study the outline above. Then answer the questions.

1. What is the topic of the report? _____

2. How many paragraphs will there be? _____

3. What is main topic of the first paragraph? _____

_____

4. How many details tell about the second main idea? _____

Use the form on the next page to develop an outline for preparing an interesting and unusual dish that your family enjoys.

© Scholastic Inc.

How to Prepare _____

I. **Background about the dish**

    A. _____

    B. _____

    C. _____

    D. _____

    E. _____

II. **Ingredients**

    A. _____

    B. _____

    C. _____

    D. _____

    E. _____

III. **Equipment**

    A. _____

    B. _____

    C. _____

    D. _____

    E. _____

IV. **Steps**

    A. _____

    B. _____

    C. _____

    D. _____

    E. _____

Share your outline with someone you know.

Read All About It

A **news story** *reports just the facts about an event and answers the questions* who, what, when, where, why, *and* how. *The most important information is included at the beginning of the article in a paragraph called the* **lead**.

Grass Fires Burn Out of Control   headline

WHERE did it happen? ⟶ GREENSBURG—Grass fires, fueled by wind gusts up to 50 miles per hour, spread into a residential area early Tuesday morning. All residents had to be evacuated. Within minutes over 25 homes were engulfed by flames and destroyed. According to officials, no injuries have been reported.

WHY did it happen?

WHEN did it happen?

WHO was affected?

  Planes and helicopters battling the blaze had to be grounded because the heat of the flames was so intense.

Write a news story using the information below. Remember to write about the facts and events in the order they occurred. Follow the model lead above.

Who: Roseville Emergency Rescue Team
When: April 10, 2003; 5 A.M.
Where: Slate Run River
What: team and rescue vehicles sent;
   worked for three hours; rescued residents
How: used helicopter and boats
Why: residents along river stranded by flash flood after storm

_____

_____   _____

_____

_____

_____

_____

_____

_____

Use your imagination to write a news story on a piece of paper for one of the following headlines or one of your own.

Mystery of the Missing Dinosaur Solved   **Students Protest School Lunch Menu**

City High Wins Championship   **First Female Elected President**

Scholastic Success With

CHARTS, TABLES & GRAPHS

The Winning Team

This table displays the win-loss record for five major-league baseball teams in 2017. Use the table to choose the best answer to each question below.

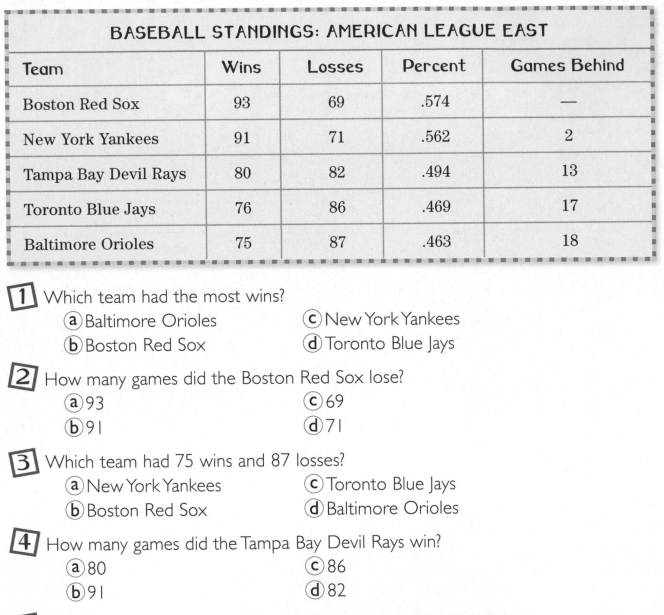

BASEBALL STANDINGS: AMERICAN LEAGUE EAST

Team	Wins	Losses	Percent	Games Behind
Boston Red Sox	93	69	.574	—
New York Yankees	91	71	.562	2
Tampa Bay Devil Rays	80	82	.494	13
Toronto Blue Jays	76	86	.469	17
Baltimore Orioles	75	87	.463	18

1 Which team had the most wins?

   a Baltimore Orioles   **c** New York Yankees

   b Boston Red Sox   **d** Toronto Blue Jays

2 How many games did the Boston Red Sox lose?

   a 93   **c** 69

   b 91   **d** 71

3 Which team had 75 wins and 87 losses?

   a New York Yankees   **c** Toronto Blue Jays

   b Boston Red Sox   **d** Baltimore Orioles

4 How many games did the Tampa Bay Devil Rays win?

   a 80   **c** 86

   b 91   **d** 82

5 How many of these teams won more than half of their games?

   a 2   **c** 4

   b 3   **d** 5

Measuring Up

Mrs. Umberto made this table to use when she buys clothing for her children. Use the table to answer the questions below.

MY CHILDREN'S CLOTHING SIZES

Child	Height (inches)	Weight (pounds)	Size
Emilio	60	103	14
Teresita	54	75	12
Pablo	52	60	8
Juana	43	51	5

1 How tall is Emilio? _____

2 How much more does Teresita weigh than Juana?

_____

3 Which two children are about the same height?

_____

4 What size clothing does Juana wear?

_____

5 According to this table, how do children's clothing sizes change as children grow taller?

_____

Tori's Sandwich Study

Tori asked her classmates to name their favorite sandwiches. She made a tally chart showing how many kids chose each kind. Use the chart to choose the best answer to each question below.

OUR FAVORITE SANDWICHES	
KIND OF SANDWICH	NUMBER OF KIDS
Ham and cheese	✓✓✓✓
Tuna fish	✓✓✓
Peanut butter and jelly	✓✓✓✓✓
Egg salad	✓✓

1 How many kids named tuna fish as their favorite kind of sandwich?
  ⓐ 2   ⓒ 4
  ⓑ 3   ⓓ 5

2 How many kids named egg salad?
  ⓐ 2   ⓒ 4
  ⓑ 3   ⓓ 5

3 Which kind of sandwich was named by the most kids?
  ⓐ ham and cheese   ⓒ peanut butter and jelly
  ⓑ tuna fish   ⓓ egg salad

4 If each kid named only one favorite sandwich, how many kids in all answered Tori's question?
  ⓐ 4   ⓒ 12
  ⓑ 5   ⓓ 14

Pete's Chores

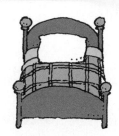

Pete made this tally chart to show how often he did chores around the house. He recorded his chores for one week. Use the chart to choose the best answer to each question below.

MY WEEKLY RECORD	
CHORE	NUMBER OF TIMES
Making bed	✓✓✓✓✓✓
Taking out trash	✓
Setting table	✓✓✓✓
Picking up toys	✓✓✓✓
Feeding cats	✓✓✓

1. Which chore did Pete do most often?
   - (a) making bed
   - (b) setting table
   - (c) picking up toys
   - (d) feeding cats

2. How many times did Pete take out the trash?
   - (a) 5
   - (b) 4
   - (c) 3
   - (d) 1

3. How many times did Pete set the table?
   - (a) 4
   - (b) 5
   - (c) 6
   - (d) 7

4. How many times in all did Pete do chores?
   - (a) 13
   - (b) 14
   - (c) 17
   - (d) 20

Drew's Newspaper Route

Drew made a pictograph to show how many newspapers he delivers on each street of his newspaper route. Use the graph to choose the best answer to each question below.

MY DAILY DELIVERIES

Gold Street	
Harold Street	
Lower Road	
Morris Drive	
Burnham Street	

Each stands for one newspaper.

1 How many newspapers does Drew deliver on Morris Drive?
- (a) 6
- (b) 7
- (c) 8
- (d) 9

2 On which street does Drew deliver the most newspapers?
- (a) Harold Street
- (b) Gold Street
- (c) Morris Drive
- (d) Lower Road

3 How many more newspapers does Drew deliver on Burnham Street than on Lower Road?
- (a) 7
- (b) 5
- (c) 3
- (d) 1

4 What is the total number of newspapers Drew delivers on his newspaper route?
- (a) 38
- (b) 36
- (c) 33
- (d) 30

Cool Inventions

Third graders in the Town School asked all the students to name the most important invention of the last 200 years. This pictograph shows how many students chose each of the inventions listed. Use the graph to answer the questions below.

KIDS' CHOICES	
Automobile	🧍🧍🧍🧍
Computer	🧍🧍🧍🧍🧍🧍🧍
Electric light	🧍🧍🧍
Telephone	🧍🧍🧍🧍
Television	🧍🧍🧍🧍🧍🧍

KEY
🧍 = 5 students

1 Which invention was named by the most students?

_____

2 How many students named television as the most important invention?

_____

3 Which two inventions were named by an equal number of students?

_____

4 How many more students named the computer than the electric light?

_____

The Class Field Trip

Mrs. Smith's class took a field trip to the park, and a park ranger explained how different trees grow to different heights. This bar graph shows the trees' heights. Use the graph to choose the best answer to each question below.

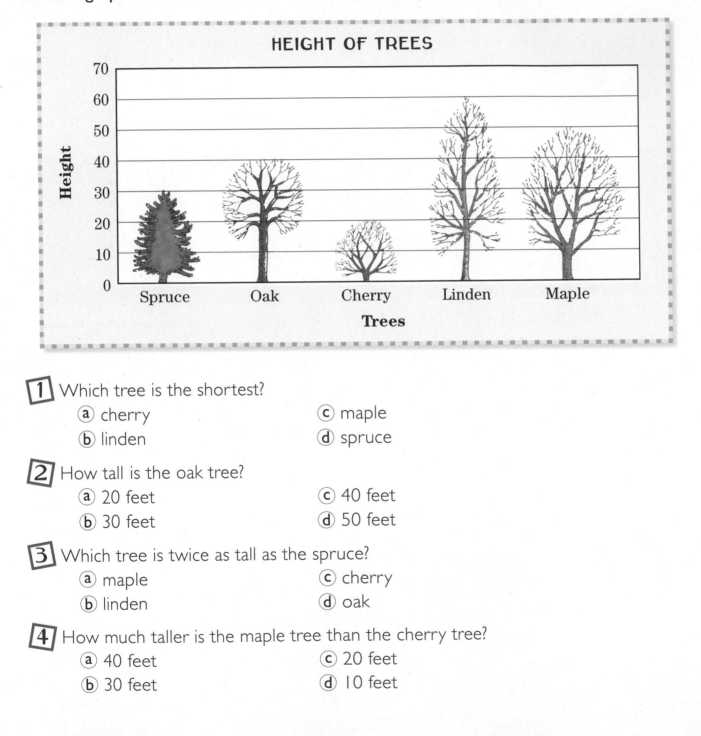

1 Which tree is the shortest?
    ⓐ cherry   ⓒ maple
    ⓑ linden   ⓓ spruce

2 How tall is the oak tree?
    ⓐ 20 feet   ⓒ 40 feet
    ⓑ 30 feet   ⓓ 50 feet

3 Which tree is twice as tall as the spruce?
    ⓐ maple   ⓒ cherry
    ⓑ linden   ⓓ oak

4 How much taller is the maple tree than the cherry tree?
    ⓐ 40 feet   ⓒ 20 feet
    ⓑ 30 feet   ⓓ 10 feet

Hannah and Her Cousins

Hannah's cousins live in five different states. She made this bar graph to show how many cousins live in each state. Use the graph to answer the questions below.

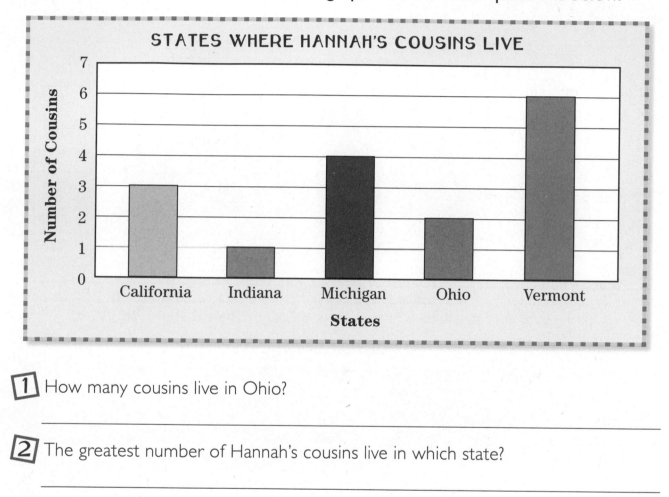

1 How many cousins live in Ohio?

_____

2 The greatest number of Hannah's cousins live in which state?

_____

3 How many more cousins live in Michigan than in California?

_____

4 How many cousins does Hannah have altogether?

_____

Soccer Contest

Five friends held a contest to see how far they could kick a soccer ball. The bar graph below shows the results of their contest. Use the graph to choose the best answer to each question.

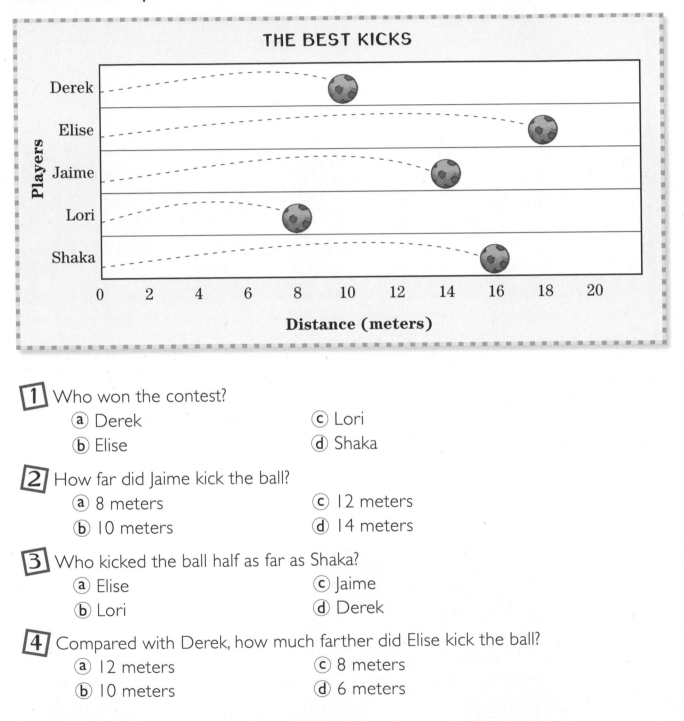

1 Who won the contest?
    ⓐ Derek
    ⓑ Elise
    ⓒ Lori
    ⓓ Shaka

2 How far did Jaime kick the ball?
    ⓐ 8 meters
    ⓑ 10 meters
    ⓒ 12 meters
    ⓓ 14 meters

3 Who kicked the ball half as far as Shaka?
    ⓐ Elise
    ⓑ Lori
    ⓒ Jaime
    ⓓ Derek

4 Compared with Derek, how much farther did Elise kick the ball?
    ⓐ 12 meters
    ⓑ 10 meters
    ⓒ 8 meters
    ⓓ 6 meters

Scouts' Honors

The Adventure Scouts earn badges by doing special projects. Their scout leader made this bar graph to show how many scouts have earned each type of badge. Use the graph to answer the questions below.

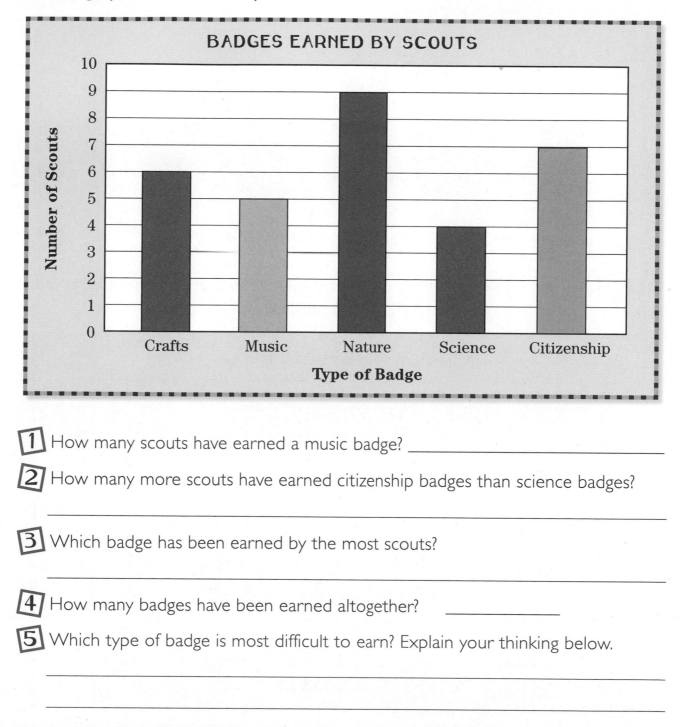

1. How many scouts have earned a music badge? _____

2. How many more scouts have earned citizenship badges than science badges?

   _____

3. Which badge has been earned by the most scouts?

   _____

4. How many badges have been earned altogether? _____

5. Which type of badge is most difficult to earn? Explain your thinking below.

   _____

   _____

Zack's Lazy Afternoon

Zack spent an afternoon at Sunrise Pond. He made this tally chart to show how many animals he saw at the pond.

KIND OF ANIMAL	NUMBER
Turtle	✓
Duck	✓✓✓✓✓
Frog	✓✓✓
Beaver	✓✓
Fish	✓✓✓✓✓✓✓

Then Zack started making a bar graph of the animals he saw at the pond, but didn't have time to finish it. Use the tally chart to finish Zack's bar graph.

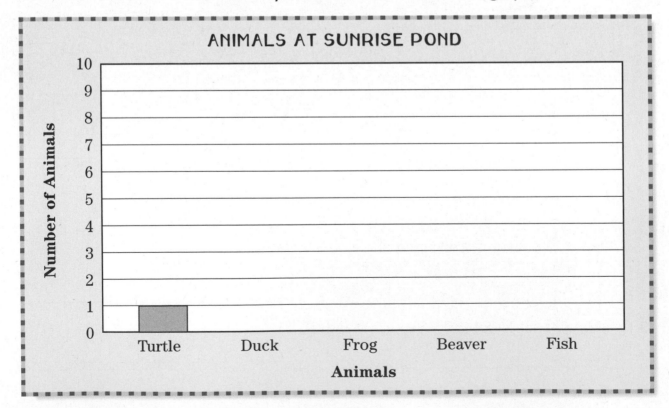

The Class Takes a Trip

Mrs. Fieldstone's students live in Boston, Massachusetts. They took a vote to decide where to go for their class trip in May and made a circle graph to help analyze the results. Use the graph to answer the questions.

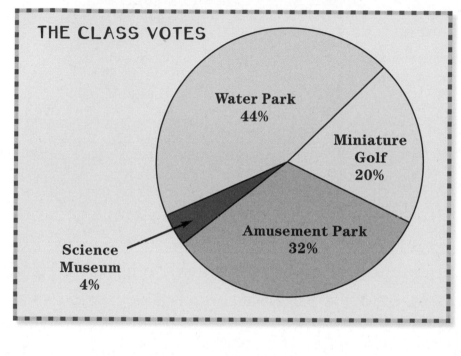

THE CLASS VOTES

Water Park 44%

Miniature Golf 20%

Amusement Park 32%

Science Museum 4%

1 Which choice received the fewest votes?

_____

2 If there are 25 students in the class, how many voted for miniature golf?

_____

3 Which two activities together were picked by about $\frac{3}{4}$ of the students?

_____

4 Which activity was chosen by about $\frac{1}{3}$ of the students?

_____

5 How do you think the votes would be different if the class trip took place in February instead of May?

_____

_____

Recycling Efforts

Every week, the town of Galway collects trash for recycling. The circle graph on the right shows what kinds of items are collected. Use the graph to choose the best answer to each question below.

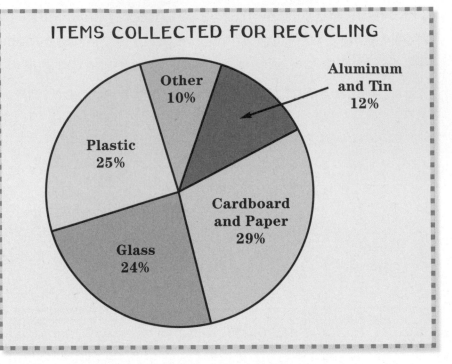

ITEMS COLLECTED FOR RECYCLING

1 Cardboard and paper make up what percentage of the recycled items?
- ⓐ 12%
- ⓑ 24%
- ⓒ 25%
- ⓓ 29%

2 What fraction shows what part of the recycled items are plastic?
- ⓐ $\frac{1}{4}$
- ⓑ $\frac{1}{3}$
- ⓒ $\frac{1}{2}$
- ⓓ $\frac{2}{3}$

3 Of every 100 items recycled, how many are glass?
- ⓐ 10
- ⓑ 12
- ⓒ 15
- ⓓ 24

4 What percentage of the recycled items are aluminum and tin?
- ⓐ 10%
- ⓑ 12%
- ⓒ 24%
- ⓓ 25%

5 One half of the items in the "Other" category were batteries. If batteries were shown on the graph, what percentage would they represent?
- ⓐ 50%
- ⓑ 10%
- ⓒ 5%
- ⓓ 3%

Best-Selling Books

The line graph below shows how many books were sold each day at a school book fair. Use the graph to answer the questions.

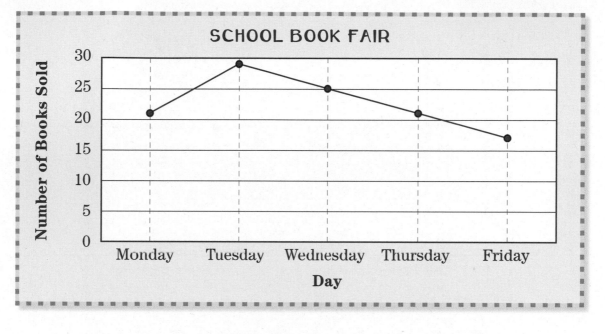

SCHOOL BOOK FAIR

Number of Books Sold

Day: Monday, Tuesday, Wednesday, Thursday, Friday

1 How many books were sold on Monday? _____

2 On what day were the same number of books sold as on Monday?

_____

3 How many more books were sold on Tuesday than on Thursday?

_____

4 What was the greatest number of books sold in one day?

_____

5 If the sales trend continued to Saturday, how many books would you expect to sell on Saturday?

_____

Compare the Squares

The line graph below shows the areas of squares of different sizes. Use the graph to answer the questions.

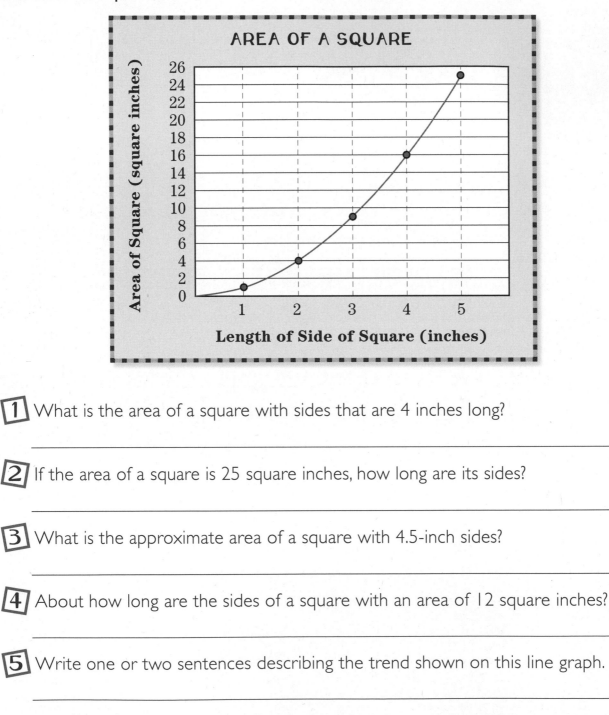

1 What is the area of a square with sides that are 4 inches long?

_____

2 If the area of a square is 25 square inches, how long are its sides?

_____

3 What is the approximate area of a square with 4.5-inch sides?

_____

4 About how long are the sides of a square with an area of 12 square inches?

_____

5 Write one or two sentences describing the trend shown on this line graph.

_____

_____

Adorable Animals

Do you know what a baby goat is called? The chart below provides the names for many baby animals. Use the chart to choose the best answer to each question.

NAMES FOR BABY ANIMALS			
Animal	Name for Baby	Animal	Name for Baby
Bear	Cub	Fox	Kit
Cow	Calf	Goat	Kid
Deer	Fawn	Kangaroo	Joey
Dog	Pup	Sheep	Lamb

1 What is the name for a baby deer?
- (a) cub
- (c) fawn
- (b) calf
- (d) pup

2 What is a baby fox called?
- (a) kit
- (c) cub
- (b) kid
- (d) lamb

3 Which kind of animal has cubs?
- (a) goat
- (c) kangaroo
- (b) sheep
- (d) bear

4 A "joey" is what kind of animal?
- (a) cow
- (c) kangaroo
- (b) fox
- (d) sheep

5 A baby goat is a —
- (a) kid
- (c) pup
- (b) lamb
- (d) calf

Joel's Trip Planner

Joel made a chart for his family to help them plan trips to local parks. Use the chart to answer the questions below.

THINGS TO DO AT LOCAL PARKS	
Blue Summit Park	
Lilac Lake Park	
Mead Canyon Park	
Pinetop Park	
Underwood Park	

KEY

Hiking Trails

Picnic Area

Swimming Beach

Campground

1 What can visitors do at Underwood Park?

_____

2 How many parks have a picnic area? _____

3 Which parks have a swimming beach?

_____

4 Which park offers the most activities?

_____

5 In which park can you ONLY camp or hike?

_____

Ordering Dinner

The Magic Meal Restaurant has a special children's menu. Use the chart to choose the best answer to each question below.

CHILDREN'S MENU

Sandwiches   *Served with potato chips and a pickle*

Egg Salad $2.50
Ham Salad $3.00
Tuna Fish $2.75
Grilled Cheese $2.50

Dinners   *Served with salad and a dinner roll*

Macaroni and Cheese $3.75
Spaghetti $3.00
Chicken Pot Pie $4.00
Beef Stew $4.00

Drinks

Milk, Chocolate Milk, Lemonade $1.00

Desserts

Dish of Ice Cream or Pudding $1.50

1 How much does a grilled cheese sandwich cost?
   (a) $2.50   (c) $3.00
   (b) $2.75   (d) $3.50

2 Which food is served with any dinner on the menu?
   (a) ice cream   (c) salad
   (b) potato chips   (d) pudding

3 Which drink is listed on the menu?
   (a) milk shake   (c) orange juice
   (b) lemonade   (d) hot chocolate

4 How much does a spaghetti dinner cost?
   (a) $4.00   (c) $3.00
   (b) $3.75   (d) $2.50

The Bookworm Club

Use this chart from the Bookworm Club to answer the questions below.

OUR BOOKS OF THE MONTH		
Item Number	Title	Price
1	*Amy Grows Up*	$3.25
2	*Beginner's Luck*	$2.95
3	*Dinosaur Dig*	$4.50
4	*Famous Firsts*	$3.95
5	*Jump Rope Games*	$4.25
6	*Lightning and Thunder*	$2.95
7	*Never Say Never*	$3.50
8	*Queen Mary of Scotland*	$2.95
9	*Science in Your Kitchen*	$3.25
10	*Yellowstone Park*	$4.50

1 What is the title of item number **1** on the book list?

_____

2 How much does the book *Queen Mary of Scotland* cost?

_____

3 What is the item number of the book *Jump Rope Games*?

_____

4 Look at this part of a book order form. Fill in the missing information.

Item Number	Title	Price
3		

Niko's Aquarium

Niko wants to set up an aquarium for tropical fish.
He is reading a library book about aquariums
before he begins this project. Use the table to
choose the best answer to each question below.

TROPICAL FISH AQUARIUMS
Contents

1 Niko wonders which fish get along well in an aquarium. Which chapter should he read to find this information?

ⓐ chapter 1   ⓒ chapter 5
ⓑ chapter 3   ⓓ chapter 6

2 Which of Niko's questions about tropical fish aquariums is probably answered in Chapter 2?

ⓐ How much gravel should I put in the bottom of the tank?
ⓑ How often should I feed my fish?
ⓒ How can I be sure I'm buying healthy fish?
ⓓ How much will a five-gallon tank cost?

3 Where should Niko start reading to find out how to clean the sides of his aquarium?

ⓐ page 5   ⓒ page 21
ⓑ page 11   ⓓ page 29

4 Which chapter explains how to find information about tropical fish online?

ⓐ chapter 2   ⓒ chapter 5
ⓑ chapter 4   ⓓ chapter 6

Reading/
Language arts: Table

Card Sharks

Do you like to play cards? Use the table to choose the best answer to each question below.

LET'S PLAY CARDS
Contents

Chapter 1   Words Used by Card Players 7
Chapter 2   Games for One Player
      Beehive...11
      Hit or Miss...12
      Solitaire 14

Chapter 3   Games for Two Players
      Baby Snap 15
      Gops 17
      Spade Oklahoma 19

Chapter 4   Games for a Group
      Authors 21
      Jacks...22
      Rolling Stone 24

1 Which chapter has information about games for two players?
- (a) chapter 1
- (b) chapter 2
- (c) chapter 3
- (d) chapter 4

2 Where should you start reading if you need to find out what a "wild card" is?
- (a) page 7
- (b) page 12
- (c) page 21
- (d) page 24

3 Which game might be a good one to play with three friends?
- (a) *Beehive*
- (b) *Jacks*
- (c) *Hit or Miss*
- (d) *Gops*

4 The directions for playing *Spade Oklahoma* begin on which page?
- (a) page 14
- (b) page 15
- (c) page 17
- (d) page 19

School Birthdays

The table below shows how many students in Grades 3 and 4 at the Rand School were born during each month. Use the table to answer the questions.

BIRTHDAY UPDATE												
Month of Birth	Sep.	Oct.	Nov.	Dec.	Jan.	Feb.	Mar.	Apr.	May	June	July	Aug.
Number of Students	2	1	2	3	2	4	6	9	6	5	4	3
Season	Fall			Winter			Spring			Summer		

1. How many students were born in November?_____

2. What month had the same number of births as February?

_____

3. How many students were born in the fall?

_____

4. During which season were the most students born?

_____

5. In which month would it be most likely to have two students share the same birthday?

_____

Presidential Studies

The table below shows information about recent presidents of the United States. Use the table to choose the best answer to each question.

U.S. PRESIDENTS			
Number	Name	Birth Year	Years in Office
37	Richard M. Nixon	1913	1969–1974
38	Gerald R. Ford	1913	1974–1977
39	Jimmy Carter	1924	1977–1981
40	Ronald Reagan	1911	1981–1989
41	George H.W. Bush	1924	1989–1993
42	William J. Clinton	1946	1993–2001
43	George W. Bush	1946	2001–2009
44	Barack Obama	1961	2009–2017

1 Who was the 40th president of the United States?
   ⓐ Gerald Ford   ⓒ Ronald Reagan
   ⓑ Jimmy Carter   ⓓ George H.W. Bush

2 In what year was Richard Nixon born?
   ⓐ 1911   ⓒ 1924
   ⓑ 1913   ⓓ 1946

3 Which president spent the shortest time in office?
   ⓐ Richard Nixon   ⓒ Jimmy Carter
   ⓑ George W. Bush   ⓓ Gerald Ford

4 Who was president in 1992?
   ⓐ Jimmy Carter   ⓒ George H.W. Bush
   ⓑ Ronald Reagan   ⓓ Bill Clinton

5 Which number president is Barack Obama?
   ⓐ 44   ⓒ 42
   ⓑ 43   ⓓ 41

Beautiful Bridges

The chart below lists six of the longest suspension bridges in the United States. Use the chart to answer the questions.

SUSPENSION BRIDGES OF THE UNITED STATES			
Year Completed	Bridge	Location	Main Span (feet)
1931	George Washington	New York–New Jersey	3,500
1937	Golden Gate	California	4,200
1950	Tacoma Narrows	Washington	2,800
1957	Mackinac Straits	Michigan	3,800
1964	Verrazano–Narrows	New York	4,260
1968	Delaware Memorial	Delaware	2,150

1 Which bridge has the longest main span?

_____

2 Which bridge was completed in 1957, and where is it located?

_____

3 Where is the Golden Gate Bridge, and when was it completed?

_____

4 How long is the main span of the George Washington Bridge?

_____

5 If the chart listed these bridges from shortest to longest, which two bridges would be listed first?

_____

The Wild Wild West

The chart below provides information about six states in the western United States. Use the chart to answer the questions.

WESTERN STATES				
State	Capital	Date of Statehood	State Bird	State Flower
Colorado	Denver	1876	Lark Bunting	Rocky Mountain Columbine
Idaho	Boise	1890	Mountain Bluebird	Syringa
Nevada	Carson City	1864	Mountain Bluebird	Sagebrush
Oregon	Salem	1859	Western Meadowlark	Oregon Grape
Utah	Salt Lake City	1896	Seagull	Sego Lily
Washington	Olympia	1889	Willow Goldfinch	Western Rhododendron

1 What is the capital of Washington? _____

2 In what year did Idaho become a state? _____

3 Which of these states gained statehood first? _____

4 What is Colorado's state bird?   _____

5 Salem is the capital of which state?   _____

6 What is Nevada's state flower?   _____

7 Which states have the same state bird, and what bird is it?

_____

The Story of Paper

The flow chart below shows how paper is made. Use the chart to answer the questions.

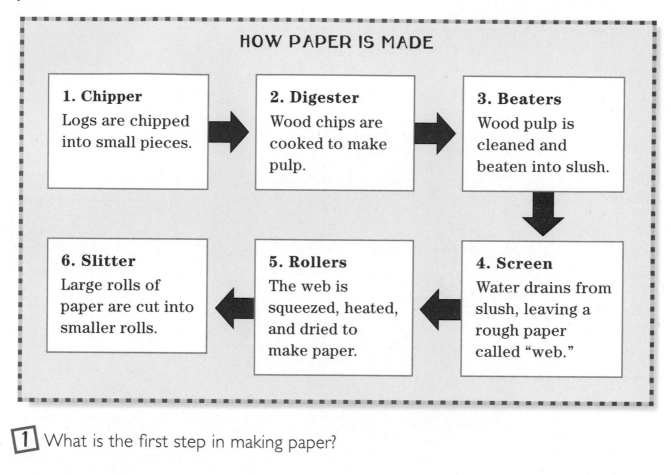

HOW PAPER IS MADE

1. Chipper
Logs are chipped into small pieces.

2. Digester
Wood chips are cooked to make pulp.

3. Beaters
Wood pulp is cleaned and beaten into slush.

6. Slitter
Large rolls of paper are cut into smaller rolls.

5. Rollers
The web is squeezed, heated, and dried to make paper.

4. Screen
Water drains from slush, leaving a rough paper called "web."

1 What is the first step in making paper?

_____

2 What happens in the "beaters"?

_____

3 In which step does slush become rough paper?

_____

4 What tasks are done with the use of heat?

_____

_____

Building Houses

The pictograph below shows the number of new houses built in five different counties last year. Use the graph to answer the questions.

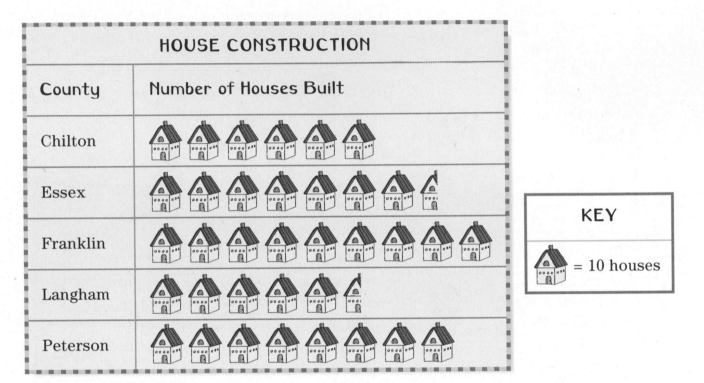

HOUSE CONSTRUCTION

County	Number of Houses Built
Chilton	
Essex	
Franklin	
Langham	
Peterson	

KEY

= 10 houses

1 How many houses were built in Chilton County last year?

_____

2 In which county were the most houses built?

_____

3 In which county were the fewest houses built?

_____

4 How many more houses were built in Peterson County than in Langham County?

_____

5 A total of 42 houses were built in Winwood County last year. How would this number be shown on the graph? (Draw a picture on the back of this paper.)

How Does Susan's Garden Grow?

Susan made a bar graph showing the heights of the flowers in her garden. Use the graph to choose the best answers to the questions below.

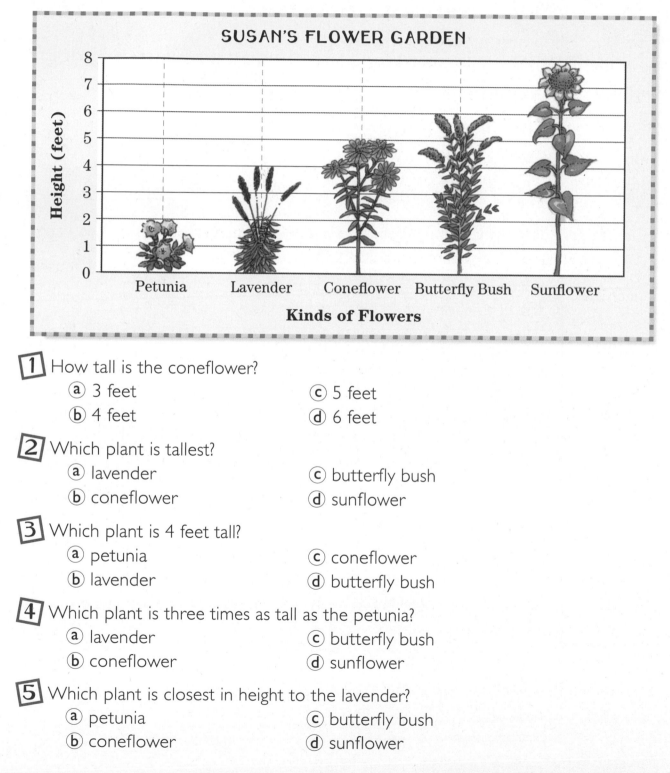

SUSAN'S FLOWER GARDEN

Height (feet)

Petunia   Lavender   Coneflower   Butterfly Bush   Sunflower

Kinds of Flowers

1 How tall is the coneflower?
- (a) 3 feet
- (b) 4 feet
- (c) 5 feet
- (d) 6 feet

2 Which plant is tallest?
- (a) lavender
- (b) coneflower
- (c) butterfly bush
- (d) sunflower

3 Which plant is 4 feet tall?
- (a) petunia
- (b) lavender
- (c) coneflower
- (d) butterfly bush

4 Which plant is three times as tall as the petunia?
- (a) lavender
- (b) coneflower
- (c) butterfly bush
- (d) sunflower

5 Which plant is closest in height to the lavender?
- (a) petunia
- (b) coneflower
- (c) butterfly bush
- (d) sunflower

Alex the Sports Reporter

Alex conducted a survey of his classmates about their favorite team and individual sports. He made these charts to show the results of his survey. Use the charts to make your own bar graphs.

FAVORITE TEAM SPORTS	
Basketball	卌 卌 lll
Soccer	卌 卌 ll
Hockey	卌 lll
Softball	卌 l

FAVORITE INDIVIDUAL SPORTS	
Tennis	卌 卌 lll
Running	卌
Golf	卌 l
Swimming	卌 卌 卌

1. On the grid below, make a bar graph to show how many students picked each *team* sport. Be sure to include labels and a title.

2. On the grid below, make a bar graph to show how many students picked each *individual* sport. Be sure to include labels and a title.

Mindy Minds the Money

Mindy and her Dad made a circle graph to show how the family's money was spent each month. Use the graph to choose the best answer to each question below.

OUR MONTHLY EXPENSES

Clothing 6%

Transportation 10%

Entertainment 3%

Rent 34%

Food 25%

Household Bills (heat, telephone, etc.) 22%

1 Which is the largest cost each month?
- ⓐ food
- ⓑ rent
- ⓒ clothing
- ⓓ transportation

2 How much of the money spent each month goes to food?
- ⓐ More than $\frac{1}{2}$
- ⓑ $\frac{1}{3}$
- ⓒ Less than $\frac{1}{6}$
- ⓓ $\frac{1}{4}$

3 The least amount of money is spent on _____.
- ⓐ household bills
- ⓑ clothing
- ⓒ transportation
- ⓓ entertainment

4 What part of the family's money is spent on clothing each month?
- ⓐ 3%
- ⓑ 6%
- ⓒ 10%
- ⓓ 22%

5 When Dad takes the bus to work each day, that cost is part of what category?
- ⓐ transportation
- ⓑ household bills
- ⓒ clothing
- ⓓ entertainment

6 Which cost is probably higher in winter than in summer?
- ⓐ rent
- ⓑ transportation
- ⓒ household bills
- ⓓ entertainment

Population Growth

The line graph below shows the number of people living in Newtown between 1900 and 2000. Use the graph to answer the questions.

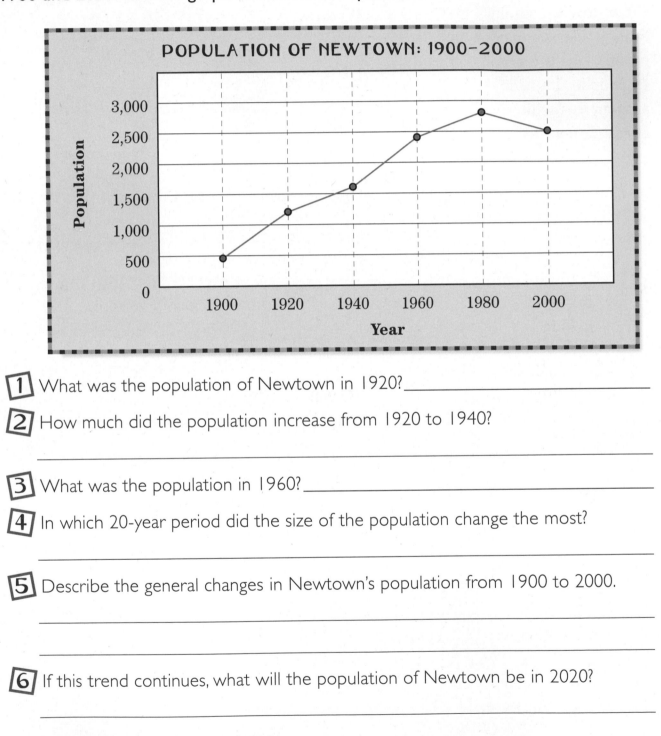

1 What was the population of Newtown in 1920?_____

2 How much did the population increase from 1920 to 1940?

_____

3 What was the population in 1960?_____

4 In which 20-year period did the size of the population change the most?

_____

5 Describe the general changes in Newtown's population from 1900 to 2000.

_____

_____

6 If this trend continues, what will the population of Newtown be in 2020?

_____

A Trip Through Time

The timeline below shows when different ways of telling time were invented. Use the timeline to answer the questions.

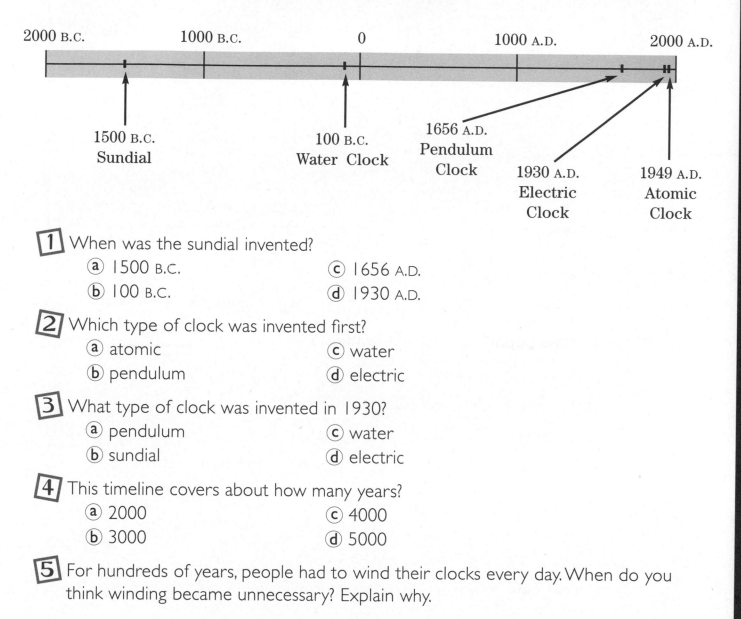

TIME MACHINE TIMELINE

2000 B.C.   1000 B.C.   0   1000 A.D.   2000 A.D.

1500 B.C.
Sundial

100 B.C.
Water Clock

1656 A.D.
Pendulum
Clock

1930 A.D.
Electric
Clock

1949 A.D.
Atomic
Clock

1 When was the sundial invented?
  (a) 1500 B.C.   (c) 1656 A.D.
  (b) 100 B.C.   (d) 1930 A.D.

2 Which type of clock was invented first?
  (a) atomic   (c) water
  (b) pendulum   (d) electric

3 What type of clock was invented in 1930?
  (a) pendulum   (c) water
  (b) sundial   (d) electric

4 This timeline covers about how many years?
  (a) 2000   (c) 4000
  (b) 3000   (d) 5000

5 For hundreds of years, people had to wind their clocks every day. When do you think winding became unnecessary? Explain why.

_____

_____

Mimi's Sunny Vacation

Mimi made a table to show when the sun rose and set each Saturday during her summer vacation. Use the table to answer the questions below.

SUNRISE AND SUNSET ON SUMMER SATURDAYS					
Date	Sunrise	Sunset	Date	Sunrise	Sunset
June 23	5:08 AM	8:25 PM	July 28	5:33 AM	8:08 PM
June 30	5:11 AM	8:25 PM	August 4	5:40 AM	8:00 PM
July 7	5:14 AM	8:23 PM	August 11	5:47 AM	7:51 PM
July 14	5:20 AM	8:20 PM	August 18	5:55 AM	7:41 PM
July 21	5:26 AM	8:15 PM	August 25	6:02 AM	7:30 PM

1 What time did the sun rise on July 21?

_____

2 On which date did the sun set at exactly 8:00 PM?

_____

3 Which Saturday had the earliest sunrise?

_____

4 How much earlier did the sun set on August 18 than on August 11?

_____

5 Which Saturday had exactly 15 hours between sunrise and sunset?

_____

6 How do the times of sunrise and sunset change from June 23 to the end of August?

_____

Weather Reporting

Fourth-grade students involved in a nation-wide project recorded the weather conditions each day for a week. Use the table to answer the questions below.

WEATHER DATA: SEPTEMBER 24-30					
Day	High Temperature	Low Temperature	Wind Speed (knots)	Precipitation	Conditions
Sunday	68°F	42°F	0–5	0	Sunny
Monday	69°F	44°F	0–5	0	Sunny
Tuesday	72°F	43°F	5–10	0	Cloudy
Wednesday	70°F	38°F	10–15	0	Partly Cloudy
Thursday	64°F	36°F	25–30	1.2 inches	Rainy
Friday	52°F	30°F	20–25	0.3 inches	Rainy
Saturday	52°F	32°F	10–15	0	Partly Cloudy

1 What were the high and low temperatures on Sunday?

_____

2 Which day was warmest? _____

3 On which days did the temperature go as low as the freezing point of 32°F?

_____

4 What were the weather conditions on Wednesday?

_____

5 In all, how much rain fell during the week? _____

6 Write one or two sentences describing how the weather changed from Sunday to Saturday.

_____

_____

Dining With Dinosaurs

This "Dino" chart provides specific information about different kinds of dinosaurs. Use the chart to choose the best answer to each question below.

DINOSAUR FACTS

Name	What It Means	Size	Weight	Food
Ankylosaurus	Crooked lizard	25 feet	3 tons	plants
Baryonyx	Heavy claw	30 feet	3,300 pounds	fish
Eoraptor	Dawn thief	3 feet	11–16 pounds	meat, insects
Maiasaura	Good mother lizard	30 feet	3 tons	plants
Plateosaurus	Broad lizard	20–26 feet	2,000–4,000 lb.	plants
Seismosaurus	Earthquake lizard	120–150 feet	40 tons	plants
Spinosaurus	Spined lizard	40 feet	4 tons	fish
Velociraptor	Fast thief	6 feet	30 pounds	meat

1 How much did the dinosaur called *Maiasaura* weigh?
- ⓐ 30 pounds
- ⓑ 3 tons
- ⓒ 4 tons
- ⓓ 40 tons

2 Which dinosaur's name means "broad lizard?"
- ⓐ *Ankylosaurus*
- ⓑ *Eoraptor*
- ⓒ *Plateosaurus*
- ⓓ *Spinosaurus*

3 How many feet long was the dinosaur called *Velociraptor*?
- ⓐ 3 feet
- ⓑ 6 feet
- ⓒ 25 feet
- ⓓ 30 feet

4 Which of these dinosaurs ate fish?
- ⓐ *Ankylosaurus*
- ⓑ *Maiasaura*
- ⓒ *Velociraptor*
- ⓓ *Spinosaurus*

5 Which is the largest, heaviest dinosaur listed in the chart?
- ⓐ *Seismosaurus*
- ⓑ *Plateosaurus*
- ⓒ *Eoraptor*
- ⓓ *Baryonyx*

How Hurricanes Get Their Names

When hurricanes form each year, the National Hurricane Center gives each one a name. The chart at right shows some of the names for hurricanes in the Atlantic Ocean in the years 2011, 2012, and 2013. Use the chart to answer the questions.

HURRICANE NAMES: ATLANTIC OCEAN		
2011	**2012**	**2013**
Arlene	Alberto	Andrea
Bret	Beryl	Barry
Cindy	Chris	Chantal
Don	Debby	Dorian
Emily	Ernesto	Erin
Franklin	Florence	Fernand
Gert	Gordon	Gabrielle
Harvey	Helene	Humberto
Irene	Isaac	Ingrid
Jose	Joyce	Jerry
Katia	Kirk	Karen

1 What name was given to the first hurricane in 2012?

_____

2 What name was given to the fifth hurricane in 2013?

_____

3 What name came after Franklin in 2011?

_____

4 What name beginning with the letter "D" was used in 2013?

_____

5 From this chart, what can you tell about the "rules" used in naming hurricanes? Explain your idea.

_____

_____

_____

Speedy Animals

The bar graph below shows how fast some animals can run. Use the graph to answer the questions.

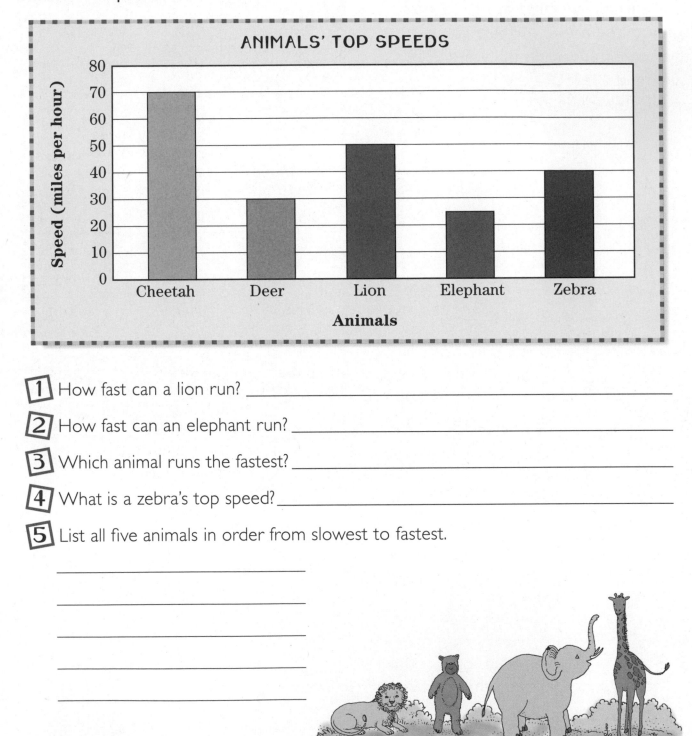

1 How fast can a lion run? _____

2 How fast can an elephant run? _____

3 Which animal runs the fastest? _____

4 What is a zebra's top speed? _____

5 List all five animals in order from slowest to fastest.

_____

_____

_____

_____

_____

All About Energy

The circle graph shows the sources of energy used in the United States today. Use the circle graph to choose the best answer to each question.

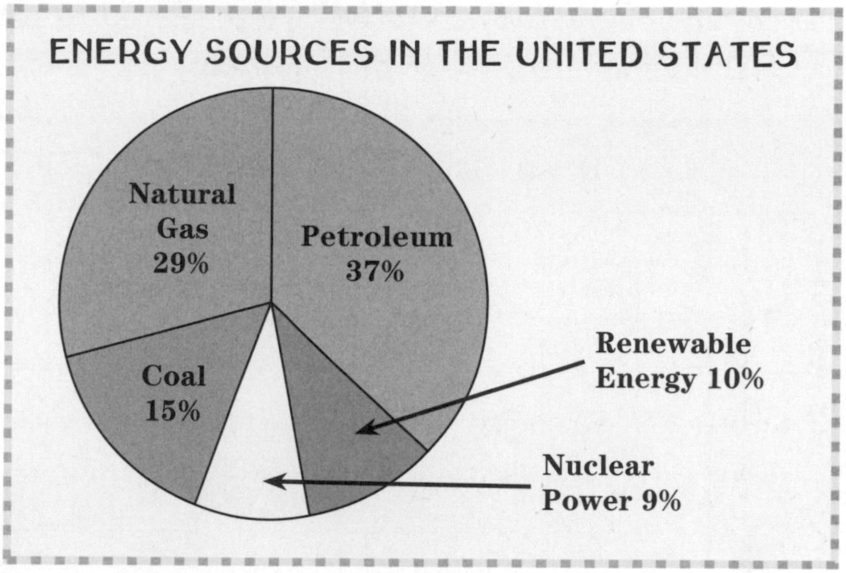

ENERGY SOURCES IN THE UNITED STATES

Natural
Gas
29%

Petroleum
37%

Coal
15%

Renewable
Energy 10%

Nuclear
Power 9%

1. Which energy source provides nearly 30% of the power in the United States?
   - (a) petroleum
   - (b) coal
   - (c) nuclear power
   - (d) natural gas

2. What portion of the energy used in the United States comes from coal?
   - (a) 29%
   - (b) 15%
   - (c) 10%
   - (d) 9%

3. More than one third of the energy used in the United States comes from which source?
   - (a) petroleum
   - (b) natural gas
   - (c) nuclear power
   - (d) renewable energy

4. What percentage of energy used in the United States comes from fossil fuels (petroleum, natural gas, and coal)?
   - (a) 44%
   - (b) 52%
   - (c) 66%
   - (d) 81%

5. From this graph, you can conclude that nearly _____ of energy in the United States comes from sources other than fossil fuels.
   - (a) 9%
   - (b) 10%
   - (c) 20%
   - (d) 25%

Cleveland's Weather Update

The line graph below shows the average temperature each month in Cleveland, Ohio. Use the graph to answer the questions.

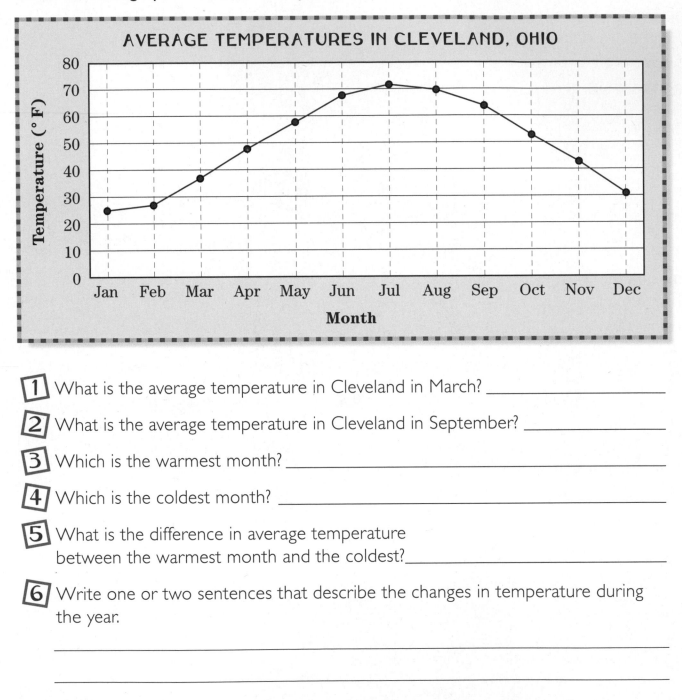

1 What is the average temperature in Cleveland in March? _____

2 What is the average temperature in Cleveland in September? _____

3 Which is the warmest month? _____

4 Which is the coldest month? _____

5 What is the difference in average temperature
between the warmest month and the coldest?_____

6 Write one or two sentences that describe the changes in temperature during
the year.

_____

_____

_____

Scholastic Success With

MAPS

What Is a Map?

A map is a flat drawing of a part or all of Earth. A map shows a place from above much as a picture taken high in the sky or from space does. In fact, mapmakers study aerial photographs to help them make more accurate maps.

map reader's Tip

Another word for mapmaker is cartographer. This word comes from the Latin word *carta*, which means "paper" and the Greek word *graphia*, which means "to write."

Since a map shows a large area in a small space, mapmakers use **symbols** to stand for buildings, roads, cities, and other things. A symbol is a drawing or color that represents something else. You can find out what each symbol means by checking the map key or legend.

Study the map key for the map on the next page. Then answer the questions.

1. This symbol ------- stands for _____.

2. The capital of Wyoming is _____.

3. Las Vegas is a city in _____.

4. Two states that share a border with Canada are _____ and _____.

5. Boise is the capital of _____.

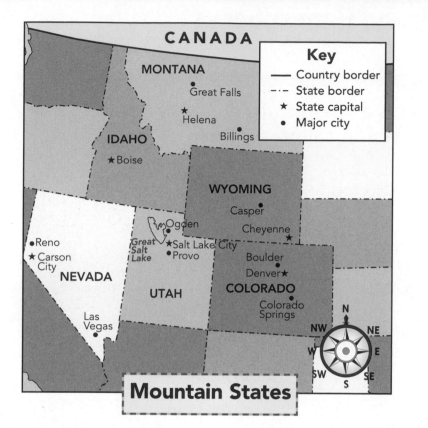

Mountain States

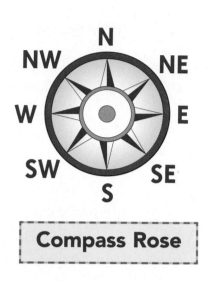

Compass Rose

A map also has a symbol called a **compass rose** that shows directions. The four main directions are north, south, east, and west. These are called the **cardinal directions**. A compass rose might show **intermediate directions** too. They are northeast, southeast, southwest, and northwest. Often, abbreviations are used to show the directions on a compass rose.

Use the compass rose to answer these questions.

6. The direction between east and south is _____.

7. The letters NW stand for _____.

8. Colorado is _____ of Idaho.

9. Montana is _____ of Wyoming.

10. A plane traveling from the capital of Idaho to the capital of Nevada would go in a _____ direction. Draw its route on the map.

Globes and Hemispheres

As you know, Earth is a large, round planet. To see all of Earth, you would have to orbit it in a spacecraft! An easier way to see Earth is to look at a small model called a globe.

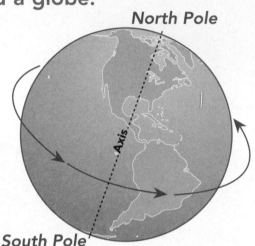

A globe shows Earth's four oceans and seven continents. A globe also shows how Earth turns on an imaginary center line called an **axis**. At the ends of this line are the North and South poles. Pole means "end." These poles help you find directions on Earth. North is toward the North Pole, and south is toward the South Pole.

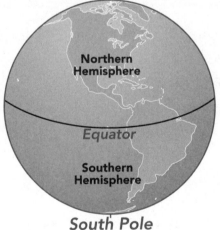

Another imaginary line on a globe is called the **equator**. The equator runs around the center of Earth and divides it into two halves called **hemispheres**. The northern half is called the Northern Hemisphere, and the southern half is called the Southern Hemisphere.

Still another imaginary line divides Earth into the Eastern and Western hemispheres. This line is called the **Prime Meridian**. This line runs from the North Pole to the South Pole.

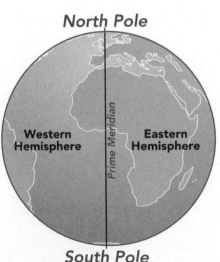

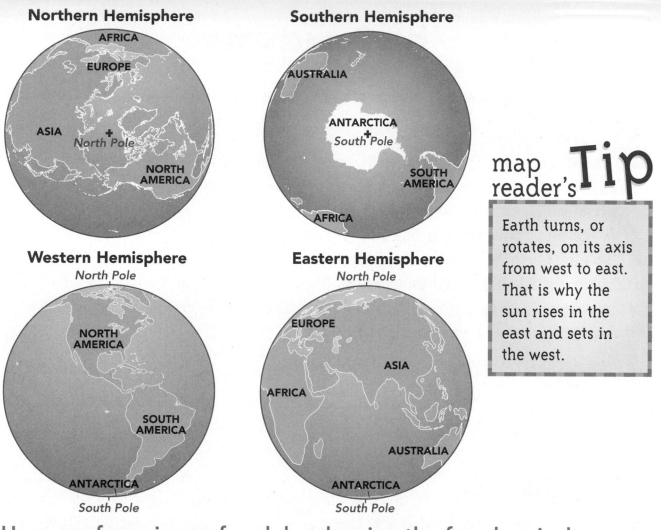

Northern Hemisphere

AFRICA
EUROPE
ASIA
+ North Pole
NORTH AMERICA

Southern Hemisphere

AUSTRALIA
ANTARCTICA
+ South Pole
SOUTH AMERICA
AFRICA

Western Hemisphere

North Pole
NORTH AMERICA
SOUTH AMERICA
ANTARCTICA
South Pole

Eastern Hemisphere

North Pole
EUROPE
ASIA
AFRICA
AUSTRALIA
ANTARCTICA
South Pole

map reader's **Tip**

Earth turns, or rotates, on its axis from west to east. That is why the sun rises in the east and sets in the west.

Here are four views of a globe showing the four hemispheres. Use the pictures on these pages to answer these questions.

1. How many hemispheres does Earth have? _____

2. What is the hemisphere nearest the South Pole? _____

3. What line divides the Eastern and Western hemispheres? _____

4. In which direction is the North Pole from the equator? _____

5. What line divides the Northern and Southern hemispheres? _____

6. What is Earth's axis? _____

7. Name one continent in the Northern Hemisphere. _____

8. Name one continent in the Eastern Hemisphere. _____

Map Projections

A globe is the best way to represent Earth, but globes are not easy to put in your pocket and carry around. Also, you cannot see all of a globe at one time. So mapmakers have developed flat maps that show all of Earth. The different ways of drawing the round Earth on flat maps are called **projections**. You can see two different projections on these pages.

No flat map can show Earth perfectly. Look at the Mercator projection. It was developed in 1569 by Gerardus Mercator. A Mercator map shows the true shapes of Earth's land, but it distorts sizes, especially near the poles. On a Mercator map, Greenland looks as big as South America. In fact, South America is eight times bigger than Greenland!

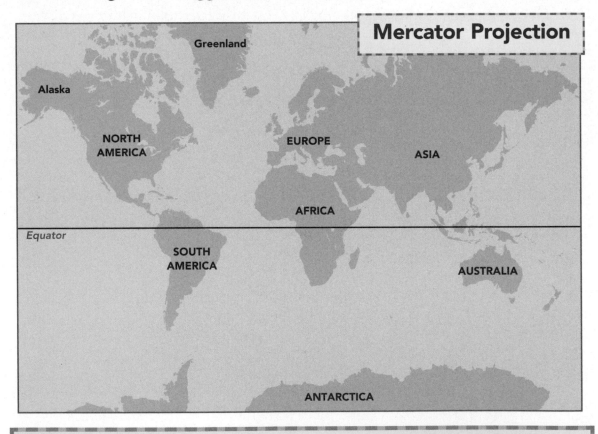

Mercator Projection

Greenland

Alaska

NORTH
AMERICA

EUROPE

ASIA

AFRICA

Equator

SOUTH
AMERICA

AUSTRALIA

ANTARCTICA

map reader's **Tip**   Other types of projections on world maps include **Mollweide**, **Polar**, and **Interrupted** projections.

© Scholastic Inc.

Robinson Projection

![Robinson projection world map with Equator labeled]

The map above shows the Robinson projection. It is used by many geographers today. The land sizes are more accurate on this map, but the shapes get distorted near the outer edges. Compare the shape of Alaska on the two maps. Use the maps to answer the questions.

1. How is a world map different from a globe? _____

2. On which map does Antarctica look bigger? _____

3. Which map is more like a globe? _____

4. On which map does the distance from

   Greenland to Antarctica look greater? _____

5. Which map looks more like a peeled orange? _____

   Why do you think this is so? _____

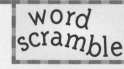 There are five types of map projections named in this lesson. Can you unscramble them?

LAROP   RATROMEC   PETDURNITRE   ILEMDEWLO   BOSNIRON

_____   _____   _____   _____   _____

Using a Map Grid and Index

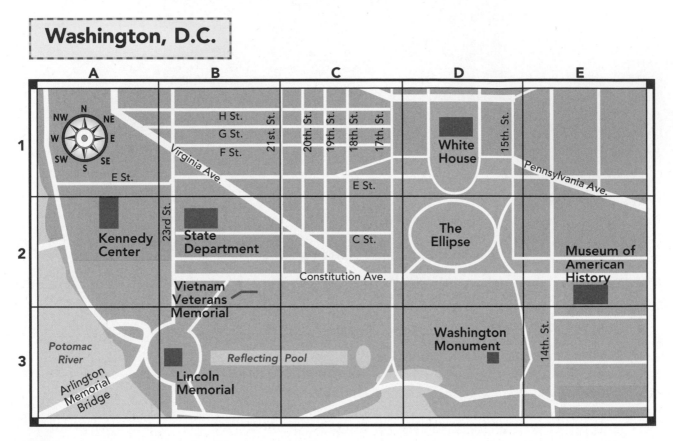

Washington, D.C.

ometimes mapmakers place a pattern of lines called a **grid** over a map. The squares formed by the grid are marked with letters and numbers. On this map the letters run across the top; the numbers run down the side. The first square in the top left corner of the map is A1. Can you find it? What is the name of the square immediately to the right of A1?

Use the map to answer these questions.

1. What landmark is in D3? _____

2. In which grid square is the White House? _____

3. What avenue runs from A1 to C2? _____

4. In which grid squares is Pennsylvania Avenue? _____

5. What body of water do you see in A2? _____

© Scholastic Inc.

map reader's **Tip**

Index

Arlington Memorial Bridge A3
The Ellipse D2
Kennedy Center A2
Lincoln Memorial B3
Museum of American History . . . E2
Reflecting Pool B3, C3
State Department B2
Vietnam Veterans Memorial B2
Washington Monument D3
White House . . . . DI

The D.C. in the city's name stands for District of Columbia. Washington, D.C., is not part of a state, but rather a "federal district." A mayor and city council make laws, but the U.S. Congress has final authority over Washington, D.C.'s government.

Suppose you are visiting Washington, D.C., and want to see some of its sights. A **map index** can help you locate different places. A map index is an alphabetical listing of place names on a map. This index gives the grid square or squares for each place.

Use the index to answer these questions.

6. You are at the Museum of American History.

What is your grid location?_____

7. In which square would you look for the State Department?_____

8. What place is listed after the Reflecting Pool on the index?_____

9. What is the grid location of the Lincoln Memorial? _____

10. You are going to a concert at the Kennedy Center.

Where can you find it on the map? _____

Understanding Latitude

You know that the equator is an imaginary line that runs around the middle of Earth. Mapmakers create other imaginary lines on globes and maps as well. Look at the lines on this globe. These lines run parallel to the equator and are called parallels or lines of **latitude**. You can use lines of latitude to measure places north and south of the equator.

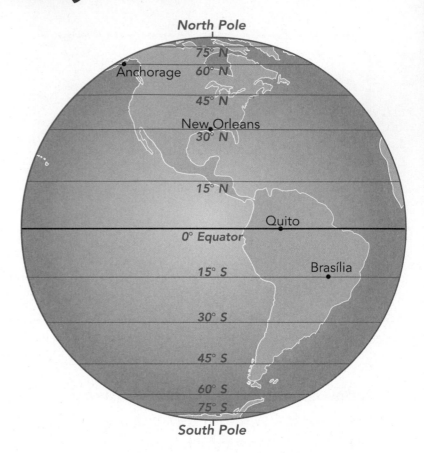

Lines of latitude are measured in degrees, shown by the symbol °. For example, the equator is 0°. Parallels north of the equator are marked in degrees north (N), and parallels south of the equator are marked in degrees south (S). The North Pole is at 90° north and the South Pole is at 90° south. Use the map to answer these questions.

1. Find the 60°N latitude line. What city is located there? _____

2. At what degree of latitude is New Orleans? _____

3. Look at the Southern Hemisphere. What city is at 15°S? _____

4. Quito, a city in Ecuador, is at 0°.
What is another name for this line of latitude? _____

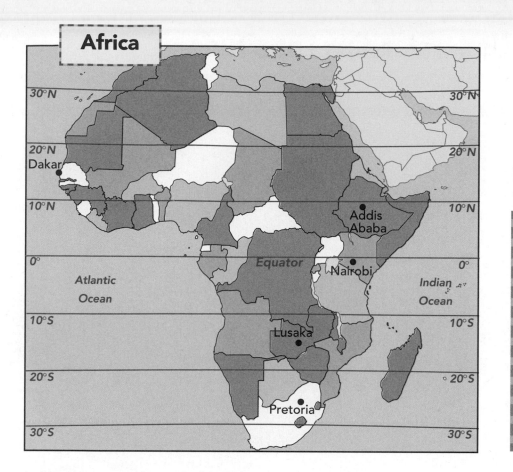

© Scholastic Inc.

map reader's Tip

The distance between two parallels that are one degree apart is about 69 miles or 111 kilometers. This distance varies slightly because the Earth is not a perfect sphere.

Most maps do not show every line of latitude. Look at the globe on page 208 again. It shows the lines of latitude for every 15 degrees. How many degrees apart are the lines of latitude on this map of Africa?

5. What city is almost on the equator? _____

6. Find the line of latitude marked 10°N.
What city is located near this parallel? _____

7. Is Dakar in the northern or southern latitudes? _____

8. Find a city at about 15°S. About how many
degrees north of Pretoria is it? _____

9. Most of Africa is between _____ and _____ lines of latitude.

10. All in all, Africa covers about _____ degrees of latitude.

Understanding Longitude

You know that lines of latitude measure the distance north and south on a globe. Lines of **longitude** measure Earth in degrees from east to west.

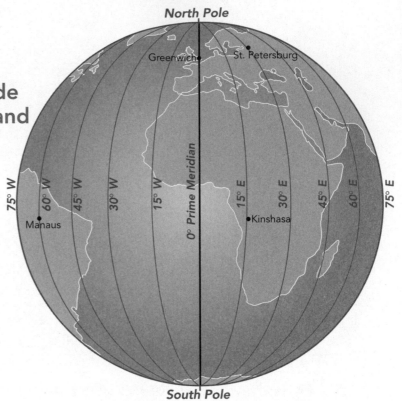

These lines are also called meridians. You read that the Prime Meridian divides Earth into the Eastern and Western hemispheres. The Prime Meridian is 0°. From the Prime Meridian to 180° longitude is exactly halfway around Earth.

1. In which direction do lines of longitude run? _____

2. Find the 15°W longitude line. What does the W stand for? _____

3. Find the 60°W longitude line. What city is located there? _____

4. At what degree of longitude is St. Petersburg? _____

5. Find a city in Africa at 15°E longitude. _____

6. Greenwich, a city in England, is at 0°.

   What is another name for this line of longitude? _____

7. Why can't you see 90° W longitude on this globe? _____

8. Most of Africa is between _____ and _____ lines of longitude.

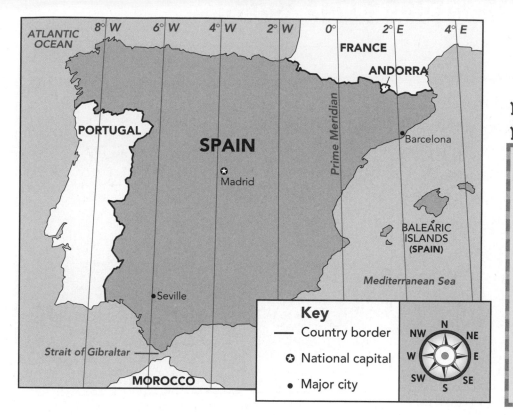

Unlike latitude, lines of longitude are not all the same distance apart from each other. They are farthest apart at the equator. At the North and South poles, they all come together.

Most maps do not show every line of longitude. The globe on page 210 shows the lines of longitude for every 15 degrees. How many degrees apart are the lines of longitude on this map of Spain?

Write True or False before each statement.

_____ **9.** Spain is entirely in the west longitudes.

_____ **10.** The Prime Meridian runs through Spain.

_____ **11.** Madrid is at about 4°W longitude.

_____ **12.** Spain covers less than 20 degrees of longitude.

word search

Find the following words from this lesson: **meridian, longitude, north, south, east, west, earth.**

```
L H E T M J J O Z
F C S E E A R T H
V I O U R T S A E
E D U T I G N O L
J N T X D B E Z Q
U E H D I C S A N
F K R S A W E S T
H T R O N I X P O
```

Using a Map Scale

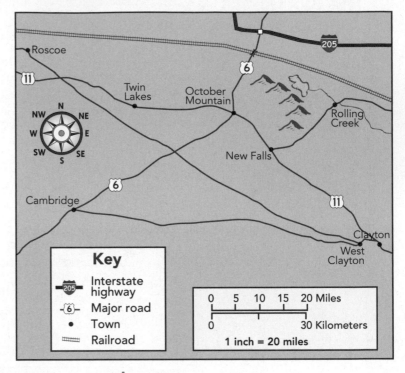

When you are traveling, it is useful to know how far you have to go. To show distances accurately on a map, mapmakers use a **scale**. A map scale helps you measure distance on a map. Look at the scale on this map. It shows that one inch equals twenty miles. That means that one inch on the map stands for twenty miles on Earth.

Use a ruler to measure distances on the map. Circle the correct answers.

1. From Twin Lakes to October Mountain, it is about _____.

   a. 20 miles   b. 40 miles   c. 50 miles

2. Between Clayton and New Falls there are _____.

   a. 20 miles   b. 30 miles   c. 40 miles

3. The distance from Cambridge to West Clayton is _____.

   a. 20 miles   b. 60 miles   c. 80 miles

4. The distance between Roscoe and West Clayton is less than _____.

   a. 100 miles   b. 20 miles   c. 60 miles

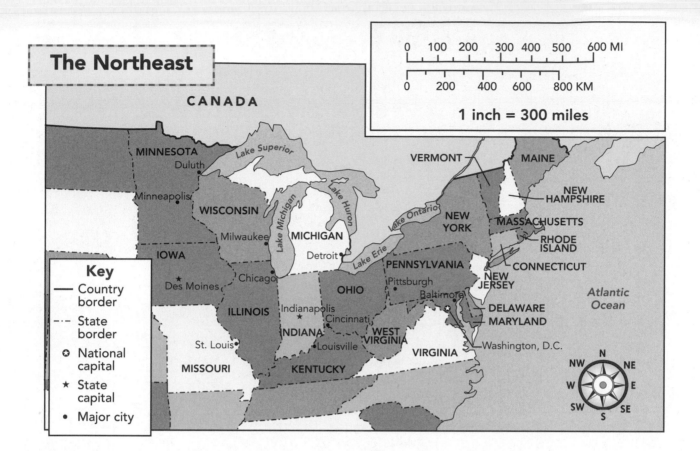

The Northeast

A map scale usually shows distance in both miles and kilometers. A kilometer is a measurement in the metric system. A mile is a longer distance than a kilometer. On this map scale you can see that 300 miles is a longer distance than 400 kilometers. Notice that the abbreviation for miles is MI and the abbreviation for kilometers is KM. Use the map to answer these questions.

5. How many miles does one inch represent on this map? _____

6. How many miles is it from St. Louis to Cincinnati? _____
About how many kilometers is this? _____

7. About how many miles is it from Milwaukee to Pittsburgh? _____

8. How many kilometers is it between
Minneapolis and Des Moines? _____

9. About how many kilometers is it from
Indianapolis to Washington, D.C.? _____

Comparing Maps and Scales

Not all maps have the same scale. The maps on this page show the same place, but they have different scales.

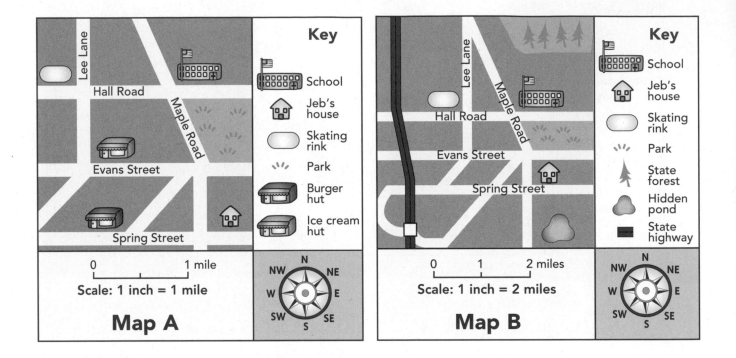

Use the map to answer these questions.

1. What does one inch stand for on the Map A scale? _____

2. How many miles does one inch stand for on Map B? _____

3. How long is Hall Road on Map A? _____

   How long is it on Map B? _____

4. Which map shows a smaller area? _____

5. Which map shows a larger area? _____

6. Which map would be more useful for getting from the state highway to

   Jeb's house? _____

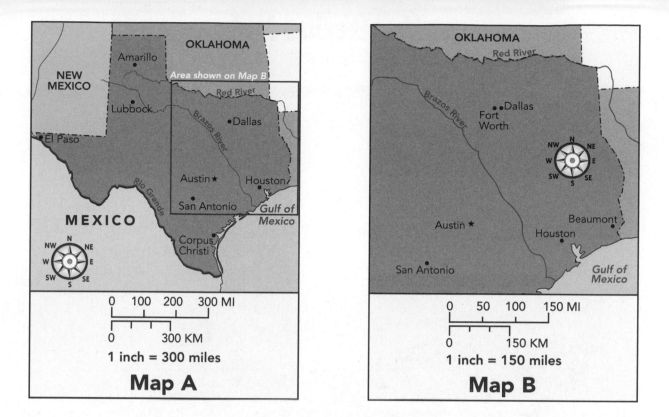

Map A

Map B

The maps on this page are the same size, but they show areas of different sizes. One map shows the whole state of Texas. The other map shows just the eastern part of the state.

Use the maps to answer the questions.

7. How many miles does one inch stand for on each map? _____

8. Why isn't El Paso on Map B? _____

9. Name two cities on Map B that are not shown on Map A. _____

10. About how many miles is it between El Paso and Lubbock? _____

11. Which map would you use if you were driving all the way across the state of Texas? _____

A Vegetation Map

The different kinds of trees and plants that grow in an area are called vegetation. This map shows **vegetation** on the continent of Africa.

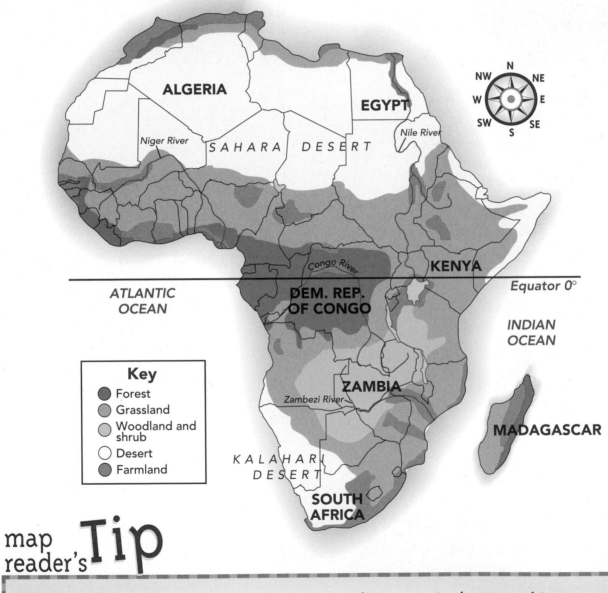

Key
- Forest
- Grassland
- Woodland and shrub
- Desert
- Farmland

map reader's Tip

The cacao tree is one special kind of vegetation that grows in the West African countries of Ghana, Ivory Coast, and Nigeria. The seeds from these trees produce most of the world's chocolate.

Use the map to answer these questions.

1. What does this symbol ◯ stand for? _____

2. Deserts cover two-fifths of Africa.

   In what part of Africa do you find the largest desert? _____

3. Would you expect the population in Africa's desert regions to be large

   or small? Why? _____

4. Grasslands also cover much of Africa.

   What is the symbol for this vegetation on the map? _____

5. How would you describe the vegetation in Zambia? _____

6. Name two African nations that are mostly desert. _____

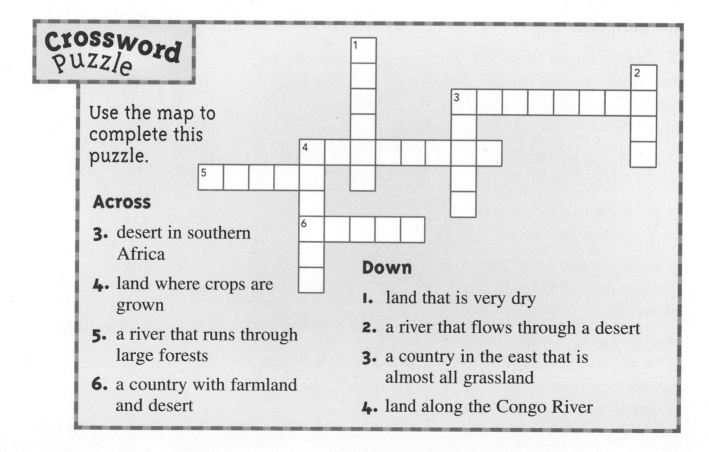

Crossword Puzzle

Use the map to complete this puzzle.

Across

3. desert in southern Africa

4. land where crops are grown

5. a river that runs through large forests

6. a country with farmland and desert

Down

1. land that is very dry

2. a river that flows through a desert

3. a country in the east that is almost all grassland

4. land along the Congo River

Looking at Landforms

As you know, Earth's surface has both land and water. The pictures on this page show some of the landforms found on Earth. Read each of these descriptions. Then write the name of the correct landform on each line under the picture.

1. _____

A **canyon** is a deep, narrow valley with high, steep sides.

A **mountain** is high, steep, rugged land that rises sharply from the surrounding area.

2. _____

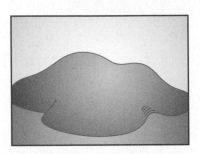

3. _____

A **hill** is an area of raised land that is lower and more rounded than a mountain.

A **plain** is a broad area of open, flat land.

A **plateau** is a large area of high, flat land.

4. _____

5. _____

A **valley** is the land that lies between hills or mountains.

A **volcano** is a mountain with a cone shape that is formed by lava that erupts from a crack in the earth's surface.

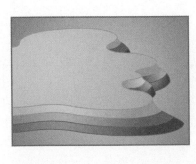

6. _____

7. _____

Many landforms are formed where land and water come together. The pictures on this page show some examples. Read the description of each one. Then write the name of each landform under the correct picture.

A **cape** is a small, narrow point of land that sticks out into a body of water.

A **peninsula** is an area of land that is surrounded by water on three sides.

An **isthmus** is a narrow strip of land that connects two large areas of land.

8. _____

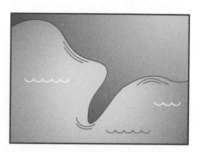

9. _____

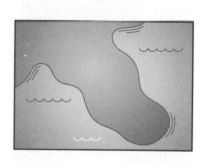

10. _____

Many bodies of water, including oceans, rivers, and lakes, cover Earth. The pictures show still other bodies of water. Read each description and write the name under the correct picture.

A **strait** is a narrow channel that connects two larger bodies of water.

A **gulf** is an arm of an ocean or sea that is partly enclosed by land.

A **bay** is a smaller body of water partly enclosed by land.

11. _____

12. _____

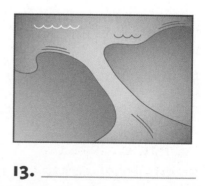

13. _____

A Profile and Contour Map

You know that mountains are high, but how high are they? The drawing on this page shows the **profile**, or side view, of two mountains.

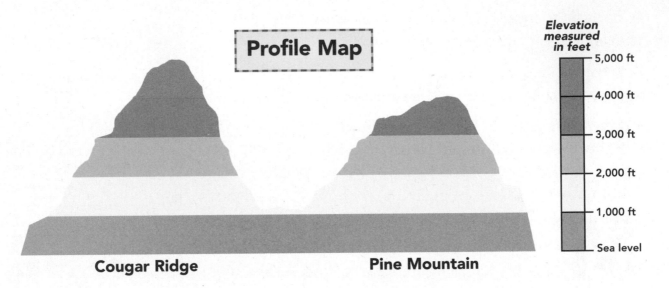

Profile Map

Elevation measured in feet

- 5,000 ft
- 4,000 ft
- 3,000 ft
- 2,000 ft
- 1,000 ft
- Sea level

Cougar Ridge   **Pine Mountain**

The key tells you the **elevation** of different parts of the mountains. Elevation is the height of any place on land above **sea level**. Sea level is the average height of the ocean's surface. It is zero elevation. Land that rises 500 feet higher than sea level has an elevation of 500 feet.

1. What does the color yellow stand for on the mountains?_____

2. Which mountain is higher?_____
   What is its elevation? _____

3. What color represents an elevation of 800 feet? _____

4. Forest rangers are building a hut at the top of Pine Mountain.
   At what elevation will it be? _____

5. Suppose you are climbing Cougar Ridge
   and are halfway to the top. What is the elevation? _____

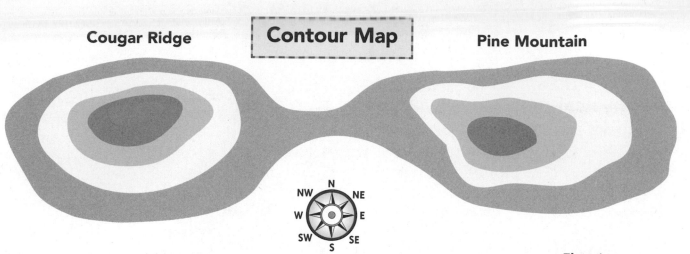

Cougar Ridge

Contour Map

Pine Mountain

Elevation measured in feet

- 5,000 ft
- 4,000 ft
- 3,000 ft
- 2,000 ft
- 1,000 ft
- Sea level

The map on this page is a **contour map**. It shows the same mountains as the profile on page 220, but it shows the view from above. The lines on the contour map show the elevations of different parts of the mountains. When the lines on a contour map are close together, they show that the land is steep. When the lines are far apart, they show a more gradual slope.

Imagine you are a mountain guide planning treks up these mountains. Draw the following routes on the contour map.

6. For expert hikers draw a dotted line up the steepest side of Cougar Ridge Mountain. Write the elevation at the top.

7. Mark a point halfway up this mountain with an X so the hikers can take a rest.

8. For the beginning hikers draw a double line up the least steep side of Pine Mountain. Write the elevation at the top.

9. For an all-day hike draw a continuous line from the lowest point on the map to the highest point on the map.

map reader's **Tip**

Some land on Earth is actually below sea level. For example, Death Valley in California is 282 feet below sea level. It is the lowest land in the Western Hemisphere.

© Scholastic Inc.

A Physical Map

A **physical map** shows natural features of a place. These might include lakes, rivers, and the elevation of the land. The physical map on this page shows the main islands of Hawaii.

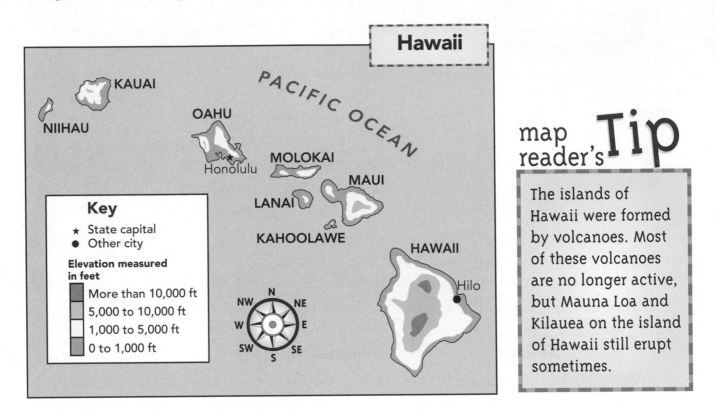

map reader's Tip

The islands of Hawaii were formed by volcanoes. Most of these volcanoes are no longer active, but Mauna Loa and Kilauea on the island of Hawaii still erupt sometimes.

1. What elevation does the color green stand for? _____

2. Which island has the highest elevation? _____

3. What landforms would you expect to see on the highest island? _____

4. Find Hawaii's capital, Honolulu. What is the elevation of this city? _____

5. Which islands are less than 5,000 feet high? _____
_____

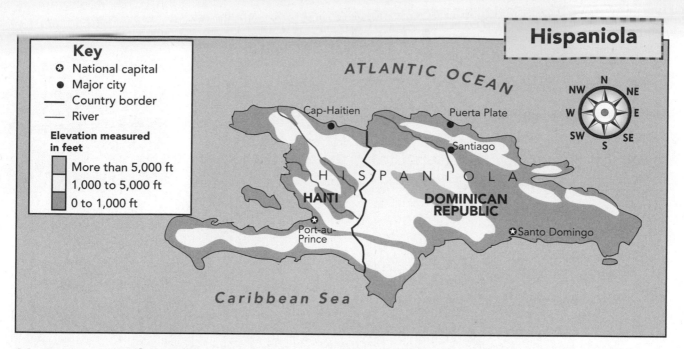

Hispaniola

Here is another physical map. It shows the two countries on the island of Hispaniola in the Caribbean Sea.

1. What are the two countries shown on this map? _____

2. What color is used to show elevations at sea level on this map? _____

3. In which country do you find the highest elevation?
   What landform would you expect to find there? _____

4. Find Santo Domingo, the capital of the Dominican Republic.
   What is the elevation of this city? _____

5. Find the border between the two countries.
   What is the elevation for most of it? _____

6. Rivers flow from high land to lower land. Find the rivers on this map.
   In which direction are they flowing? _____

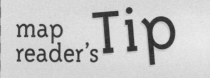

Hispaniola is the second largest island (after Cuba) in the West Indies. The explorer Christopher Columbus landed on Hispaniola in 1492.

A Product Map

Some maps give information about the economy of a place. The map on this page shows the main crops and farm products produced in North Dakota. It is called a **product map**.

North Dakota is a leading producer of flax, which is used to make paint.

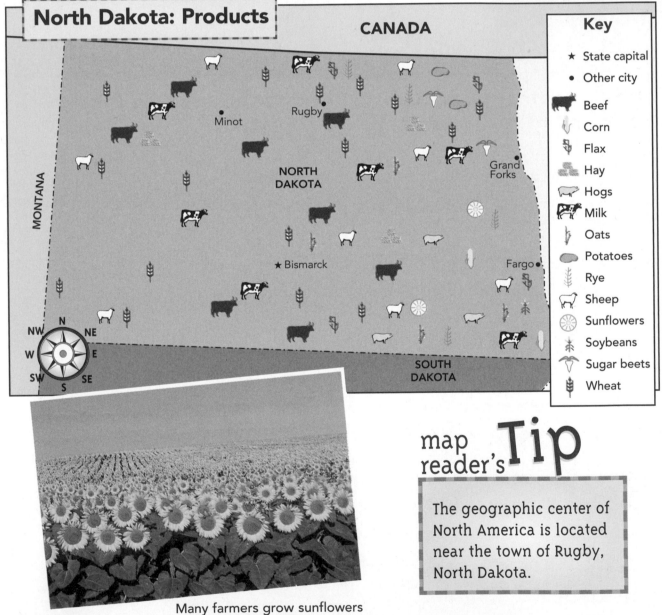

North Dakota: Products

CANADA

MONTANA

Minot

Rugby

NORTH DAKOTA

Grand Forks

Bismarck

Fargo

SOUTH DAKOTA

Key

★ State capital
• Other city
Beef
Corn
Flax
Hay
Hogs
Milk
Oats
Potatoes
Rye
Sheep
Sunflowers
Soybeans
Sugar beets
Wheat

N NE E SE S SW W NW

Many farmers grow sunflowers for their oil and seeds.

map reader's Tip

The geographic center of North America is located near the town of Rugby, North Dakota.

Write TRUE or FALSE on the line next to each sentence.

_____ 1. More crops are grown in the western part of the state than the eastern part.

_____ 2. Wheat and other grains such as rye and oats are grown in many parts of the state.

_____ 3. 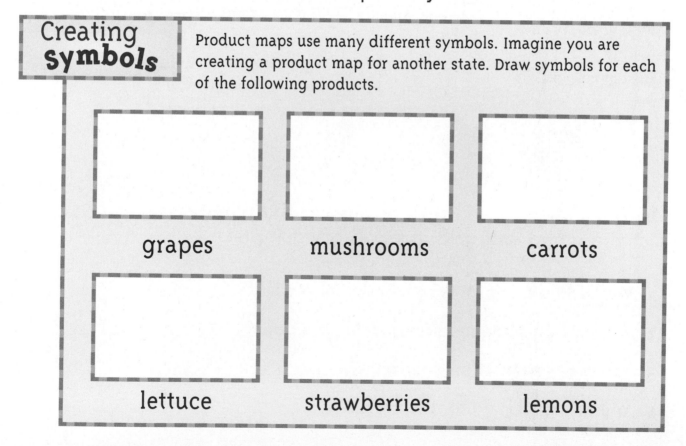 is the symbol for hay on this map.

_____ 4. Fruit is an important farm product in North Dakota.

_____ 5. Some farmers in the state raise dairy cows.

_____ 6. Steaks are probably a big meat product in North Dakota.

_____ 7. Sunflowers grow mostly in the southeastern part of the state.

_____ 8. The soil in North Dakota is probably fertile.

Creating symbols

Product maps use many different symbols. Imagine you are creating a product map for another state. Draw symbols for each of the following products.

grapes	mushrooms	carrots
lettuce	strawberries	lemons

A History Map

Most maps show what the world is like today. But some maps can show you what a place was like long ago. These are called history maps.

The map on these pages shows Colonial Williamsburg in Virginia. Some people call this community a "living museum." That's because Colonial Williamsburg was rebuilt to show how people lived in 1775. Looking at this map is like stepping back in time.

Glossary of Colonial Terms

apothecary	. . . . pharmacy or drugstore
blacksmith	. . . . . maker of iron tools, knives, and horsehoes
cooper	. . . . barrelmaker
gaol	. . . . jail
milliner	. . . . hatmaker
rural trades	. . . . farm equipment
tavern	. . . . restaurant
wheelwright	. . . . wheelmaker
windmill	. . . . . . grinder of grain into flour

A

1 SCOTLAND STREET

2 PRINCE GEORGE STREET

3 College of William and Mary

4 BOUNDARY STREET

Use the glossary and grid to answer the questions. List the name and grid location of each place.

1. You drop off your horse's harness for repair. _____

2. You pick up some medicines for your mother. _____

3. You order a barrel for your father. _____

4. You drop off an ad for the newspaper. _____

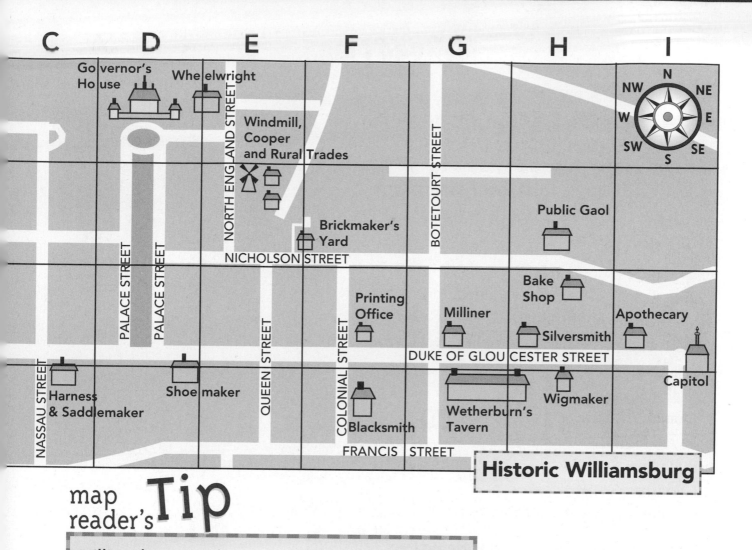

Historic Williamsburg

map reader's **Tip**

> Williamsburg was the capital of Virginia from 1699 to 1780. Today, Virginia's capital is Richmond.

5. You leave a basket of corn to be ground into corn meal. _____

6. You join your father for dinner. _____

7. You stop to look at hats in a store window. _____

8. You help your father take a horse to get new shoes. _____

9. Mmmm. You can't resist those baked apple pies! _____

10. You buy a candlestick for your sister's wedding. _____

A Road Map

Have you ever taken a vacation by car? Then your family probably used a **road map**. A road map shows the main highways that go from place to place. It also shows smaller, secondary roads.

On a road map, the numbers for roads are shown in different symbols. Some kinds of highways that you might travel on are:

interstate highway

U.S. highway

state or county road

1. What interstate highway runs east and west across Iowa? _____

2. If you travel from Cedar Rapids to Waterloo, what interstate can you take? _____

3. Interstate 29 connects Iowa with which two other states. _____

4. What does this symbol —(3)— stand for? _____

5. Name two routes you could take from Dubuque to South Dakota. _____

6. On which highways is Ames? _____

7. What cities does Interstate 35 run through? _____

8. Describe the best route from Council Bluffs to Mason City. _____

map reader's Tip

"Inter" means between or among. Interstate highways cross between states. Interstate routes that go east and west have even numbers. North-south interstate routes have odd numbers.

Iowa: Highways

E-Z Trip Planner

Imagine you are planning a trip from Davenport to Sioux City. Use the E-Z Trip Planner to list the highways you will travel on. Don't forget to pick a place for a lunch break!

Highway	Direction
Lunch break	

A Weather Map

What's the weather like today? One way to find out is to look out the window. Another way to check the weather is to look at a weather map like the one shown here.

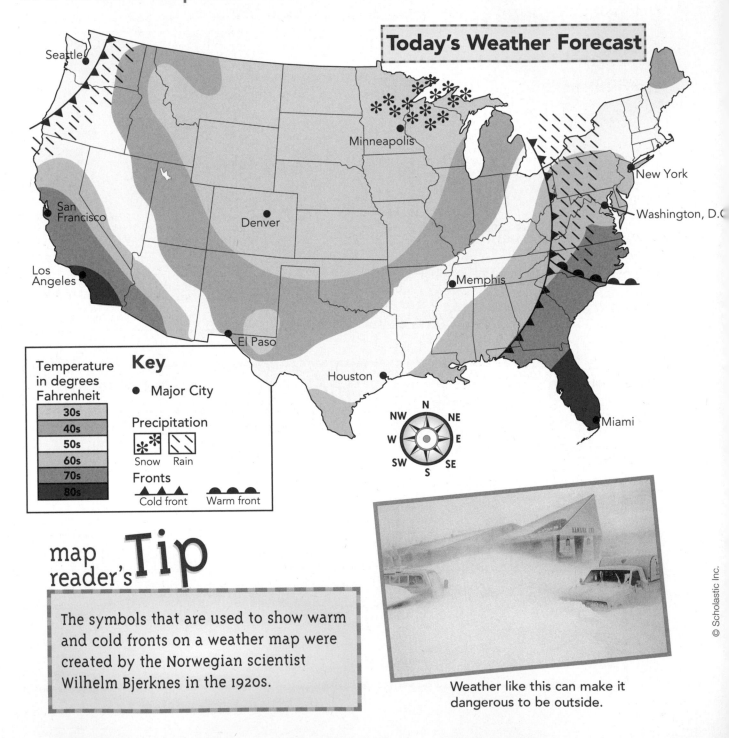

Today's Weather Forecast

Seattle
San Francisco
Los Angeles
El Paso
Denver
Minneapolis
Memphis
Houston
New York
Washington, D.C.
Miami

Key

Temperature in degrees Fahrenheit

| 30s |
| 40s |
| 50s |
| 60s |
| 70s |
| 80s |

● Major City

Precipitation

Snow   Rain

Fronts

Cold front   Warm front

Compass: N, NE, E, SE, S, SW, W, NW

map reader's Tip

The symbols that are used to show warm and cold fronts on a weather map were created by the Norwegian scientist Wilhelm Bjerknes in the 1920s.

Weather like this can make it dangerous to be outside.

A cold front is a zone of cold air moving in as warm air retreats. A cold front usually means clouds and showers. A warm front is a zone of warm air advancing as cold air retreats. Clouds and rain often occur just ahead of a warm front. Weather systems usually move from west to east across North America.

1. In which part of the country is there a warm front? _____

2. What is the temperature in Seattle today? _____

3. What city is about to get snow? _____

4. Name two cities with temperatures in the 80s. _____

5. If you were in Denver today, how would you dress? _____

6. What kind of weather is heading toward Washington, D.C.? _____

7. Is it cooler in San Francisco or Los Angeles today? _____

8. You live in Memphis and are planning a hike.

Will you have good weather for this activity? _____

Weather or Not Find the area of your hometown on the weather map. Then fill out the chart below with your prediction for the weather for today and the next two days. Use the symbols provided.

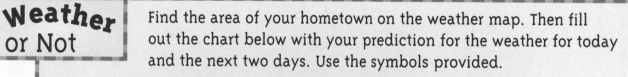

Today	Tomorrow	Day After Tomorrow

A Climate Map

Weather changes from day to day, but climate remains more or less the same.

C limate is the pattern of weather that an area has over a period of time. Does an area get a lot of rain during the year? Is it mostly hot or mostly cold? The map shown here is a climate map. It shows the different kinds of climate regions in the United States.

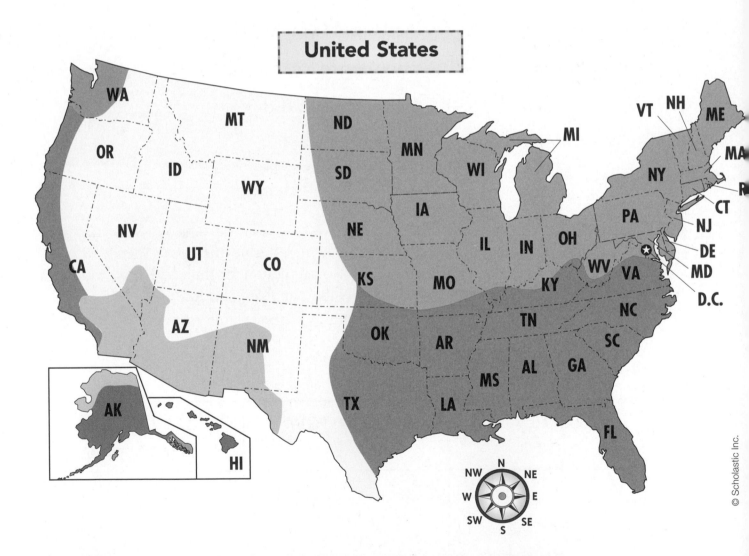

United States

© Scholastic Inc.

map reader's Tip

Different factors affect climate. Elevation is one. Another is latitude or how far a place is from the equator. Landforms also affect climate.

Map Key

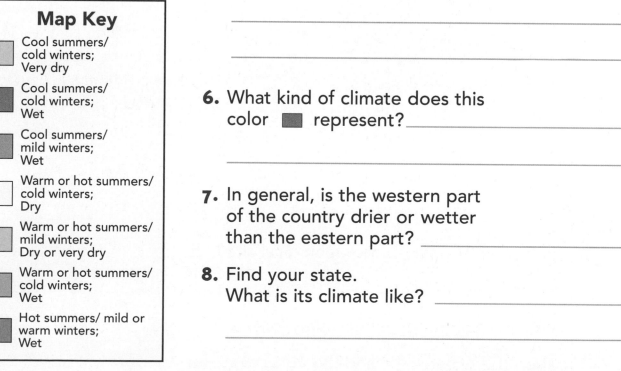

	Cool summers/ cold winters; Very dry
	Cool summers/ cold winters; Wet
	Cool summers/ mild winters; Wet
	Warm or hot summers/ cold winters; Dry
	Warm or hot summers/ mild winters; Dry or very dry
	Warm or hot summers/ cold winters; Wet
	Hot summers/ mild or warm winters; Wet

1. How would you describe the climate in the northeastern part of the United States?

_____

_____

2. Find an area where summers are hot and winters are mild. Where is it?_____

3. How many kinds of climates does Texas have? _____

4. Describe one climate in Alaska. _____

_____

_____

5. What is the climate like along most of the west coast?

_____

_____

6. What kind of climate does this color ■ represent?_____

_____

7. In general, is the western part of the country drier or wetter than the eastern part? _____

8. Find your state. What is its climate like? _____

_____

A News Map

News maps help readers locate and understand events around the globe. Here is the first paragraph of a news story and a map that goes with it.

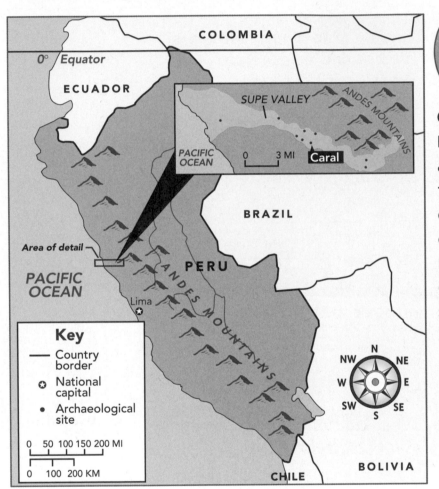

Oldest City in the Americas

Researchers working at an archaeological site in Peru say that they think it is the oldest city in the Americas. The site, called Caral, dates back to 2600 B.C. Scientists used radiocarbon dating of plant fibers from the site to determine its age. They believe that a civilization existed at Caral for five centuries. Until now, scientists thought that the earliest civilization in Peru was on the coast.

1. In which direction is Caral from Lima?_____

2. What is the symbol for an archaeological site? _____

3. In which valley is Caral?_____

4. In which mountain range is the valley located? _____

5. Is Caral on the ocean or inland? _____

© Scholastic Inc.

This news story takes place in another part of the world, the country of Cambodia in Southeast Asia.

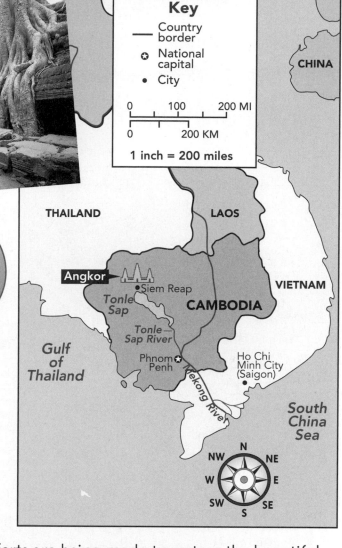

Temples and Trees Embrace

Angkor was one of the world's great cities between the ninth and fifteenth centuries. Its huge temples were famous. When the empire at Angkor collapsed, the jungle crept in and the temples lay hidden by trees and undergrowth. Although the temples were rediscovered by explorers many years later, only part of the jungle was cleared away. Today, efforts are being made to restore the beautiful temples. But in many cases the trees have become part of the buildings.

6. What countries border Cambodia on the north? _____

What country borders Cambodia on the east? _____

7. What city is Angkor near? _____

8. In which direction is Angkor from Phnom Penh? _____

9. About how far is Angkor from the Mekong River? _____

10. What body of water is Angkor near? _____

Planning With a Map

The map on this page shows Yellowstone National Park, one of the most popular parks in our country. It's a great place to take a vacation!

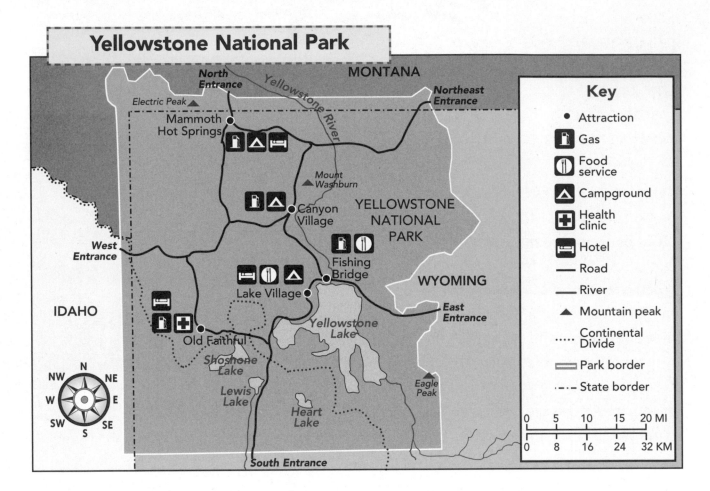

1. Yellowstone is located in three different states. What are they?_____

2. How many road entrances are there to the park? _____

3. Old Faithful Geyser is the park's most famous attraction.

   In which direction is the geyser from Yellowstone Lake?_____

map reader's Tip

The Continental Divide runs through Yellowstone Park. Rain that falls on the west side of this line flows to the Pacific Ocean. Rain that falls on the east side of this line flows to the Atlantic Ocean.

Handy Dandy Planning Guide

Use the guide below to plan a three-day visit to Yellowstone Park.

	Day 1	Day 2	Day 3
Sights to See			
Places to Swim or Fish			
Mountain to Hike			
Hotel			

4. Which river flows out of the north end of the park?_____

5. What is the largest lake in the park? _____

6. Look at the scale on this map. About how many miles is it from the east side of the park to the west side? _____

Maps and Charts

Sometimes maps don't provide all the information you need. The chart on the next page tells what the abbreviations in the map below stand for. It also provides the nickname of each state.

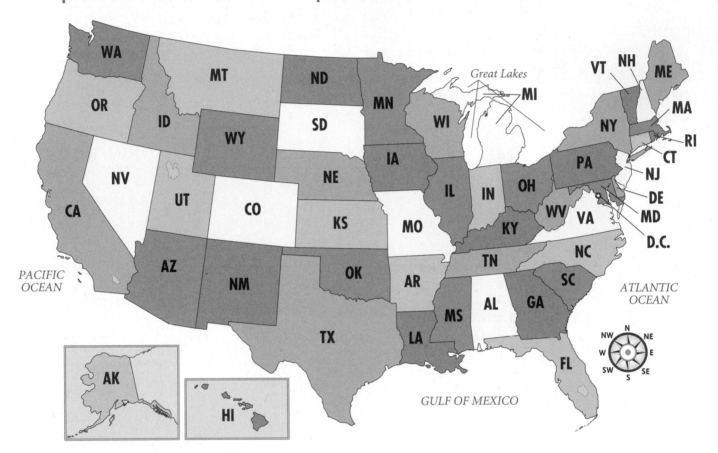

Use the map and the chart to answer these questions.

1. What two states bordering the Great Lakes have nicknames that are animals? _____

2. What is the abbreviation of the Mountain State? _____

3. Which ocean does the Ocean State border? _____

4. What is the nickname of Nebraska? _____

   What does this tell you about the crops grown there? _____

STATE NAME	ABBREVIATION	NICKNAME	STATE NAME	ABBREVIATION	NICKNAME
Alabama	AL	Heart of Dixie	Montana	MT	Treasure State
Alaska	AK	The Last Frontier	Nebraska	NE	Cornhusker State
Arizona	AZ	Grand Canyon State	Nevada	NV	Silver State
Arkansas	AR	Land of Opportunity	New Hampshire	NH	Granite State
California	CA	Golden State	New Jersey	NJ	Garden State
Colorado	CO	Centennial State	New Mexico	NM	Land of Enchantment
Connecticut	CT	Constitution State	New York	NY	Empire State
Delaware	DE	First State	North Carolina	NC	Tar Heel State
Florida	FL	Sunshine State	North Dakota	ND	Peace Garden State
Georgia	GA	Peach State	Ohio	OH	Buckeye State
Hawaii	HI	The Aloha State	Oklahoma	OK	Sooner State
Idaho	ID	Gem State	Oregon	OR	Beaver State
Illinois	IL	Prairie State	Pennsylvania	PA	Keystone State
Indiana	IN	Hoosier State	Rhode Island	RI	Ocean State
Iowa	IA	Hawkeye State	South Carolina	SC	Palmetto State
Kansas	KS	Sunflower State	South Dakota	SD	Coyote State
Kentucky	KY	Bluegrass State	Tennessee	TN	Volunteer State
Louisiana	LA	Pelican State	Texas	TX	Lone Star State
Maine	ME	Pine Tree State	Utah	UT	Beehive State
Maryland	MD	Free State	Vermont	VT	Green Mountain State
Massachusetts	MA	Bay State	Virginia	VA	Old Dominion
Michigan	MI	Wolverine State	Washington	WA	Evergreen State
Minnesota	MN	North Star State	West Virginia	WV	Mountain State
Mississippi	MS	Magnolia State	Wisconsin	WI	Badger State
Missouri	MO	Show Me State	Wyoming	WY	Equality State

5. Which state in the northwest probably has a lot of pine trees? _____

Which state in the northeast is similar?_____

6. Which state on the Gulf of Mexico
has a nickname that is a bird? _____

7. Why do you think Florida is called the Sunshine State? _____

Map Review 1

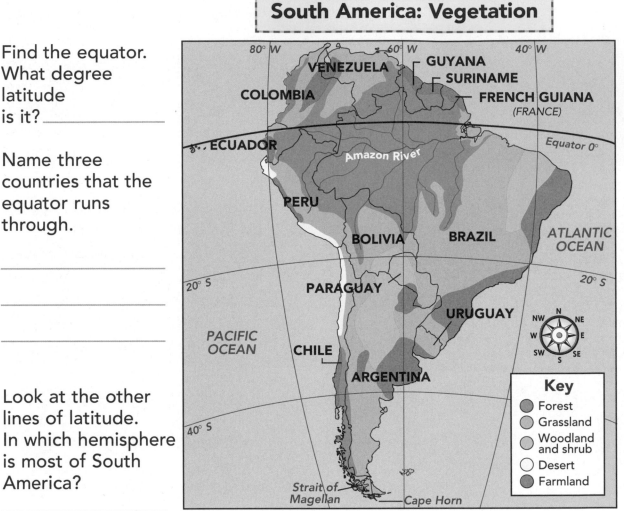

South America: Vegetation

1. Find the equator. What degree latitude is it? _____

2. Name three countries that the equator runs through.

   _____

   _____

   _____

3. Look at the other lines of latitude. In which hemisphere is most of South America?

   _____

4. At about what longitude is the westernmost part of Ecuador? _____

5. What does this symbol ◯ stand for? _____

6. Where are the deserts in South America? _____

7. How would you describe the vegetation in Guyana? _____

8. In which part of Brazil would you expect to find the Amazon Rain Forest? _____

© Scholastic Inc.

Map Review 2

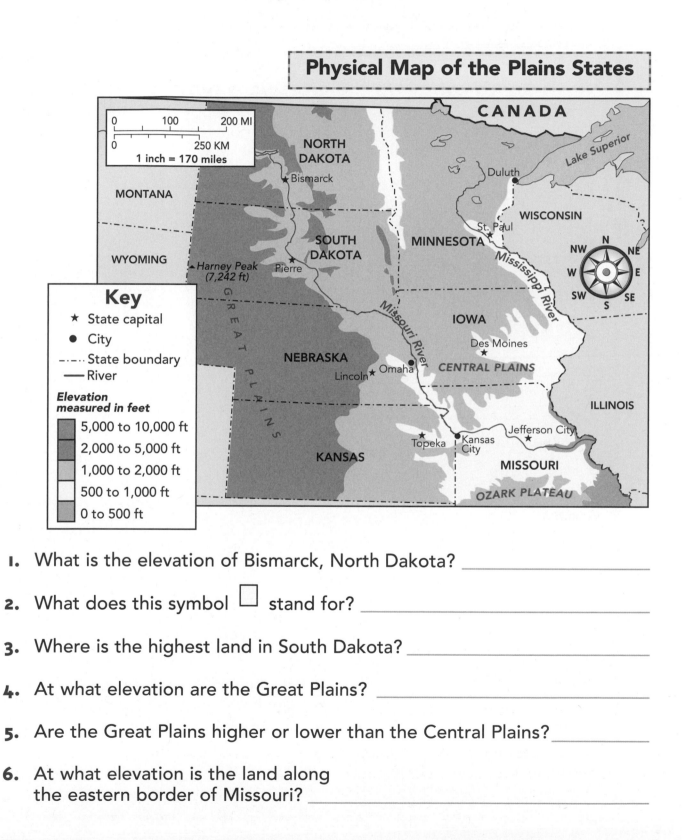

Physical Map of the Plains States

1. What is the elevation of Bismarck, North Dakota? _____

2. What does this symbol ☐ stand for? _____

3. Where is the highest land in South Dakota? _____

4. At what elevation are the Great Plains? _____

5. Are the Great Plains higher or lower than the Central Plains? _____

6. At what elevation is the land along
   the eastern border of Missouri? _____

Thinking About Maps

Use what you have learned about maps
to complete the crossword puzzle.

Across

4. a way to measure
   distance on a map

5. half of Earth

8. a map that is a side view

9. a drawing that stands
   for something on a map

10. 0° latitude

Down

1. plants that grow in a place

2. A mountain is a kind of
   _____.

3. the pattern of weather
   in a place

4. a narrow channel of water

6. the height of land above
   sea level

7. an area of high, flat land

9. there are 50 of these

Glossary

axis
An axis is an imaginary center line on which Earth turns.

canyon
A canyon is a deep, narrow valley with high, steep sides.

cape
A cape is a small, narrow point of land that sticks out into a body of water.

cardinal directions
Cardinal directions are the four main directions—north, south, east, and west.

climate
Climate is the kind of weather that an area has over a period of time.

compass rose
A compass rose is a symbol that shows directions.

contour map
A contour map has lines that show the elevations of different parts of land.

elevation
Elevation is the height of land above sea level.

equator
The equator is an imaginary line that runs around the center of Earth and divides it into the Northern and Southern hemispheres. The equator is 0° latitude.

grid
A grid is a pattern of lines that form squares.

gulf
A gulf is an arm of an ocean or sea that is partly enclosed by land.

hemisphere
A hemisphere is half of Earth. Earth can be divided into Northern and Southern hemispheres or Eastern and Western hemispheres.

intermediate directions
Intermediate directions are directions between the four main directions. They are northeast, southeast, southwest, and northwest.

isthmus
An isthmus is a narrow strip of land that connects two large areas of land.

latitude
Lines of latitude run around Earth parallel to the equator. They are marked in degrees north and south.

longitude
Lines of longitude are meridians that measure Earth in degrees from east to west.

map index
A map index is an alphabetical listing of place names on a map. A map index gives the grid square for each place.

peninsula
A peninsula is an area of land that is surrounded by water on three sides.

physical map
A physical map shows natural features of Earth.

plateau
A plateau is a large area of high, flat land.

Prime Meridian
The Prime Meridian is an imaginary line at 0° longitude. The Prime Meridian divides Earth into Eastern and Western hemispheres.

profile map
A profile map shows the side view of a place.

product map
A product map shows the products produced in a region.

projections
Map projections are different ways of showing Earth on a flat surface.

road map
A road map shows the main roads and highways that go from place to place in an area.

scale
A map scale helps you measure distance on a map.

sea level
Sea level is the average height of the ocean's surface. It is zero elevation.

strait
A strait is a narrow channel that connects two larger bodies of water.

symbol
A symbol is a drawing or color that represents something else.

vegetation
Vegetation is the different kinds of trees and plants that grow in an area.

volcano
A volcano is a mountain with a cone shape that is formed by lava that erupts from a crack in Earth's surface.

Old Bones

What unusual discoveries have scientists made about animals that lived long ago? Fill in the blanks in this article to find out.

Ten million years ago, a group of animals gathered at a watering hole in Nebraska. Barrel-bodied _____,
15-foot camels, and other creatures came to drink. Then a volcano
_____ 1,000 miles away. Wind carried the
volcanic ash great distances. The ash rained down over the animals
and buried them.

Word Bank
erupted
fossil
preserved
rhinoceroses
scattered

Dr. Michael Voorhies grew up in Nebraska. As a boy, in 1971, a
strange thing happened. He found a baby rhino skull in Nebraska. He dug around it.
It was still attached to a skeleton. He kept digging and found five more rhino skeletons.

So far, _____ scientists have found more than 240 complete
animal skeletons in that area. They even discovered the remains of a tiny three-toed horse.

Finding so many skeletons in one place is very unusual. Usually bones are
_____ far apart by wind, waves, or animals. But these remains were
_____ exactly where they were by the volcanic ash that buried them.

Think About It!

Why was the discovery of the Nebraska animal bones so important?

Why Penguins Wear Tuxedos

Have you ever noticed that penguins look like funny little men in tuxedos? Fill in the blanks to find out how their distinctive look may help keep them safe.

Walking around on two legs with their arms flapping around,

penguins are a _____ and adorable sight.

But how did they get their special look?

Most _____ of penguin developed a

similar color pattern. They have black or dark blue feathers on their backs

and white feathers on their chests and _____.

Scientists think that this basic pattern _____

because it protected penguins so well from their enemies, such as seals, in the

water. From below, its white chest and stomach hide a penguin in the glare of

_____. From above, its dark back makes a penguin hard

to see against the darkness of the water.

Word Bank

comical
evolved
species
stomachs
sunlight

Think About It!

Why do scientists think that penguin species developed a similar color pattern?

Elephant Orchestra

Read the animal behavior article.
Then follow the directions in the Text Marking box.

"Elephants like music," says musician and neuroscientist David Sulzer. "If you play music, they'll come over." At a conservation center in Thailand, he saw this for himself. He watched elephant trainers sing to the animals to soothe them. Sulzer already knew that elephants could recognize melodies. He wondered if they would play music themselves.

An elephant named Pratiah playing the drums

So Sulzer collected a band of elephants at the center to find out. He first built a variety of huge, unbreakable percussion instruments the elephants could play with their trunks or feet. He built 22 such instruments. These included drums, gongs, flutes, cymbals, and king-sized xylophones the elephants could play with a large mallet. Sulzer's instruments resemble traditional Thai ones and sound like them, too.

Sulzer soon found that elephants were indeed musicians. They could bang, stomp, tap, and blow to play distinct musical notes. With the help of the trainers, Sulzer got his elephant orchestra to play Thai melodies the tuskers recognize.

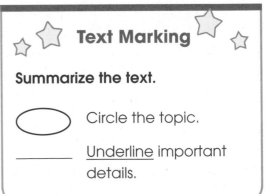

Text Marking

Summarize the text.

◯ Circle the topic.

___ Underline important details.

The Thai Elephant Orchestra has been a success. They have made three albums. And they'll play for peanuts (or bananas or apples). But the best part is that these talented musicians help raise much-needed money to house and protect other endangered elephants.

Answer each question. Give evidence from the article.

1. The purpose of a *conservation center* (paragraph 1) is to _____.

    ○ A. soothe and calm wild animals   ○ C. provide musical entertainment

    ○ B. offer a safe home for wildlife   ○ D. raise funding for special equipment

What in the text helped you answer?

_____

2. Which of the following would make another good title for this article?

    ○ A. How to Fund Conservation Centers   ○ C. Massive Musicians

    ○ B. David Sulzer's Work   ○ D. A Visit to Thailand

What in the text helped you answer?

_____

3. Look back at your text markings. Write a one-paragraph summary of the key information provided in the article.

_____

_____

_____

_____

4. In this article, "play for peanuts" has two meanings. Explain what they are.

_____

_____

_____

_____

The Bear Facts

You probably know at least two things about bears: They're big and they can be scary. Fill in the blanks to learn more about two different kinds of bears.

Although black bears and polar bears are different in many

ways, they also have a lot in common. Their body shape is

_____, and they both have thick coats of fur.

_____ bear cubs of all kinds are very tiny and

stay with their mother for a year or more.

A major difference between black bears and polar bears

is their size. A full-grown black bear can be four to five feet long

and weigh 150 to 400 pounds. The huge polar bear, at six to eight feet long, can weigh up to

1,500 pounds! Black bears eat mostly green plants, berries, nuts, ants, and small animals such

as _____. The _____ food of polar bears is

seals, although they also eat birds' eggs and berries.

Black bears have black or dark brown fur. Polar bears have fur that is yellowish-white.

What's another way the two types of bears differ? Black bears _____

during the winter, while polar bears remain active.

Word Bank

- chief
- hibernate
- newborn
- rodents
- similar

Think About It! How are the black bear and the polar bear alike and different?

Return of the Wolves

Read how wolves are important to Yellowstone's food web. Then try the science investigations.

The lives of predator and prey are closely connected. A drop in the number of prey, for example, means fewer predators can survive. But what happens when a top predator is completely removed? The United States accidentally found out in the 20th century when it hunted wolves out of existence in Yellowstone National Park, which sits where Wyoming, Montana, and Idaho meet.

The wolves were targeted because they sometimes killed cattle and other livestock. They also competed with human hunters for elk and other game. Many people thought the world would be better without wolves. But once the wolves were gone, their absence sent ripples of change throughout the Yellowstone **food web**—a complex network of **food chains**, or orders of animals and plants in which each feeds on the one below it.

Population Explosion

Wolves' biggest prey had been elk. Once wolves weren't there to eat them, the number of elk increased. The larger numbers of hungry elk did a lot of damage to the willow trees that line the park's river.

But elk aren't the only animals that rely on willows. Beavers use them for food and for materials to build dams. Without access to willows, the number of beavers decreased—and so did the number of beaver dams.

And the changes didn't stop there. Beaver dams affect the flow of rivers and create shady pools that some fish need to raise babies. So fish populations were also thrown off balance.

Park officials tried to fix the problems by hunting elk to decrease their population. But it didn't help enough. Then they wondered—could returning wolves to Yellowstone put things back in balance?

A Reintroduction

In the 1990s, new wolves were released into the park. Since then, scientists have watched the wolf population and studied the food web. The number of elk has decreased. To avoid wolves, the elk must stay on the move and eat a wider variety of plants. That means less damage to the willows. And as willow trees have recovered, the population of beavers has bounced back.

Scientists hope that, slowly but surely, wolves will help restore the natural balance of the food web in Yellowstone.

Investigation 1

What happens when an animal disappears from a food chain?

Materials
★ sandwich and gallon-sized plastic bags
★ dry spinach pasta
★ dry macaroni
★ dry spaghetti
★ dry bow-tie pasta
★ watch or clock
★ recording sheet (next page)

1. Gather the materials you will need.

2. Follow the steps of Chow Time Simulation from the box below.

3. Pick the pieces off the floor. Count all the remaining pasta plants and animals. Record the numbers on the next page.

4. **Predict:** What would happen if a disease killed most of the mice? In this simulation, that would mean that only one friend or family member is a mouse. (Split the rest of the players between snakes and hawks.)

5. Repeat the Chow Time Simulation using the changes in Step 4.

6. Count all the plants and animals from each group. Record the numbers on your sheet. How did your results change? Why?

7. What would happen if instead the hawks were all killed by disease, leaving the snakes to eat mice with no time limit? Make a prediction.

8. Repeat the Chow Time Simulation using the changes in Step 7.

9. Count all the plants and animals. Record the numbers on your sheet. If this were a real food chain, what would happen next?

10. How was this simulation like a real food chain? How was it different?

Chow Time Simulation

1. Ask five friends or family members to play with you. Divide yourselves evenly into three groups: mice, snakes, and hawks. Mice and snakes each get a sandwich bag. Hawks each get a gallon-sized bag.

2. Clear a playing space. Scatter the spinach pasta onto the floor. These are "plants" that the mice eat.

3. **Mice,** pick up one plant and put it in your bag. Repeat for about 5 seconds.

4. **Mice,** count the plants in your bag. For every plant "eaten," place one dry macaroni on the floor. Each one represents one mouse.

5. **Snakes,** your turn next. Repeat Steps 4 and 5, but pick up only the macaroni "mice." For each "mouse" eaten, place one piece of spaghetti on the ground.

6. **Hawks,** your turn at last. Repeat Steps 4 and 5, but pick up only the spaghetti "snakes." For each "snake" eaten, place one piece of bow-tie pasta on the ground.

© Scholastic Inc.

1. Do Steps 2 and 3 of the investigation. Record the numbers in the chart below.

2. Predict: What would happen if a disease killed most of the mice?

_____

_____

3. Now do Steps 5 and 6 of the investigation. Record the numbers below. How did your results change? Why?

_____

_____

4. Predict: What would happen if the hawks were all killed by disease, leaving the snakes to eat mice with no time limit?

_____

_____

5. Do Steps 8 and 9 of the investigation. Record the numbers below.

	No. of Plants	No. of Mice	No. of Snakes	No. of Hawks
Original simulation				
Simulation with only one mouse				
Simulation with no hawks				

6. If this were a real food web, what would happen next?

_____

_____

7. How was this simulation like a real food web? How was it different? Write your answers on a separate sheet of paper.

Investigation 2

Invent a game to teach about food webs.

1. Gather the materials you will need.

2. Make a food web using local plants, animals, and other living things. **Your food web should focus on how nutrients cycle through the ecosystem.** Start by brainstorming local wildlife. Then research what eats what. **Many animals will eat more than one food. Many foods can be eaten by more than one animal.** Include at least 10 living things on your web. Be sure to have at least one of each of these: **plant**, **herbivore** (plant eater), **carnivore** (meat eater), and **decomposer** (something that breaks down dead things, putting nutrients back in the soil).

3. Draw your food web on your recording sheet. No pictures needed; just a box for each living thing and arrows showing how nutrients move from thing to thing. **Have the arrow point from the food toward the eater, because that's where the nutrients are going next.**

4. Now imagine your food web was drawn big on the pavement, like a hopscotch game. How could you turn it into a game to teach friends or family members how food webs work? Consider these:

   • Will kids move from square to square? Or will they stay on one square and something else does the moving?

   • If they are on a square that's eaten by more than one animal, how will they decide which arrow to follow?

   • What will happen when they get to a new square?

   • How long will they play?

   Write your game rules on your recording sheet.

5. Copy your food web onto pavement with chalk. Play the game to test the rules. Make any changes or improvements.

6. Invite friends or family members to play your game. Show them how it works and watch them play.

7. On a separate sheet of paper, tell how your game worked with friends or family members. What did they like? Did anything confuse them? What do you think they learned? Are there any changes you would make for the next version?

Materials

★ research tools (books, Internet, and so on)

★ chalk and pavement

★ recording sheet (next page)

© Scholastic Inc.

1. Do Steps 2 and 3 of the investigation. Draw your food web in the box below.

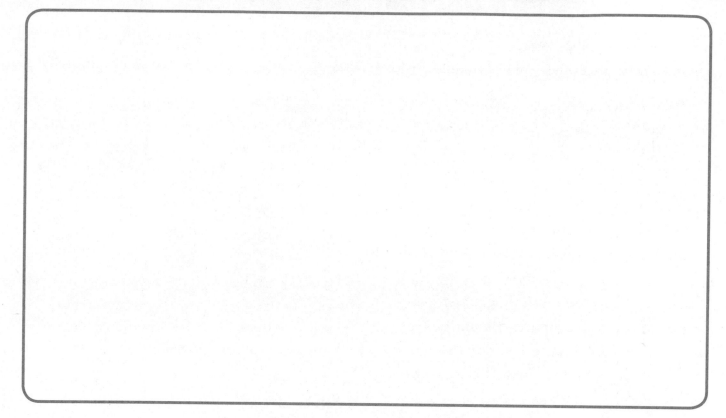

2. Now do Step 4 of the investigation. Write your game rules below.

_____

_____

_____

_____

_____

_____

3. Do Steps 5 and 6 of the investigation. What did the kids like? Did anything confuse them? What do you think they learned? Are there any changes you would make for the next version? Record your answers on a separate sheet of paper.

© Scholastic Inc.

"How Did That Taste, Doggie?"

Read the life science essay.
Then follow the directions in the Text Marking box.

If you have ever spent any time with dogs, you have noticed how much better their sense of smell is than yours. They can smell things before you do. They can detect smells that you cannot. But how does a dog's sense of taste compare with ours?

Their sense of taste is not as good as ours. You get one clue simply by watching them gobble up food as if they are starving and don't seem to even taste what they are wolfing down. Well, dogs just don't seem to care much about taste. That's because they have fewer taste buds than you do.

Taste buds are groups of cells that let us know how things taste. They tell us whether foods are sweet, salty, sour, bitter, or savory. Taste buds are located on the surface of the tongue. There are also some on the roof of the mouth and in the back of the mouth. The more taste buds you have, the better your sense of taste is. Whereas humans have about 9,000 of these, canines have about 1,700.

But compared to cats, dogs are foodies. Poor cats have only about 470 taste buds in their mouths.

A puppy wolfing down dinner

⭐ **Text Marking** ⭐

Find the main idea and supporting details.

⬭   Circle the main idea in each paragraph.

_____   Underline supporting details for each main idea.

Answer each question. Give evidence from the essay.

1. Which of the following words has the same meaning as *detect* (paragraph 1)?

    ○ A. avoid   ○ B. enjoy   ○ C. identify   ○ D. taste

What in the text helped you answer?

_____

2. Which statement is *true* about the connection between number of taste buds and the ability to taste different things?

    ○ A. An animal with more taste buds has a weaker sense of taste.
    ○ B. An animal with more taste buds senses more kinds of smells.
    ○ C. The fewer taste buds an animal has, the weaker its sense of taste.
    ○ D. There is no connection because all animals can taste the same things.

What in the text helped you answer?

_____

_____

3. In your own words, explain what you think it means to "wolf down" food.

_____

_____

_____

4. Suggest a different title that would work for this piece. Explain your thinking.

_____

_____

_____

Which One Doesn't Belong?

Three words in each group are related. Cross out the word that does not belong. Write a title for the remaining words. Then think of a word to add in place of the word you crossed out. The first one has been done for you. If you are not sure of the meaning of a word, use a dictionary or a science book.

1. manatee   blue whale   ~~minnow~~ _seal_   sea lion   <u>Endangered Mammals</u>

2.   iris   eardrum   pupil   cornea   _____

3.   root   petals   stamen   pistil   _____

4.   wedge   lever   pulley   battery   _____

5.   centimeter   decimeter   kilogram   meter   _____

6.   biology   geometry   botany   zoology   _____

7.   incisors   molars   canines   plaque   _____

8.   volume   thermometer   barometer   anemometer   _____

9.   nitrogen   baking soda   oxygen   carbon dioxide   _____

10.   cirrus   cumulus   stratus   circus   _____

11.   flock   gosling   herd   colony   _____

12.   climate   forest   grassland   desert   _____

13.   larva   chrysalis   pupa   hibernation   _____

14.   alligator   seal   tortoise   gecko   _____

Kingdoms in Science

Scientists classify living things into five kingdoms based on their similarities. Body structure, cell structure, method of reproduction, and ways they obtain nutrients and energy are all considered.

One-celled organisms with no separate nucleus, such as bacteria, are classified in the MONERAN kingdom.

Those with a single cell having a nucleus and other structures are in the PROTIST kingdom. Algae and amoebas are in this group.

FUNGI, the third kingdom, have many cells but cannot move. They are unable to use the sun's energy to make food. Molds and mushrooms are fungi.

PLANTS are also many-celled and cannot move, but they are able to use the sun's energy "" to make food.

ANIMALS are many-celled. Most can move, but they must get their energy by consuming other organisms or their remains.

The five kingdoms represent living things from the very simplest to the most complex.

Complete each analogy with a word from the passage.

1. Easy is to difficult as simple is to _____.

2. Planet is to universe as animal is to _____.

3. Bacteria is to Moneran as _____ is to Fungi.

4. Consume is to use as _____ is to get.

5. Nucleus is to nuclei as fungus is to _____.

Draw a line to connect each word with its definition.

6. organism   **a.** use the sun's energy to make food

7. scientific   **b.** classification of living things

8. plants   **c.** a complex structure

9. nutrients   **d.** nourishment

10. kingdom   **e.** exhibiting the principles of science

Leafy Jaws

Sometimes a story or a chapter in a textbook may have so many new words that you hardly understand what you have just read. One of the ways to become a better reader is to know and understand all the words you come across as you read. Then practice reading the words aloud.

Look at the following words found in the article on the next page. Each word is a noun that names an animal. Match each word with the picture of the animal it names.

_____ shark

_____ tarantula

_____ grizzly bear

_____ crocodile

All of these animals are carnivores. By thinking about what these four creatures have in common, you can guess what a carnivore is. Circle the correct meaning.

a. an animal that has fur   **b.** an animal that kills and eats other creatures

c. an animal that can swim   **d.** an animal that has sharp claws and teeth

Here are some of the other nouns you will find in the article. Match each word with its definition. Look for clues in the definitions to help you understand the words you do not know.

1. _____ a sweet liquid secreted by flowers   **a.** botanist

2. _____ a small container in which plants are grown   **b.** diameter

3. _____ one who studies plants   **c.** exoskeleton

4. _____ places where young plants are grown for sale   **d.** habitat

5. _____ the width of a circle   **e.** nectar

6. _____ a creature hunted or caught for food   **f.** nurseries

7. _____ a place where a creature lives   **g.** prey

8. _____ an external supporting structure of insects   **h.** terrarium

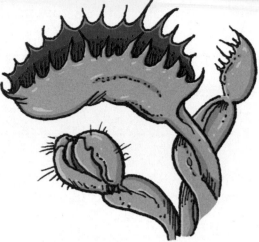

Carnivorous creatures are those that can capture, kill, and digest insects or other animal life. Carnivorous creatures include crocodiles, grizzly bears, sharks, tarantulas, and Venus flytraps. You might have expected there to be carnivorous reptiles, mammals, fish, and insects. But did you expect to find a plant on the list of carnivores? Even early botanists doubted that such a plant could exist, but the Venus flytrap is a true carnivore that captures its insect meals in its leafy jaws.

The Venus flytrap is native to the sunny bogs and wetlands of North and South Carolina. Since the soil in this region is too poor to meet the plant's needs, it supplements its diet with the minerals it gets by devouring insects. A mature Venus flytrap is usually about six inches in diameter, and the four to eight "traps" at the end of its leaves are about one inch long. Small flies, spiders, and crickets are the typical "prey" of a Venus flytrap.

To attract prey, the leaves forming the trap secrete a sweet nectar. When an insect lands on or climbs in the trap, it brushes against tiny "trigger" hairs inside the trap. When these hairs detect motion, the leaves of the trap can tightly shut within half a second. The plant then begins secreting digestive juices that dissolve the insect, so its nutrients can be absorbed. In about five to twelve days, the trap reopens, and all that remains of the insect is its shell or exoskeleton, which blows away. Each of the leafy traps can close only a limited number of times. Once this limit is reached, the trap eventually dies and falls away, and the plant grows new traps to replace it.

Today, the Venus flytraps growing in the wild are endangered because of the destruction of their native wetlands, pollution, and over-collection. There are strict fines for taking them out of their habitat in the Carolinas. However, you can obtain domestic Venus flytraps from reputable plant nurseries.

A carefully set-up and maintained terrarium can duplicate the sunny, humid, moist growing conditions the Venus flytrap needs in order to grow. You also have to provide your plant with crickets and other small insects. Sometimes well-meaning growers will try to feed their Venus flytrap hamburger. The leaves were not designed to catch cows, and trying to feed the plant hamburger will only kill it. Remember, too, that the traps can only open and close so many times. Poking its leaves with a pencil to make the traps snap shut may cause the traps to wear out and die before the plant can grow new ones. With the right care and growing conditions, the Venus flytrap will be a fascinating addition to your in-home garden.

1. Why do you think botanists doubted that the Venus flytrap existed?

_____

_____

_____

2. You learned the process the Venus flytrap uses to attract, trap, and devour its prey. Complete the following summary of that process by adding the correct words.

First, the plant attracts insects by secreting a sweet __ __ __ __ __ __.

When the flytrap's trigger hairs __ __ __ __ __ __ motion, they close up on the insect.

The plant then __ __ __ __ __ __ __ __ digestive juices that dissolve the insect.

When the leaves open in five to twelve days, all that remains is the insect's

__ __ __ __ __ __ __ __ __ __ __.

3. Circle the correct answers about owning a Venus flytrap.

You should get your Venus flytrap by
- ○ A. going to the Carolinas and digging it up.
- ○ B. ordering one from a reputable nursery.

You should grow the Venus flytrap
- ○ A. in a terrarium that duplicates the plant's natural habitat.
- ○ B. in your backyard.

You should feed the Venus flytrap
- ○ A. crickets.
- ○ B. hamburger.

© Scholastic Inc.

Helpful Houseplants

They sit on a desk or table and look pretty.
You need to remember to water them.
But what are houseplants actually good for?
Fill in the blanks to find out.

Scientists say houseplants do more than

_____ homes and offices. They can

also improve the _____ of the air we

breathe. Buildings today are often airtight and have plenty of

_____. This makes them energy-efficient,

but it also makes it hard for fresh air to enter.

Many houseplants can "clean" the stale air trapped inside

buildings. Plant leaves take in the carbon dioxide gas from the air.

In return, they give out clean _____. Plants also take

other dangerous gases from the air. For instance, a type of daisy takes in benzene,

a _____ found in gasoline. Spider plants take in carbon

monoxide. So why not keep a lot of houseplants around? They just might help you

breathe easier.

Word Bank

chemical

decorate

insulation

oxygen

quality

Think About It!

What are some benefits of houseplants?

Water

Read the article and answer the questions.

Water is vital, or needed, for life on Earth. All animals and plants need water to survive. Plants and animals that live on "dry" land can get water from soil, streams, rivers, lakes, puddles, dew, or rain. Water is also vital for human life. People collect and store water for drinking and washing, for our pets and farm animals, and for supplying water to crops. Each person needs to take in about two quarts of water daily to stay alive and healthy. Like many other substances, water can exist in more than one form. It can exist as a solid, liquid or gas. All of these forms occur naturally. The liquid form is the one we think of most often. This is simply water as in the water that we drink or that comes out of a hose. The solid form, which is ice, exists in very cold places and the gaseous form, which is water vapor, exists in the air around us. Water vapor also exists in steam produced from hot springs or geysers.

1. What is the main idea of this article? (Circle the answer)

- ○ A. Water is needed for life on Earth.
- ○ B. Each person needs to drink about two quarts of water each day.
- ○ C. Water on dry land comes from soil, streams, rivers, lakes, puddles, dew, or rain.

2. Name three different forms of water.

_____

3. Water vapor is what form of water? (Circle the answer)

    ○ A. solid   ○ B. liquid   ○ C. gas

4. What form of water is ice?

_____

5. Where are some example of places that you might find water vapor?

_____

6. The word "vital" means: (Circle the answer)

    ○ A. friendly   ○ B. needed   ○ C. not very good

© Scholastic Inc.

Coastlines

Read the article and answer the questions.

The coastline is always changing. It changes by the second, as waves roll in and then fall back again. It also changes by the hour as the sea rises and falls in tides. It also changes by the month from the constant battering by heat, cold, wind, and rain which shapes and reshapes it. On rocky coasts, steep cliffs bear evidence of the enormous power of the sea to erode, or wear away, and to shape the land. Hard rocks can resist the wearing by the sea better than some other elements as they remain behind while softer rocks collapse and erode and form bays and other coastal structures. On low coasts where the sea is shallow, beaches and banks are built up as waves bring in and drop off elements such as pebbles, sand, and mud. In this way, the sea can be constructive. Everywhere you look on a coastline, there is evidence of a mixture of different effects of the sea.

1. What is the main idea of this article? (Circle the answer)

○ A. The sea batters the land.

○ B. A coastline is in a constant state of change.

○ C. Waves leave behind pebbles, sand, and mud.

2. What can change a coastline? (Circle the answer)

○ A. weather ○ B. wrecked boats ○ C. heat and cold

3. What does the word "erode" mean? (Circle the answer)

○ A. to wear away ○ B. sea animals ○ C. wrecked boats

4. How can the sea be constructive to a shallow coastline?

_____

5. What are some things that are dropped off by waves to build beaches?

_____

6. How can the sea be destructive?

_____

Zapped

Read the article and answer the questions.

Getting struck by lightning is a serious thing. A bolt of lightning is powerful. It can contain enough volts of electricity to flash on all the lights of a medium-sized town. If you were struck by a bolt of lightning, there are many harmful things that could happen. The lightning's heat would instantly turn your sweat to steam. That steam could burn your skin or blow off your clothes and shoes. The electricity could race through your eyes and ears, blurring your vision and bursting your eardrums. The explosive force of the lightning could break your bones. Your muscles, including your heart, could stop working.

Each year about 30 people in America die from lightning strikes. Another 270 Americans are struck, but the strike is not fatal, or deadly. To avoid being struck by lightning, there are some things you should do. You should stay inside during a thunderstorm or remain in your car. You should avoid contact with metal pipes. You should also stay away from corded phones, computers, and other electrical equipment because if lightning strikes your house, it can travel through metal and wires.

1. What is the main idea of this article? (Circle the answer)

    ○ A. Sometimes lightning is not deadly.

    ○ B. Sweat can turn to steam.

    ○ C. Lightning is powerful and can be dangerous.

2. What are three things that might happen to you if you are struck by lightning?

_____

3. About how many people in America are killed by lightning each year?

_____

4. What are some things you should do during a thunderstorm to avoid lightning?

_____

5. A word that means "deadly" is: (Circle the answer)

    ○ A. bursting   ○ B. harmful   ○ C. fatal

Washed Away

Read about beach erosion.
Then try the science investigations.

Before Hurricane Ivan hit this barrier island in Alabama in 2004

After the hurricane: Waves and storm surge have split the island in two.

Before Hurricane Ivan hit this beach in Alabama in 2004

After the hurricane: The front of the 5-story building collapsed and the pilings under the house were exposed.

Hurricanes are powerful storms that form over the ocean. Hurricane winds can reach more than a hundred miles per hour. Winds that strong can uproot trees and blow the roofs off houses. But a lot of the damage from hurricanes actually comes from water. When a hurricane hits the coast, high winds can stir up massive waves and flooding. All that moving water can carry away sand and soil, a process called **erosion**.

Beaches naturally undergo erosion all the time, as waves and tides move sand around. "[But] when a big storm hits, the effects of erosion are much stronger," says Gerald Galloway, an engineer who works on flood prevention. The result: major damage to homes and businesses built along the shore.

Storm Stoppers

To safeguard homes, some towns in hurricane-prone areas along the East Coast decided to follow nature's example and build sand dunes. Dunes can hold back floodwaters and help cut down on erosion. Building artificial dunes has paid off. When big storms have hit, these towns have suffered much less damage than those without dunes.

Now more communities are turning to dunes to help them weather future storms. To build the dunes, engineers use ships to dredge up sand from the seafloor. Machines pump and spray it onto beaches. Bulldozers then shovel the sand into dune-shaped mounds.

It's not a perfect solution. Dredging the sand can damage underwater habitats. And it may have to be done all over again after a hurricane strikes.

Stay or Go?

To weather the next storm, people need to rethink their rebuilding efforts, says Galloway. Houses need to be made stronger to resist damage or raised to sit high above floodwaters.

Another option is for people to rebuild somewhere else entirely. Some say it's too costly and dangerous for people to rebuild in places that could be repeatedly struck by hurricanes. But many residents don't want to leave their beaches or their communities.

It's a complex problem. But it can't be ignored. "Nature can be a very powerful force," says Galloway. "When the next storm comes, we've got to be prepared to deal with it."

Investigation 1

Build a beach and make waves!

1. Gather the materials you will need.

2. Place a funnel into an empty 1-liter soda bottle. Pour in 240 ml (1 cup) of sand. Then pour in 240 ml of water. Replace the bottle cap. Remove any label from the bottle.

3. Shake the bottle to mix the sand and water. As soon as you stop shaking, lean the top of the bottle against the stack of books. Wait about 10 seconds for the sand to settle.

4. Gently lay the bottle on its side. Some of the sand should rise out of the water, making a beach.

5. Look at the shape of the beach. Look at the shape of the sand below the water. Find the line where the water meets the sand. Measure from that line to the bottom end of the bottle. Write that beach measurement on your recording sheet.

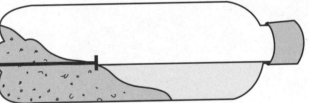

6. Carefully hold the bottle in both hands, keeping it horizontal. Rock it to make small, gentle waves. Let the waves go about halfway up your beach. Keep making waves for about 1 minute.

7. Gently put down your bottle. How has your beach changed? What about the sand under the water? Record your observations on the next page. Measure your beach again. Did your beach change size?

8. **Predict:** How will your results be different with stronger waves? Record your predictions.

9. Repeat Steps 3–7, but this time make larger waves. Allow your waves to go all the way up your beach.

10. What differences did you notice between the gentle and the strong waves? Which took you more energy to make? Which waves had more energy? How do you know? Which were more like hurricane waves?

Materials
★ funnel
★ empty 1-liter soda bottle with cap
★ 240 ml (1 cup) sand
★ 240 ml (1 cup) water
★ ruler
★ watch
★ stack of books, about 13 cm (5 in.) high
★ recording sheet (next page)

1. Do Steps 2-7 of the investigation. Record your measurements and observations in the chart below.

2. **Predict:** How will your results be different with stronger waves?

_____

_____

3. Now do Step 9 of the investigation. Record your measurements and observations in the chart below.

	Starting beach measurement	Ending beach measurement	How has the beach changed?	How has the sand under the water changed?
Gentle waves				
Strong waves				

4. What differences did you notice between the gentle and the strong waves?

_____

_____

5. Which took you more energy to make?

_____

6. Which waves had more energy? How do you know?

_____

_____

7. Which were more like hurricane waves?

_____

Investigation 2

Experiment with different ways to control beach erosion.

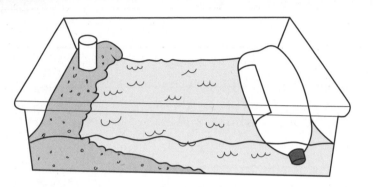

1. Gather the materials you will need.

2. Pour 4 liters of sand into a clear plastic container. Add just enough water to wet the sand. Push the sand to one end of the container to make a sloped beach. Carefully add water to the container until it's 2.5-cm (1-in.) deep. Add a model building or two to your beach.

3. Place an empty soda bottle in the water. Gently push it down to make a wave. Watch the wave roll up on your beach. Make 20 waves in a row. (If the water slops out of your container, make your waves smaller.) What happens to your beach and your buildings? Record your observations on your recording sheet.

4. Push the sand back to its original condition. Reposition your buildings.

5. Look at your selection of inventor's materials. Choose one. Add it to your model beach. (You can leave it on top, bury it completely, or leave it sticking partway out.)

6. Repeat Steps 3 and 4. Record your observations. Do the same with two other materials.

7. Make an Erosion Control Plan using one or more of your materials. Describe it on your recording sheet. Then repeat Steps 3 and 4 to test it. Record your observations.

8. How could you improve your Erosion Control Plan? Think of one thing to change. Describe your change on your recording sheet and repeat Steps 3 and 4.

9. Keep improving and testing until you have the best erosion control possible. (If needed, use a separate sheet of paper to record your test data.)

10. **Think:** With your erosion control in place, would beach lovers still want to visit? How might your design affect wildlife?

Materials

★ 4 liters of sand

★ large, clear plastic storage container

★ water

★ model buildings

★ empty 2-liter soda bottle

★ inventor's materials: toothpicks, pipe cleaners, plastic bags, waterproof cardboard from milk cartons, aluminum foil, cloth scraps

★ recording sheet (next page)

1. Do Steps 2 and 3 of the Investigation. What happened to your beach and buildings? Record your observations below.

_____

_____

2. Now do Steps 4–6 of the investigation. Record your observations below.

Materials	Observations

3. Do Steps 7–8 of the investigation. Record your observations below.

Erosion Control Plan	Observations
Original design:	
Improvement 1:	
Improvement 2:	

4. With your erosion control in place, would beach lovers still want to visit? How might your design affect wildlife? Record your answers on a separate sheet of paper.

Pickles on Ice

Read the environment essay.
Then follow the directions in the Text Marking box.

Do thoroughfares in your area ice over in winter? Are sidewalks treacherous for walking? If so, would you ever think to grab a jar of pickles?

Icy roads can be dangerous. Cities and towns spend heavily each winter spreading rock salt on roads to melt the ice. However, the problem with using rock salt is that it is hazardous to the environment. Salt seeps into the ground and into our fresh water, damaging plants and trees. Salt also harms wildlife and pets.

This challenge has pushed transportation departments in some states to seek safer materials to use. One solution is to replace rock salt with *brine*. Brine is salty water. It is found in the juice of beets, pickles, potatoes, and cheese. Brine has three advantages over rock salt. First, it causes less harm to the environment. It also works better than rock salt at very low temperatures. Moreover, using brine saves money for taxpayers.

Indiana has begun to use beet brine to melt ice on its roadways. Surfaces in Tennessee are being de-iced with potato brine. New Jersey ice is being melted with pickle brine. Cheese brine is now used to combat Wisconsin's icy streets. Yes, states may have found an effective answer to a slippery problem.

Truck de-icing a road in winter

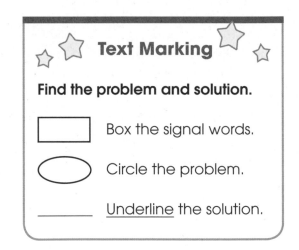

Text Marking

Find the problem and solution.

☐ Box the signal words.

◯ Circle the problem.

___ Underline the solution.

Answer each question. Give evidence from the essay.

1. Which of the following is the best meaning of *brine*?

    ○ A. a winter danger   ○ C. slippery ice

    ○ B. liquid with salt in it   ○ D. a kind of cheese

What in the text helped you answer?

_____

2. Why may rock salt NOT be the best way to melt ice on roads in winter?

    ○ A. Rock salt works too slowly.

    ○ B. Rock salt is the same color as ice.

    ○ C. Rock salt causes potholes in roads.

    ○ D. Rock salt can harm living things and the environment.

What in the text helped you answer?

_____

_____

3. What transportation problems do cities and towns face in winter weather?

_____

_____

_____

4. Give three reasons from the text that explain why using brine to melt ice is a good idea.

_____

_____

_____

Twisters

Read the story and answer the questions.

Tornadoes, sometimes called twisters, occur, or happen, all over the world. Most of them occur in the United States. Approximately 1,000 tornadoes form each year in the United States. A tornado is a funnel cloud. In the Northern Hemisphere, tornadoes rotate counter-clockwise. In the Southern Hemisphere, they rotate clockwise. A tornado forms when a warm air mass is pushed upward very quickly by a colder air mass. Then, more warm air rushes in and starts to twist. The twisting grows stronger until a funnel is formed. Not all funnels touch the earth. When tornadoes do touch the earth's surface, the violent rotating winds can demolish almost everything in their paths. A spinning wind can reach speeds of more than 200 miles per hour. The best protection against a tornado is to take cover in a basement. If a basement is not available, you should crouch down in a bathtub or under a sturdy piece of furniture and you should stay away from windows.

1. Another word for *occur* is:

    ◯ A. spin   ◯ B. destroy   ◯ C. happen

2. In which direction do tornadoes rotate in the Southern Hemisphere?

_____

3. How does a tornado form?

_____

_____

4. How fast can a spinning wind go?

_____

5. Name three places you could hide if a tornado is coming.

_____

_____

Volcano Trackers!

Read about new tools that help tell when an eruption may happen. Then try the science investigations.

BOOM! **Lava** bursts high in the air before flowing in hot-red rivers down the mountain. Hot ash shoots into the atmosphere, covering an entire continent like a giant cloud. Thousands of people flee their homes toward safety. When a volcano suddenly comes to life, watch out!

Scientists want to learn how to tell when an eruption may be brewing. They hope to develop better warning systems so people can be prepared for the next big boom. Volcanoes do give some warning signs before they erupt. But in the past, these signs have been hard to measure. That's because working near volcanoes is extremely dangerous, and scientists couldn't get close enough.

Now, new technology is helping scientists study volcanoes from far away. High-tech instruments placed near cracks in the earth's crust can sense gases that could mean **magma** is moving underground. Before an eruption, the crust can rise a little, like a balloon filling with air.

Scientists have placed devices on rocks to detect these movements. They're also measuring vibrations that pulse throughout the crust during earthquakes, which are often the first sign that a volcano is coming alive. Information from these sensors gives scientists a clearer picture of how volcanoes behave. Over time, it may help them figure out which volcano could blow next.

Inside a Volcano

What gives a volcano its fiery force? Follow these steps to find out.

1. Under the soil is a solid layer of rock called the **crust**. Under the crust is the **mantle**, a layer of hot, melted rock. The melted rock itself is called **magma**.

2. In some places, magma rises from the mantle into the crust. It collects in a **magma chamber**. As more and more magma rises, the pressure builds. The pressure gets so high, the magma can crack the rock around it.

3. The pressure pushes magma up through the central **vent** of a volcano.

4. The volcano erupts! Once magma is outside the volcano, it's called **lava**. The eruption may also include hot ash, rocks, and steam.

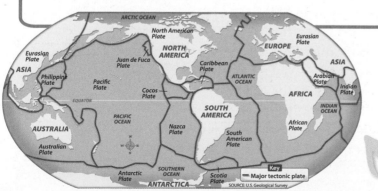

Earth's crust is broken into big pieces called *tectonic plates*. The red lines show the *boundaries*—the places where the plates touch. At some boundaries, conditions are just right for volcanoes to form.

© Scholastic Inc.

Investigation 1

Where do volcanoes form? Model how tectonic plates move to find out.

1. Gather the materials you will need.

2. Put a heaping tablespoon of whipped cream on a sheet of wax paper. Use your spoon to spread the whipped cream into a square the size of a half graham cracker. **This is a model of the earth's mantle. The whipped cream is the melted rock, or magma.**

3. Your half graham cracker is your solid rock crust. Carefully break the cracker along the line.

4. Place the two pieces next to each other on top of the whipped cream. Their broken edges should touch. **Each piece is a tectonic plate. The place where the two broken pieces match up is a boundary. The plates don't stay still. They move slowly.** You will model three ways they can move.

5. Transform boundary: Slide the crackers past one another, like trains passing on opposite tracks. Can you feel them rubbing together? How much magma (whipped cream) do you see between them?

6. Divergent boundary: Carefully move the crackers back into place. Then slowly push the crackers away from one another. **This creates a rift, a separation of plates.** How much magma do you see between the crackers? Real magma would harden into new crust.

7. Convergent boundary: Put the crackers side by side again. Push them toward one another. Let one cracker slide underneath the other. How much magma do you see between the crackers? **When Earth's plates do this, the lower plate melts into the hot mantle. It becomes new magma.**

8. Think: Volcanoes can form where magma rises through the crust. You just modeled three different ways that can happen at boundaries. Think about which ones brought magma close to the surface. Which kinds of boundaries seem best for making volcanoes?

Materials

★ plastic spoon
★ whipped cream
★ wax paper
★ half a graham cracker
★ recording sheet (next page)

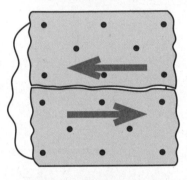

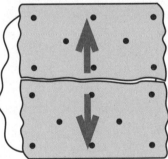

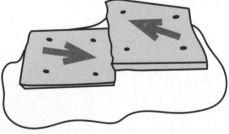

© Scholastic Inc.

1. Do Steps 2–7 of the investigation. Model the three ways plates can move. Record your observations in the chart below.

Types of boundary	How much magma do you see between the crackers?
Transform boundary	
Divergent boundary	
Convergent boundary	

2. Think: Volcanoes can form where magma rises through the crust. Which kinds of boundaries brought magma close to the surface? Which seem best for making volcanoes?

_____

_____

_____

_____

Investigation 2

Earthquakes can be a warning that a volcano is getting ready to erupt. But scientists can't stand around a volcano waiting for an earthquake to happen. Instead, they use equipment that can detect earthquakes. Invent your own Shake Detector!

1. Gather the materials you will need.

2. Put a box on a table. Give the box a little push with your hand. **Think:** What could you put in or on the box that could detect the push? Think of at least five ideas. (**Hint:** It can be anything that will react when you push the box. It can be loose inside the box. It can be attached to a side. Or it can hang from the lid. What else?)

3. Scientists need their equipment to record how hard an earthquake shakes. Look at your list. Can you change one of your ideas so it leaves a record of a shake? (Want some hints? See the Brainstorming Tips below.) Think of at least two ideas.

4. Test one of your ideas. Does it work?

   • If yes, how can you make it work even better?

   • If no, what can you change so it does work?

5. Keep testing and improving your Shake Detector. When you are done, draw a picture of it on your recording sheet. Explain how it works.

Materials

★ box

★ inventor's materials: markers, paper, string, tape, rice, bowls, marbles,

★ recording sheet (next page)

Brainstorming Tips

   • A Shake Detector might move. The harder the shake, the farther it moves.

   • A Shake Detector might spill something. The harder the shake, the more it spills.

   • A Shake Detector might leave a mark. The harder the shake, the bigger the mark.

   • A Shake Detector might make a sound that could be recorded. The harder the shake, the louder the sound.

1. Do Step 2 of the investigation. **Think:** What could you put in or on the box that could detect the push? List at least five ideas.

- _____
- _____
- _____
- _____
- _____

2. Look at your list. Can you change one of your ideas so it leaves a record of a shake? Think of at least two ideas.

- _____
- _____

3. Test one of your ideas. Does it work? How can you make it work even better?

_____

_____

4. Keep testing and improving your Shake Detector. When you are done, draw a picture of it here and label it. Explain how it works on a separate sheet of paper.

Do-It-Yourself Lava Lamp

Lava lamps first made their appearance as a novelty item in 1963. They didn't contain actual boiling lava from an active volcano, but the liquid inside did move in much the same slow, burbling manner as lava does as it inches along. Now, you can make your own lava lamp with simple materials you probably already have at home.

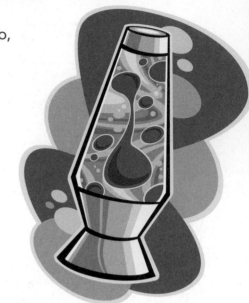

Materials

- funnel
- empty 16-oz. clear plastic water bottle with screw-on cap
- 10 oz. vegetable oil
- tap water
- food coloring in a dark color
- 1 large antacid tablet

Step-by-Step Instructions

1. Place the funnel in the bottle. Pour the oil into the funnel. Then add water until the bottle is almost full. Leave a little bit of space.

2. Add 12 drops of food coloring. Swirl gently to mix.

3. Break the antacid tablet into eight small pieces. Drop one piece of the tablet into the liquid. It will begin bubbling. When the bubbling stops, add another piece. Again, wait until the bubbling stops. Repeat until you use all the pieces.

4. When the bubbling finally stops, screw the top onto the bottle. Slowly tilt the bottle from side to side. Look for the blobby lava waves!

© Scholastic Inc.

Answer each question. Give evidence from the science activity.

1. In Step 1, why do the instructions say to leave some space at the top of the bottle?

_____

_____

2. Explain why the activity includes two different lists.

_____

_____

3. Why do you think the instructions tell you to break the antacid tablet into eight small pieces? Explain.

_____

_____

4. Which of the following things might you see *burbling*?

    ○ A. meat cooling off   ○ C. oatmeal cooking

    ○ B. a potato baking   ○ D. ice cubes melting

Tell how you chose your answer.

_____

5. Based on the introduction and the picture, which best explains what *a novelty item* is?

    ○ A. something invented at least 50 years ago

    ○ B. anything that can be used to provide light

    ○ C. a surprising new item people want to have

    ○ D. a scientific book, article, or project

What evidence in the text helped you choose your answer?

_____

_____

Natural Processes

Geology is the study of Earth and the forces that shape and change it. Some changes happen gradually over time while others happen quickly. Erosion and wind are examples of processes that cause slow changes. Volcanic eruptions and earthquakes are two processes that cause rapid changes on Earth.

Find geological processes that shape Earth in the puzzle below.

AVALANCHES	EROSION	FLOODS	GLACIERS	LANDSLIDES
MUDSLIDES	SINKHOLES	TSUNAMI	VOLCANIC ERUPTIONS	WIND

HINT:

VOLCANIC ERUPTIONS appears in the puzzle separately but the words cross each other.

```
W  N  K  T  S  U  N  A  M  I  N  G  Q
R  F  L  O  O  D  S  V  X  V  E  L  S
M  P  A  W  W  E  L  A  S  N  E  A  U
U  M  N  C  R  U  A  L  I  E  R  C  E
D  F  D  T  L  V  X  A  N  D  O  I  G
S  U  S  J  M  V  W  N  K  Y  S  E  L
L  M  L  I  U  O  J  C  H  T  I  R  A
I  W  I  N  D  L  S  H  O  K  O  S  C
D  H  D  P  G  C  T  E  L  L  N  W  I
E  G  E  Q  H  A  L  S  E  N  H  I  E
S  H  S  J  K  N  K  T  S  A  M  W  R
E  R  U  P  T  I  O  N  S  D  B  O  S
K  A  Q  R  N  C  B  U  S  Y  Q  Z  B
```

The Blackest Material Ever!

Read about how the darkest black can help scientists see light far out in space! Then try the science investigations.

A company in England has created the world's darkest material. Called Vantablack®, it is made of extremely tiny tubes of the element carbon. Scientists invented a special process to form a layer of these carbon tubes on surfaces like aluminum foil.

Why is Vantablack so dark?

You see objects when light bounces off them and into your eyes. But Vantablack **absorbs**, or soaks in, almost all of the light that hits it. Only 0.035 percent is **reflected**, or bounced off. (Regular black paint reflects about 5 percent. The darkest things in the universe—black holes—reflect 0 percent.)

Why is it important to make something so dark? Astronomers could use Vantablack to coat the inside of space telescopes. By absorbing bright light from the sun, the material could help the telescopes detect much fainter light from galaxies far away.

Seeing Light

Visible light is made up of all the colors of the rainbow. You see objects when that light bounces off them and into your eyes. When light strikes most objects, some colors are absorbed and others are reflected.

The colors of light that bounce off an object determine its color. So red objects reflect red light and absorb every other color. Objects that reflect all colors appear white. And objects that absorb all colors look black.

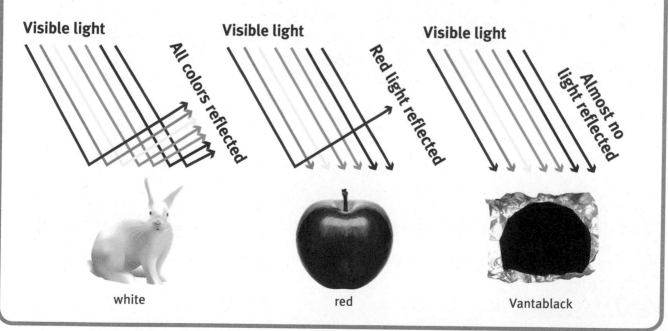

Visible light	Visible light	Visible light
All colors reflected	Red light reflected	Almost no light reflected
white	red	Vantablack

Investigation 1

IMPORTANT SAFETY REMINDER:

Never look directly at the sun or sunlight reflected in a mirror.

Catch the rainbow on paper!

1. Gather the materials you will need.

2. Place a shallow container on a sunny windowsill. Pour about 3 cm (1-1/4 in.) of water into the container. Put a mirror face-up in the bottom of the container.

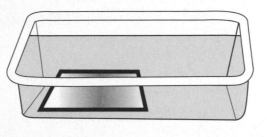

3. Turn off the lights in the room. Look for a bright patch of reflected light on the wall or ceiling. (Until the water in your container becomes still, the light patch will be somewhat "wiggly.") If all you see is a dim patch of light, keep looking. Try tilting the mirror or moving the container.

4. Adjust the mirror so that the patch of light is on a wall or ceiling as far away as possible from the window. Use lumps of clay to hold the mirror in place.

5. Wait until the water becomes still and the light patch stops wiggling. On your recording sheet, draw what you see using crayons or markers. **White light contains all the colors of the rainbow. When light waves go from the air to the water, they bend. But each color of light bends a slightly different amount. The same thing happens when light waves go from the water back into the air. Because of the differences in how they bend, the colors get spread out. The farther they travel, the more they're spread.**

6. Put a white sheet of paper in front of the light patch to "catch" the rainbow colors. Try tilting the paper around. Record your observations on the next page.

7. Keeping the colored light on your paper, move the paper closer and closer to the water and mirror. Record your observations on the next page.

8. "Catch" the light with a sheet of black paper. How does that change what you see?

9. Vantablack absorbs almost all light and reflects almost none. What do you think you would see if you repeated Step 8 with a surface covered with Vantablack? Why?

© Scholastic Inc.

IMPORTANT SAFETY REMINDER:
Never look directly at the sun or sunlight reflected in a mirror.

1. Do Steps 2–4 of the investigation. When the water and the light patch on the wall have become still, draw what you see using crayons or markers.

2. Now do Step 6 of the investigation. Record your observations below.

_____

_____

3. Do Step 7 of the investigation. Record your observations below.

_____

_____

4. Do Step 8 of the investigation. How does that change what you see?

_____

_____

5. What do you think you would see if you repeated Step 8 with a surface covered with Vantablack? Why? Write your answers on a separate sheet of paper.

Investigation 2

What do you get when you mix together different colored lights? Find out here!

1. Gather the materials you will need.

2. Cut a 10-cm (4-in.) strip off the bottom of a gallon-sized freezer bag. Cut the strip into three equal pieces. For the two corner pieces, cut one edge so you can fully unfold it. You should end up with three equal-sized plastic pieces that fold like a book.

3. Unfold one plastic piece. Use a red permanent marker to color the inside, as shown. (You may need to tilt your marker for good coverage.) Leave the plastic open to dry for 5 minutes.

4. Repeat Step 2 with the other two plastic pieces, using the blue and green markers.

5. Fold each plastic piece back into the closed position. Use a rubber band to attach each piece to a flashlight, as shown.

6. Place a sheet of paper in the bottom of a cardboard box and tape it down. Set the box on its side. Tape any box flaps up and out of your way.

7. Test the flashlights one-by-one by shining each on the paper. What color light does each flashlight make?

8. **The primary colors for pigments (like paint and ink) are red, blue, and yellow. You can mix them to make all other colors. But light has different primary colors: red, blue, and green.** On your recording sheet, predict what you will see when you overlap these colored light beams.

9. Test your predictions. Record your results on the next page.

10. Arrange the three flashlights so they are pointing at the same spot. Hold your hand right in front of the paper. What colors do you see? Explain what is happening.

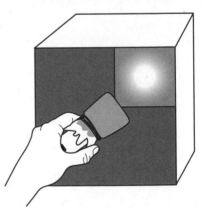

Materials

- ★ gallon-sized zip-top freezer bag
- ★ scissors
- ★ red, blue, and green permanent markers
- ★ 3 rubber bands
- ★ 3 identical LED flashlights
- ★ sheet of paper
- ★ large cardboard box
- ★ tape
- ★ recording sheet (next page)

© Scholastic Inc.

1. Do Steps 2 7 of the investigation. What color light does each flashlight make on the paper?

red filter: _____

blue filter: _____

green filter: _____

2. Predict: What will you see when you overlap these colored light beams?

Mix these colors	Resulting color	Intensity (circle one)
blue + red		brighter light / darker light / the same
red + green		brighter light / darker light / the same
green + blue		brighter light / darker light / the same
green + blue + red		brighter light / darker light / the same

3. Test your predictions. Record your results below.

Mix these colors	Resulting color	Intensity (circle one)
blue + red		brighter light / darker light / the same
red + green		brighter light / darker light / the same
green + blue		brighter light / darker light / the same
green + blue + red		brighter light / darker light / the same

4. Now do Step 10 of the investigation. What colors do you see? Explain what is happening.

_____

_____

Rainbows

Read the article and answer the questions.

 Sunlight appears colorless, but it is really made up of different colors. Sometimes you can see these colors on the surfaces of bubbles or on oil that is floating on top of water. You may also see the colors across the sky in the form of a rainbow. In each case, "white" light is being separated into different colors called a spectrum. When the sun comes out during a rain shower, you may see a rainbow. This happens because light from the sun shines on the raindrops. As the light enters each drop of rain, it is reflected, bent, and separated into all of the colors of the spectrum. All of this light reflecting off of the raindrops forms a rainbow. From a distance, the light appears as a colored arc across the sky.

 Scientists have divided the rainbow into seven bands of color, which are red, orange, yellow, green, blue, indigo, and violet. These colors always appear in the same order, with red on the outside and violet on the inside of the arc.

1. What is the main idea of the article?

_____

2. What color does sunlight appear as? (Circle the answer)

○ A. white   ○ B. the colors of the rainbow   ○ C. colorless

3. How does a rainbow form?

_____

_____

4. How many colors are in a rainbow?

_____

5. Name the colors of a rainbow in order.

_____

_____

6. Do the colors of the rainbow always appear in the same order?

_____

Floating Festival

Read about hot-air balloons. Then try the science investigations.

Each fall, hundreds of hot-air balloons float over Albuquerque (AL-buh-kur-kee), New Mexico. Some even come in wacky shapes, like a cow, octopus, or rubber ducky! The spectacle kicks off the annual Albuquerque International Balloon Fiesta—the largest in the world.

Liftoff!

How do these giant balloons get off the ground? Attached to the top of each balloon's basket is a gas burner. It heats the air inside the balloon. As the air in the balloon gets warmer, its molecules move faster and farther away from one another. Liter-for-liter, the balloon's spread-out air then weighs less than the regular air outside. In other words, the air inside is **less dense**. That difference in density makes the balloon float upwards.

Riding the Wind

Hot-air balloons don't have steering wheels. Pilots must catch a breeze that will blow them in the direction they want to go. This is one reason Albuquerque is a great place for the fiesta. During the best ballooning weather, it has a lower air current blowing from the north and a higher air current blowing from the south. A balloon can travel in one direction in the lower air current. Then the pilot can heat the air inside the balloon to lift it into the higher air current. The balloon is then blown back in the opposite direction. Finally, the pilot slowly releases hot air from the top of the balloon. The balloon sinks back to the ground, making a perfect round trip.

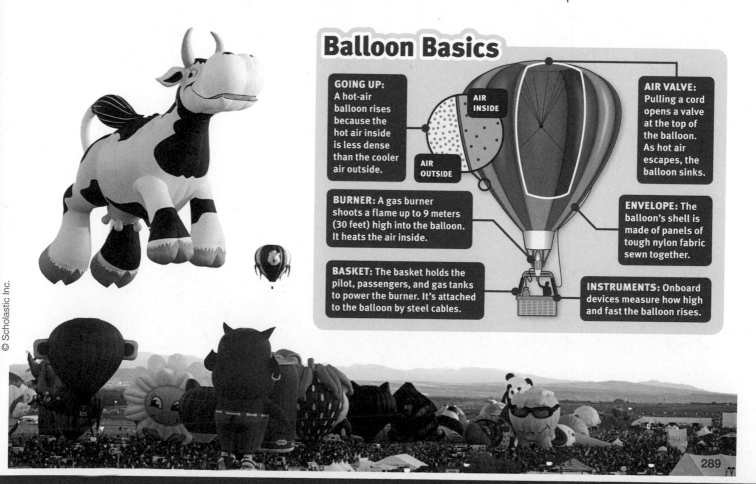

Balloon Basics

GOING UP: A hot-air balloon rises because the hot air inside is less dense than the cooler air outside.

AIR INSIDE

AIR OUTSIDE

AIR VALVE: Pulling a cord opens a valve at the top of the balloon. As hot air escapes, the balloon sinks.

BURNER: A gas burner shoots a flame up to 9 meters (30 feet) high into the balloon. It heats the air inside.

ENVELOPE: The balloon's shell is made of panels of tough nylon fabric sewn together.

BASKET: The basket holds the pilot, passengers, and gas tanks to power the burner. It's attached to the balloon by steel cables.

INSTRUMENTS: Onboard devices measure how high and fast the balloon rises.

Investigation 1

What happens when air changes temperature? Find out here!

Materials

- ★ empty aluminum can
- ★ balloon
- ★ scissors
- ★ rubber band
- ★ bowl of warm water
- ★ bowl of ice water
- ★ recording sheet (next page)

1. Gather the materials you will need.

2. Look inside the empty can. **Think:** Is it really empty? (**Hint:** If you blew up a balloon, would it be empty?) What's inside the can?

3. Cut a balloon a little below the widest part, as shown.

4. Stretch the top of the balloon over the open end of the can. The balloon should be stretched mostly flat, but don't make it super tight. Use a rubber band to hold the balloon in place. You've trapped air molecules inside the can.

5. **Predict:** What do you think will happen if you warm up the air inside the can? Record your prediction on the next page.

6. Push the can (balloon-side up) about ²/₃ of the way into a bowl of warm water. Hold it in the warm water for about 3 minutes. **Heat will travel through the metal and into the air inside the can.** What changes do you notice as the air inside the can heats up? Record your observations on the next page.

7. **Predict:** What do you think will happen if you make the air inside the can colder? Record your prediction.

8. Repeat Step 6, but this time use ice water. What changes do you notice as the air inside the can cools down?

9. **When air molecules are more spread out, we say the air is less dense.** Which is less dense—warm air or cold air? How do you know?

1. Look inside the empty can. **Think:** Is it really empty?
What's inside the can?

_____

2. Do Steps 3 and 4 of the investigation. **Predict:** What do you think will
happen if you warm up the air inside the can?

_____

_____

3. Now do Step 6 of the investigation. What changes do you notice as the air inside the
can heats up?

_____

_____

4. Predict: What do you think will happen if you make the air inside the can colder?

_____

_____

5. Do Step 8 of the investigation. What changes do you notice as the air inside the can cools down?

_____

_____

6. Which is less dense—warm air or cold air? How do you know?

_____

_____

_____

Investigation 2

A floating balloon is made of three things: a balloon skin, a string or ribbon, and a gas called helium. Helium is naturally less dense than air. (At the same temperature, a cup of helium weighs less than a cup of air.) The balloon skin and string are both denser than air. The combined density of all three together determines whether a balloon floats.

Materials

★ helium-filled balloon
★ room with a low ceiling
★ paper clips
★ inventor's materials: scrap paper, tape, yarn
★ timer
★ recording sheet (next page)

1. Gather the materials you will need.

2. Hold the balloon by the string. **Predict:** What do you think will happen if you let go of the balloon? Record your prediction. Then test it and record what happened. Is the balloon denser or less dense than the air in the room?

3. Tie a loop in the balloon string. Attach a paper clip to the loop. **Predict:** What do you think will happen if you let go of the balloon now? Record your prediction. Then test it and record what happened.

4. Add paper clips one-by-one until the balloon and string can no longer rise off the ground. How many paper clips did it take? Is the balloon—which now includes the paper clips—denser or less dense than the air in the room?

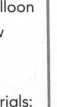

5. **Challenge:** Change the balloon so that it can hang in the air for 30 seconds without any part of it touching the ceiling or the floor. In order to do this, you will need to change the density of your balloon so it matches the density of the air in the room. (**Hint:** Think about how you changed the density in Steps 3 and 4.)

6. When your balloon can hang in midair, you can use it to look for **air currents**— streams of air that flow in a regular direction. For instance, air from a heater or air conditioner might push air in your home in a certain direction. Or air from an open window might stream toward an open door. Put the balloon in different locations and watch what happens. Record your observations on the next page.

7. You changed your balloon's density so it matched the density of the air in the room. What would happen if you took the balloon to a place where the air was colder or warmer? Pick one and experiment to find out. Record the results on the next page.

1. Do Step 2 of the investigation. **Predict:** What do you think will happen If you let go ot the balloon?

_____

2. Test your prediction. What happened?

_____

3. Is the balloon denser or less dense than the air in the room?

_____

4. Now do Step 3 of the investigation. **Predict:** What will happen if you let go of the balloon now?

_____

5. Test your prediction. What happened?

_____

6. Do Step 4 of the investigation. How many paper clips did it take to hold the balloon down?

_____

7. Is the balloon—with the paper clips—denser or less dense than the air in the room?

_____

8. Do Steps 5 and 6 of the investigation. Record your observations below.

_____

_____

9. Do Step 7 of the investigation. Record your results on a separate sheet of paper.

Rocket Man

What's it like to be in outer space? Fill in the blanks in this interview with former astronaut Tom Jones for some inside information.

Question: When did you decide to become an astronaut?

Tom Jones: When I was 10. It was 1965, and U.S. astronauts were practicing for the first trips to the moon.

Question: What does it feel like when you blast off?

Tom Jones: First there's a rumble as the engines fire up. Then there's a huge jolt. The _____ against your chest builds. It feels like a 700-pound _____ is sitting on your chest.

Question: What does it feel like to be _____?

Tom Jones: It's very _____, like you're floating underwater. With a touch of your finger, you can push off and glide wherever you want.

Question: What's cool about being in space?

Tom Jones: The _____ view of Earth. You can float over to the window and catch glimpses of oceans, snow-covered forests, and deserts.

Word Bank

gorilla
peaceful
pressure
vivid
weightless

Think About It! Name one fact and one opinion in the interview.

Blast Off!

Complete the puzzle with words related to the solar system. Use a dictionary to help you. One has been done for you.

| ASTEROIDS | ASTRONAUT | ASTRONOMY | ATMOSPHERE | GRAVITY |
| MERCURY | REVOLUTION | ROTATE | SATURN | SOLAR |

1. one who travels in space — S — — — — — — —

2. one complete path around the sun — — — O — — — — — —

3. grouping of billions of stars that form a system G A L A X Y

4. turn on an axis — — — A — —

5. study of the universe — — — R — — — — —

6. small planets with orbits between Mars and Jupiter — S — — — — — — —

7. force of attraction between objects — — — — — — Y

8. having to do with the sun S — — — —

9. the ringed planet — — T — — —

10. planet closest to the sun — E — — — — —

11. gaseous layer surrounding a planet — — M — — — — — — —

A Super Space Place

The International Space Station (ISS) was built by thousands of people from 15 countries. All these people and countries want to find out if humans can one day live in space.

Floating 220 miles above Earth, the ISS is made up of many pieces which were put together by astronauts in space. The main part of the construction began in 1998. United States space shuttles and Russian rockets transported tools and pieces of the station to help finish building it. They assembled the pieces in space! It was completed in 2011.

It is the largest structure ever to float above Earth. Although the main construction is complete, the ISS will continue to evolve as astronauts go on new missions and conduct experiments.

Some of the questions that crews who built the space station and crews that continue to visit the station are trying to answer include: How does space travel affect germs? Does the body break down food and nutrients differently in space? Some day, the station may even serve as a launchpad for missions to other planets, such as Mars.

Because of its large size, the ISS needs a lot of power. This power comes from solar energy. To create solar energy, large panels are lined with special materials. These materials collect the sun's energy for power and change the sun's rays into electricity.

So what does it cost to build such a structure? It costs more than $150 billion dollars. Although this may seem astronomical, it may be a small price to pay for a project that enables some of the world's finest scientists to work together, exploring space for the world's future.

1. Write **C** for cause or **E** for effect for each sentence.

_____ Fifteen countries built the International Space Station.

_____ People want to know if humans can one day live in space.

_____ Panels are lined with special materials that change the sun's rays into electricity.

_____ The ISS is powered by solar energy.

© Scholastic Inc.

2. Write a word from the article to match each definition. Then write each numbered letter on the matching blank below to find out the four most requested foods of astronauts.

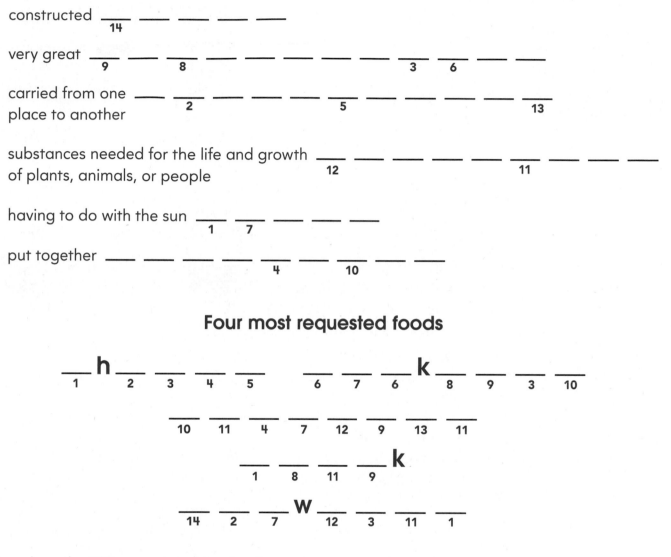

constructed ___ ___ ___ ___ ___
          14

very great ___ ___ ___ ___ ___ ___ ___ ___ ___ ___
          9   8   3   6

carried from one ___ ___ ___ ___ ___ ___ ___ ___ ___
place to another   2   5   13

substances needed for the life and growth ___ ___ ___ ___ ___ ___ ___ ___ ___
of plants, animals, or people   12   11

having to do with the sun ___ ___ ___ ___ ___
                          1   7

put together ___ ___ ___ ___ ___ ___ ___ ___ ___
                         4   10

Four most requested foods

___ h ___ ___ ___ ___   ___ ___ ___ k ___ ___ ___ ___
1   2   3   4   5   6   7   6   8   9   3   10

___ ___ ___ ___ ___ ___ ___ ___
10 11   4   7 12   9 13 11

___ ___ ___ ___ k
1   8 11   9

___ ___ ___ w ___ ___ ___ ___
14   2   7   12   3 11   1

3 How does the ISS crew spend its time?

_____

4. Why might $150 billion dollars be a small price to pay for the ISS?

_____

_____

_____

A Worldwide Pickle

Read the nutrition article. Then follow the directions in the Text Marking box.

Nature demands that living things must eat to survive. This might seem easy in a modern world of freezers, supermarkets, and restaurants. But in the past, the problem was that much food spoiled before anyone could eat it. Our ancestors knew that without food, they would die. So they needed to find ways to treat foods to make them last. They had to preserve enough food in good times to survive harsh winters, droughts, natural disasters, and seasonal shortages.

One early answer to making food last was *pickling*. Pickling is a way to preserve foods by curing them in vinegar and/or salt to prevent spoiling. Vinegar is an acid that kills most bacteria. Salt dries food out and aids in the growth of "good" bacteria that protect against the "bad" bacteria that cause rot. Nearly every culture in the world developed pickled foods.

Science has since proven that pickling not only makes food last longer, it also makes some of it easier to digest. In fact, certain foods become more nutritious after they have been pickled. Pickling can also convert inedible foods, such as some roots or plants, into healthy new forms.

Which of these pickled foods have you tried?

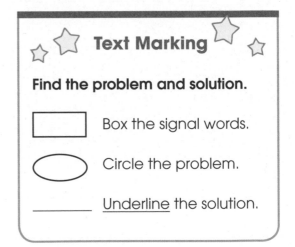

Text Marking

Find the problem and solution.

☐ Box the signal words.

◯ Circle the problem.

____ Underline the solution.

Pickled Foods From Around the World

Name	Made From...	Common in...
chutney	fruits/vegetables	India
itlog na maalat	eggs	The Philippines
jerky	meat/fish	The Americas
kimchi	cabbage/radish	Korea
sill	herring	Sweden
umeboshi	plums	Japan

Answer each question. Give evidence from the article.

1. Something that is *inedible* (paragraph 3) cannot be _____.

    ○ A. eaten   ○ B. grown   ○ C. frozen   ○ D. preserved

What in the text helped you answer?

_____

_____

_____

2. Which of the following foods could appear in the chart?

    ○ A. orange juice   ○ B. corn muffin   ○ C. ice cream   ○ D. salt pork

What in the text helped you answer?

_____

_____

_____

3. Why do you think the author includes the chart of pickled foods?

_____

_____

_____

_____

4. The title of this article has a double meaning. Explain the two meanings.

_____

_____

_____

_____

Bugs on the Menu

Read the nutrition article.
Then follow the directions in the Text Marking box.

Here's a question for you: What food has a mild, nutty flavor, is low in fat, and is loaded with nutrients? If you answered "a cricket," you would be right on target.

"Really?" you might ask. "Yuck!" you might add.

Eating insects may seem, well, disgusting to you. But that's because you haven't been introduced to what 2 billion people around the world already know: Insects are very healthy and tasty. And they are environmentally friendly, too. Eva Muller at the United Nations agrees because she knows that insects are not only harmless to eat, but nutritious and full of protein. She adds that they are a delicacy—a special food treat—in many countries.

One reason that bugs are so high in nutrients is that you eat the entire insect, including its exoskeleton, or outer body covering. (You don't eat a whole cow, however.)

Bugs are beginning to be served in restaurants here in America. Cricket taco with guacamole and fresh cream, anyone, with some delicious "crittle"* for dessert? Come, now. Just close your eyes and take a nibble. You might be pleasantly surprised.

Fried grasshoppers, a delicacy in Brazil, Ghana, Mexico, and Thailand

nutrient: a substance living things require to live and grow

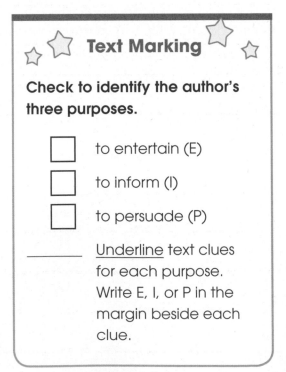

Text Marking

Check to identify the author's three purposes.

- [ ] to entertain (E)
- [ ] to inform (I)
- [ ] to persuade (P)

_____ <u>Underline</u> text clues for each purpose. Write E, I, or P in the margin beside each clue.

*"crittle" is peanut brittle flavored with chunks of cricket meat

© Scholastic Inc.

Answer each question. Give evidence from the article.

1. When would you be most likely to enjoy a *delicacy* (paragraph 2)?

- ○ A. on a desert hike
- ○ B. during a holiday party
- ○ C. while at a highway rest stop
- ○ D. during lunch in a school cafeteria

What in the text helped you answer?

_____

2. According to the article, which is NOT a reason to eat insects?

- ○ A. Eating insects is environmentally friendly.
- ○ B. Insects are very cheap to buy.
- ○ C. Insects can be very tasty.
- ○ D. Insects are very healthy.

What in the text helped you answer?

_____

3. Look back at how the author began the article. How would you describe the purpose of starting that way?

_____

_____

_____

4. Look back at your text markings regarding author's purpose. Summarize the author's point of view about eating insects.

_____

_____

_____

The Five-Second Rule

Read the health essay.
Then follow the directions in the Text Marking box.

When a person drops otherwise edible food on the floor, you might hear someone yell, "Five-second rule!" This is the belief that if you retrieve food from the floor in five seconds or less, it's still safe to eat. Is this a legitimate fact you can accept as true? Or is it simply an excuse not to waste that tasty brownie? High school senior Jillian Clarke wanted to know. She conducted a controlled scientific experiment to test this notion.

Clarke got smooth and rough tiles of equal size. First, she cleaned them thoroughly. Then she contaminated them with samples of the *E. coli* bacteria. She chose cookies and gummy bears as the test foods. In turn, she dropped one of each on the tainted tiles, picked each up in five seconds or less, and tested for the presence of *E. coli* on the foods.

The results left no doubt. Clarke found a transfer of germs in less than five seconds. Common sense prevails: It's simply not safe to eat food that has fallen on the floor. For her work, Clarke received a joke prize for "research that first makes you laugh, then makes you think."

Illness-causing *E. coli* bacteria (seen through a microscope)

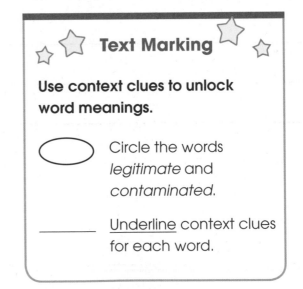

⭐ Text Marking ⭐

Use context clues to unlock word meanings.

◯ Circle the words *legitimate* and *contaminated*.

___ Underline context clues for each word.

Answer each question. Give evidence from the essay.

1. Which of the following is NOT *edible* (paragraph 1)?

     ○ A. broccoli   ○ B. brownies   ○ C. floor tiles   ○ D. gummy bears

What in the text helped you answer?

_____

2. What usually happens when people eat food that is *contaminated* with *E. coli* bacteria?

     ○ A. They become sick.   ○ C. They have endless hunger.

     ○ B. They fall on the floor.   ○ D. They perform a science experiment.

What in the text helped you answer?

_____

_____

3. Summarize what Jillian Clarke discovered as a result of her experiment.

_____

_____

_____

_____

4. Use context clues in the essay to explain the meaning of *tainted* (paragraph 2) in your own words.

_____

_____

_____

Accidents Happen

Read the health and safety article.
Then follow the directions in the Text Marking box.

What if you scrape your shin or a pet claws you by mistake? Alas, accidents occur to everyone. Minor wounds need TLC—tender loving care—and sufficient time to mend. Luckily, you can manage most small wounds without visiting a hospital; that's why it's a good idea to have basic first-aid supplies on hand at home.

First-aid kit

The first thing to do is to stop any bleeding immediately. Small cuts and scrapes usually close on their own. If not, cover the wound with a clean cloth or bandage. Then press gently on it until the bleeding stops. This could take a few seconds or minutes.

Next, it's essential to rinse the wound to avoid infection. Use lukewarm water and mild soap to gently clean the area; repeat to remove dirt and grit. If needed, wet some cotton or gauze with alcohol or peroxide and lightly clean again. Dry the area thoroughly.

Then, cover the wound to keep out harmful germs using a bandage, gauze pad, or other type of clean cover, but don't make it too tight.

Finally, be kind to your wound. Try not to bump it. When the bandage gets wet or dirty, replace it. After a scab forms, expose the wound to fresh air so it can finish healing.

Text Marking

Find the sequence of steps.

☐	Box the signal words.
_____	<u>Underline</u> the important steps.
1-2-3	Number the events in the sequence they happen.

Answer each question. Give evidence from the article.

1. Which of the following words means about the same as *sufficient*, as used in paragraph 1?

    ○ A. enough   ○ B. scarce   ○ C. painful   ○ D. restful

What in the text helped you answer?

_____

_____

2. Which is the *last* thing to do when caring for a wound?

    ○ A. Rinse the wound carefully.   ○ C. Press on the wound to stop any bleeding.

    ○ B. Let the wound get some fresh air.   ○ D. Apply some form of cover to the wound.

What in the text helped you answer?

_____

_____

_____

3. According to the article, what is the most important reason to clean and cover a wound?

_____

_____

_____

4. Does the advice explained in this article apply to all kinds of accidents? In your own words, explain your response.

_____

_____

_____

Bones

Read the article and answer the questions.

Bones are strong, yet light. Before we are born, our bones are solid. Gradually, some bones become hollow, which makes them very light, but hollow bones are still strong. As our bodies develop in the womb, our bones are made of a soft, flexible material called cartilage. By the time we are born, much of this cartilage has turned to bone. New bone tissue is constantly being made. Minerals that we get from food make the bones as hard as rock. Strong, stringy materials called collagen also run through most bones and strengthen them. The bones are a storage place for minerals. If certain minerals are needed by other parts of the body, they are released from the bones into the blood. Until the age of thirty-five, there is more new bone being created than there is old bone breaking down. By the time we reach old age, a lot of minerals and collagen have disappeared from our bones, which weakens them. These weak bones break more easily, sometimes causing elderly people to suffer from broken bones.

1. What is the main idea of this article?

_____

2. What are bones made of?

_____

3. What makes bones hard?

_____

4. Are bones solid or hollow? Explain.

_____

5. How do bones grow?

_____

6. What makes bones weak?

_____

ADDITION, SUBTRACTION, MULTIPLICATION & DIVISION

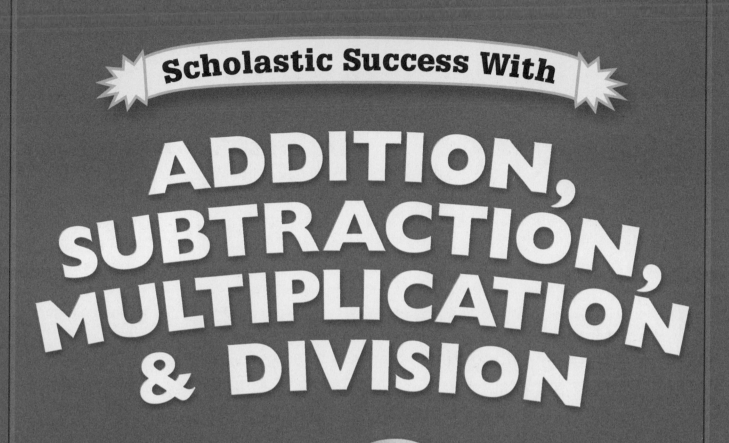

A Sick Riddle

Riddle: What sickness can't you talk about until it's cured?

Find each sum. Then use the Decoder to solve the riddle by filling in the spaces at the bottom of the page.

Decoder

66	I
57	W
42	I
216	M
19	Y
97	C
768	G
35	S
46	E
100	X
245	R
1,257	D
54	A
52	O
368	L
82	P
1,323	T
155	Q
165	N

❶ $12 + 7$ = _____

❷ $32 + 10$ = _____

❸ $50 + 4$ = _____

❹ $13 + 22$ = _____

❺ $47 + 19$ = _____

❻ $97 + 68$ = _____

❼ $204 + 41$ = _____

❽ $37 + 331$ = _____

❾ $670 + 98$ = _____

❿ $857 + 466$ = _____

___ ___ ___ ___ ___ ___ ___ ___ ___ ___
 8   3   7   1   6   9   5   10 2   4

© Scholastic Inc.

Blooming Octagon

Solve the problems. ◆ If the answer is between 1 and 300, color the
shape yellow. ◆ If the answer is between 301 and 600, color the shape
blue. ◆ If the answer is between 601 and 1,000, color the shape orange.
◆ Finish by coloring the outer shapes with the colors of your choice.

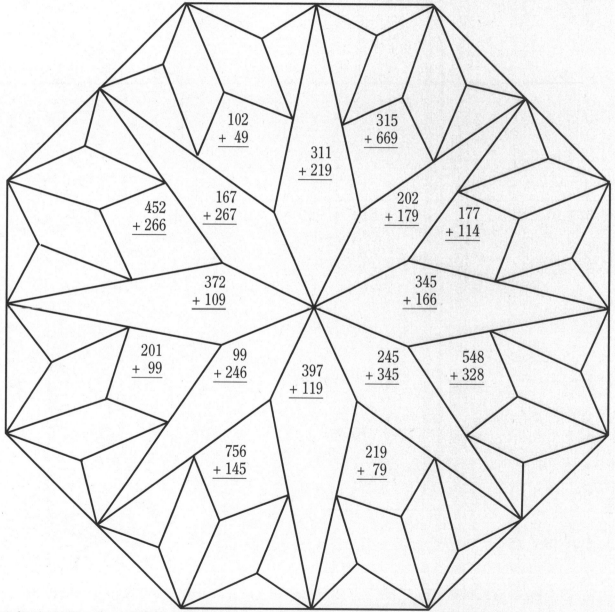

Inside the octagon, the addition problems are:

$$102 + 49$$

$$315 + 669$$

$$311 + 219$$

$$452 + 266$$

$$167 + 267$$

$$202 + 179$$

$$177 + 114$$

$$372 + 109$$

$$345 + 166$$

$$201 + 99$$

$$99 + 246$$

$$397 + 119$$

$$245 + 345$$

$$548 + 328$$

$$756 + 145$$

$$219 + 79$$

Taking It Further: Fill in the next three numbers in this pattern.

150, 300, 450, 600, _____, _____, _____.

The Big Cheese

 Always complete the operation inside the parentheses ( ) first.
Then complete the rest of the problem.

$$7 + (3 + 6) =$$
$$7 + 9 = 16$$

$$(4 + 4) + 8 =$$
$$8 + 8 = 16$$

Add.

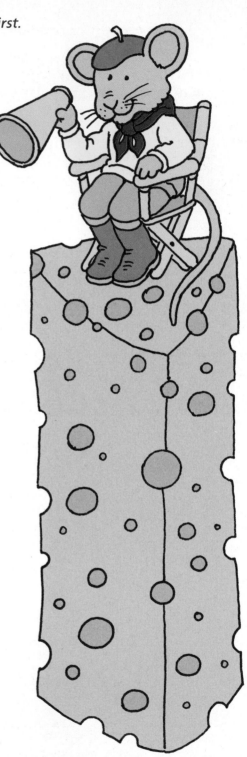

A. $(7 + 2) + 4 =$ _____ $(3 + 4) + 7 =$ _____

B. $(5 + 4) + 9 =$ _____ $9 + (2 + 3) =$ _____

C. $8 + (3 + 5) =$ _____ $6 + (2 + 4) =$ _____

D. $(2 + 6) + (5 + 2) =$ _____ $(5 + 1) + (4 + 4) =$ _____

E. $(3 + 3) + (5 + 4) =$ _____ $(4 + 3) + (6 + 2) =$ _____

F. $(6 + 6) + 3 =$ _____ $4 + (5 + 4) =$ _____

G. $5 + (4 + 8) =$ _____ $(3 + 7) + 7 =$ _____

H. $(2 + 9) + 8 =$ _____ $5 + (5 + 5) =$ _____

I. $(8 + 5) + 4 =$ _____ $(9 + 3) + 2 =$ _____

J. $(8 + 2) + (3 + 2) =$ _____ $(5 + 7) + (4 + 4) =$ _____

K. $(2 + 5) + (5 + 8) =$ _____ $(6 + 5) + (7 + 4) =$ _____

 The director ordered a big piece of cheese for each actor in the movie. He ordered 6
pieces from Charlie's Cheese Shop, 3 pieces from Holes and More, and 7 pieces from
Mouse Munchers. Write a number sentence using parentheses to solve the problem.

A-Mazing Eighteen

The answer to an addition problem is called the **sum.**

Find the path that leads from the mouse to the cheese by following the sums of eighteen. Add.

(5 + 4) + (3 + 6)	(7 + 6) + 5	(5 + 6) + (4 + 2)	(7 + 5) + 7	3 + (7 + 5)
4 + (6 + 6)	3 + (8 + 7)	(5 + 3) + (3 + 4)	(4 + 6) + 5	(5 + 9) + 3
(9 + 2) + 6	(5 + 3) + (6 + 4)	2 + (8 + 8)	8 + (6+ 2)	(4 + 5) + (2 + 5)
5 + (6 + 6)	(6 + 6) + (4 + 6)	(2 + 3) + (9 + 4)	3 + (7 + 5)	(6 + 7) + 6
(7 + 8) + 2	5 + (4 + 6)	7 + (4 + 7)	(5 + 6) + (4 + 3)	(8 + 4) + 6

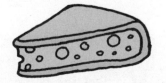

Write another number sentence with 18 as the sum. Do not use a number sentence from above.

Climbing High

To add multiple-digit numbers without regrouping, follow these steps.
1. Add the ones column.
2. Add the tens column.
3. Add the hundreds column.
4. Continue working through each column in order.

Add.

A.
$$1,136 + 2,433$$

$$9,025 + 851$$
—

B.
$$8,730 + 1,252$$
—

$$2,928 + 5,021$$

$$3,650 + 4,210$$

$$80,662 + 11,136$$

C.
$$55,100 + 31,892$$

$$60,439 + 30,310$$
—

$$81,763 + 8,231$$

$$36,034 + 41,753$$

D.
$$321,957 + 260,041$$

$$623,421 + 151,441$$
—

$$264,870 + 303,120$$

$$592,604 + 102,335$$

$$127,094 + 832,502$$
—

Mount Everest is the highest mountain in the world. To find the height of Mount Everest, begin climbing in Row D. Write the underlined numbers in order. Continue writing the numbers in Row C, Row B, and Row A. How many feet did you climb?

Reaching New Heights

To add multiple-digit numbers with regrouping, follow these steps.
1. Add the ones column.
2. If the sum is greater than 9, regroup to the tens column.
3. Add the tens column.
4. If the sum is greater than 9, regroup to the hundreds column.
5. Continue working through each column in order.

Which of these mountains is the tallest? To find out add. The sum with the greatest number in each row shows the height of the mountain in feet. Circle the height for each mountain.

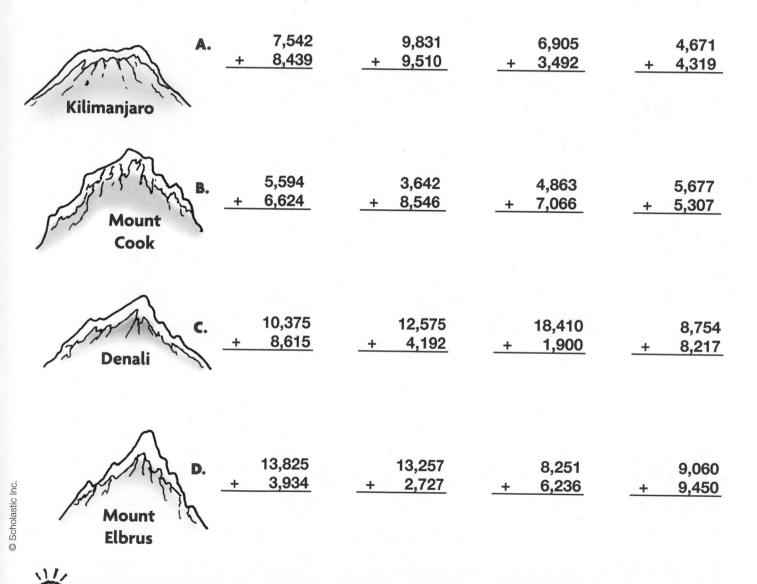

Kilimanjaro

A.
$$7,542 + 8,439$$
$$9,831 + 9,510$$
$$6,905 + 3,492$$
$$4,671 + 4,319$$

Mount Cook

B.
$$5,594 + 6,624$$
$$3,642 + 8,546$$
$$4,863 + 7,066$$
$$5,677 + 5,307$$

Denali

C.
$$10,375 + 8,615$$
$$12,575 + 4,192$$
$$18,410 + 1,900$$
$$8,754 + 8,217$$

Mount Elbrus

D.
$$13,825 + 3,934$$
$$13,257 + 2,727$$
$$8,251 + 6,236$$
$$9,060 + 9,450$$

Find the total height of the two mountains with the greatest heights.

Wild Birds

Some addition problems will require regrouping several times. The steps look like this.

1. Add the ones column. Regroup if needed.

2. Add the tens column. Regroup if needed.

3. Add the hundreds column. Regroup if needed.

4. Continue working through each column in order.

```
    1                 11                111               111
  37,462            37,462            37,462            37,462
+  22,798          + 22,798          + 22,798          + 22,798
_____          _____         _____         _____
    0                 60               260              60,260
```

Add. Then use the code to finish the fun fact below.

bald eagle

Z.	953	B.	295	R.	418	Q.	565	S.	862	X.	478
+	418	+	337	+	793	+	957	+	339	+	283

falcon

I.	2,428	C.	1,566	Y.	3,737	A.	9,289	Y.	8,754
+	6,679	+	2,487	+	6,418	+	4,735	+	368

vulture

L.	57,854	P.	29,484	E.	36,238	F.	67,139
+	45,614	+	46,592	+	46,135	+	25,089

owl

D.	240,669	O.	476,381	R.	882,948
+	298,727	+	175,570	+	176,524

What do all of these birds have in common?

They are _____ _____ _____ _____ _____   _____ _____
        632   9,107 1,211 539,396 1,201   651,951 92,228

_____ _____ _____ _____ .
76,076 1,059,472 82,373 10,155

The American Bald Eagle

 To add numbers that require regrouping in more than one column, follow these steps.
1. Add the ones column. Regroup if needed.
2. Add the tens column. Regroup if needed.
4. Add the hundreds column. Regroup if needed.
5. Continue working through each column in order.

Add. Then use the code to finish the fun fact below.

H.   8,754
       +   368

L.   7,789
       +   4,759

I.   8,997
       +   9,978

A.   8,599
       +   8,932

E.   5,476
       +   4,846

O.   9,475
       +   7,725

C.   8,838
       +   9,668

T.   6,867
       +   7,256

M.   9,891
       +   3,699

N.   92,854
       +   37,898

U.   25,748
       +   85,362

Y.   99,977
       +   82,943

R.   57,544
       +   78,587

The bald eagle is found

	17,200	130,752	12,548	182,920	17,200	130,752

14,123	9,122	10,322	130,752	17,200	136,131	14,123	9,122

17,531	13,590	10,322	136,131	18,975	18,506	17,531	130,752

18,506	17,200	130,752	14,123	18,975	130,752	10,322	130,752	14,123

Funny Bone

Use the same steps to add several addends. Some columns will require regrouping, and some will not.

Add. Then use the code to find the answer to the riddle below.

W.	T.	P.	N.	O.	E.
1,233 1,442 + 5,226	6,314 3,380 + 2,606	2,305 2,404 + 2,439	1,238 6,281 + 5,366	3,541 309 + 7,845	3,525 2,213 + 9,281
H.	**R.**	**S.**	**!**	**A.**	**U.**
444 7,283 + 8,217	4,327 4,331 + 1,746	4,024 678 + 4,505	5,441 421 + 3,954	2,653 3,338 + 2,924	5,560 4,202 + 1,541

What is the difference between a man and a running dog?

$\overline{\text{11,695}}$ $\overline{\text{12,885}}$ $\overline{\text{15,019}}$

$\overline{\text{7,901}}$ $\overline{\text{15,019}}$ $\overline{\text{8,915}}$ $\overline{\text{10,404}}$ $\overline{\text{9,207}}$

$\overline{\text{12,300}}$ $\overline{\text{10,404}}$ $\overline{\text{11,695}}$ $\overline{\text{11,303}}$ $\overline{\text{9,207}}$ $\overline{\text{15,019}}$ $\overline{\text{10,404}}$ $\overline{\text{9,207}}$.

$\overline{\text{12,300}}$ $\overline{\text{15,944}}$ $\overline{\text{15,019}}$

$\overline{\text{11,695}}$ $\overline{\text{12,300}}$ $\overline{\text{15,944}}$ $\overline{\text{15,019}}$ $\overline{\text{10,404}}$

$\overline{\text{7,148}}$ $\overline{\text{8,915}}$ $\overline{\text{12,885}}$ $\overline{\text{12,300}}$ $\overline{\text{9,207}}$ $\overline{\text{9,816}}$

Canine Calculations

The numbers being added together are called **addends**.

Use the sum to help you find the missing numbers of each addend.

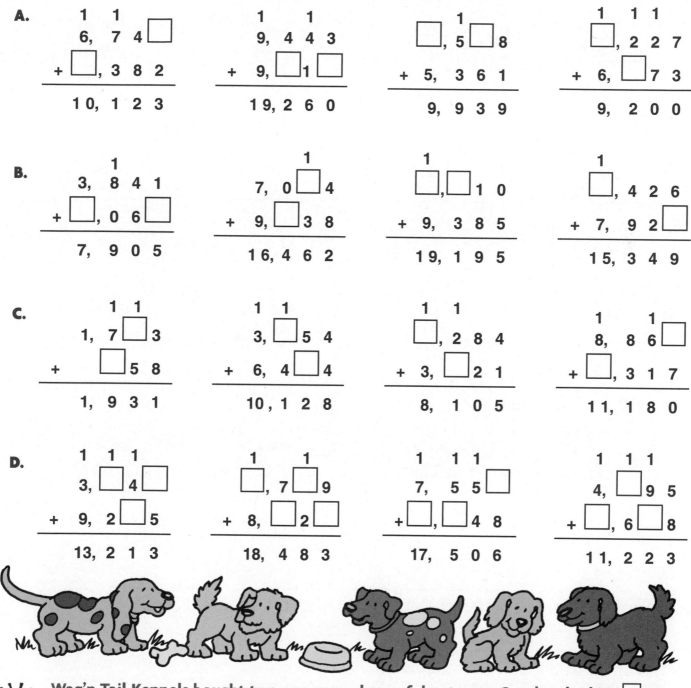

A.

```
    1  1
    6, 7 4 □
 + □ , 3 8 2
 ────────────
   10, 1 2 3
```

```
   1   1
   9, 4 4 3
 + 9, □ 1 □
 ────────────
   19, 2 6 0
```

```
       1
   □ , 5 □ 8
 + 5, 3 6 1
 ────────────
   9, 9 3 9
```

```
   1  1  1
   □ , 2 2 7
 + 6, □ 7 3
 ────────────
   9, 2 0 0
```

B.

```
      1
   3, 8 4 1
 + □ , 0 6 □
 ────────────
   7, 9 0 5
```

```
      1
   7, 0 □ 4
 + 9, □ 3 8
 ────────────
  16, 4 6 2
```

```
   1
   □ , □ 1 0
 + 9, 3 8 5
 ────────────
  19, 1 9 5
```

```
   1
   □ , 4 2 6
 + 7, 9 2 □
 ────────────
  15, 3 4 9
```

C.

```
   1  1
   1, 7 □ 3
 +    □ 5 8
 ────────────
   1, 9 3 1
```

```
   1  1
   3, □ 5 4
 + 6, 4 □ 4
 ────────────
  10, 1 2 8
```

```
   1  1
   □ , 2 8 4
 + 3, □ 2 1
 ────────────
   8, 1 0 5
```

```
   1     1
   8, 8 6 □
 + □ , 3 1 7
 ────────────
  11, 1 8 0
```

D.

```
   1  1  1
   3, □ 4 □
 + 9, 2 □ 5
 ────────────
  13, 2 1 3
```

```
   1     1
   □ , 7 □ 9
 + 8, □ 2 □
 ────────────
  18, 4 8 3
```

```
   1  1  1
   7,  5 5 □
 + □ , □ 4 8
 ────────────
  17, 5 0 6
```

```
   1  1  1
   4, □ 9 5
 + □ , 6 □ 8
 ────────────
  11, 2 2 3
```

Wag'n Tail Kennels bought two enormous bags of dog treats. One bag had 38, □69 dog treats in it. The other bag had 4 □,510 pieces of dog treats. Altogether the bags had 80,879 treats. On another piece of paper, find the number of dog treats in each bag.

Money Fun

Remember to include a decimal point and a dollar sign in the answer when adding money.

Add. Then use the code to answer the riddle below.

A.	$63.54 + 29.29	**G.**	$65.35 + 27.18	**U.**	$24.12 + 90.48	**O.**	$15.79 + 48.08

B.	$27.60 + 44.65	**N.**	$77.88 + 92.90	**E.**	$86.91 + 70.44	**R.**	$39.75 + 29.62

M.	$103.90 + 64.82	**C.**	$291.26 + 473.83	**S.**	$485.13 + 494.92	**T.**	$630.57 + 39.52

D.	$184.64 + 292.43	**Y.**	$354.60 + 261.74	**F.**	$964.36 + 252.04	**W.**	$904.86 + 95.82

Why are birds poor?

_____ _____ _____ _____ _____ _____ _____
$72.25 $157.35 $765.09 $92.83 $114.60 $980.05 $157.35

_____ _____ _____ _____ _____
$168.72 $63.87 $170.78 $157.35 $616.34
                    ,

_____ _____ _____ _____ _____ _____ _____ _____ _____ _____
$477.07 $63.87 $157.35 $980.05 $170.78 $670.09 $92.53 $69.37 $63.87 $1,000.68
                                                                        !

_____ _____ _____ _____ _____ _____ _____
$63.87 $170.78 $670.09 $69.37 $157.35 $157.35 $980.05

Bathtub Brunch

Riddle: What's the best thing to eat in a bathtub?

Find each sum. Then use the Decoder to solve the riddle by filling in the spaces at the bottom of the page.

Decoder

5,429	A
10,493	F
2,133	S
14,983	R
10,439	P
712	U
3,489	K
1,840	M
1,063	E
4,523	W
689	N
2,009	B
8,292	O
3,234	I
7,538	G
1,804	C
4,708	H
6,521	L
8,234	E

1 $1,004 + 800$ = _____

2 $512 + 177$ = _____

3 $364 + 699$ = _____

4 $1,245 + 888$ = _____

5 $1,876 + 1,613$ = _____

6 $2,010 + 6,224$ = _____

7 $5,470 + 2,068$ = _____

8 $4,526 + 3,766$ = _____

9 $1,017 + 4,412$ = _____

10 $2,588 + 7,851$ = _____

$\overline{}$ $\overline{}$ $\overline{}$ $\overline{}$ $\overline{}$ $\overline{}$ $\overline{}$ $\overline{}$ $\overline{}$ $\overline{}$
  4   10   8   2   7   6   1   9   5   3

© Scholastic Inc.

Food to Go

Figure it out!

1. Woovis the Dog found a $5 bill. Which item can he buy from the menu that will give the least change?

_____

DOGGIE DINER BREAKFAST SHOP

MENU

Kibble $1.79
Mouse Crumbs $1.39
Table Scraps $2.49
Crumbs & Cheese $3.19
Deluxe Scraps $3.79

2. Molly Mouse gets Crumbs & Cheese for breakfast. She pays with the $5 bill. With the leftover money, what can Woovis buy to eat?

_____

3. Which item can Woovis buy with the $5 bill that will give the most change?

_____

4. Which two items can Woovis buy with the $5 bill so that he gets about $1 back in change?

_____

5. Woovis ordered two items from the menu and gave the cashier the $5 bill. But the two items cost more than $6.50. Which two items did Woovis order?

_____

SUPER CHALLENGE: Can Woovis use the $5 bill to buy three different items from the menu? Why or why not?

A Penny Saved Is a Penny Earned

Write a number sentence for each problem. Solve.

A. Aimee and her 2 sisters are saving to buy a camera. Aimee has $12.89. Each of her sisters has $28.53. How much money do all the girls have combined?

B. Katie has $23.95 in her purse, $17.23 in her bank, and $76.82 in her savings account. What is the total amount of Katie's money?

C. Jonah worked in the yard for 3 days. The first day he earned $7.96. The second day he earned $2.00 more than the first day. The third day he earned $2.00 less than the first day. How much did Jonah earn altogether?

D. Jack has $9.29. He also has 79 dimes and 139 pennies. How much money does he have altogether?

E. Kelsey has 478 coins in her collection. The silver dollars equal $79.00, and the quarters equal $99.75. How much is Kelsey's collection worth in all?

F. Claire bought lemonade for herself and two friends. Each cup costs $1.75. How much did Claire spend in all?

On another piece of paper, write a word problem with a sum equal to $41.68.

Reach for the Stars

*Always complete the operation inside the parentheses ( ) first.
Then complete the rest of the problem.*

$(18 - 9) - 3 =$ _____ $18 - (9 - 3) =$ _____
$9 - 3 = 6$ $18 - 6 = 12$

Subtract. Then use the code to answer the question below.

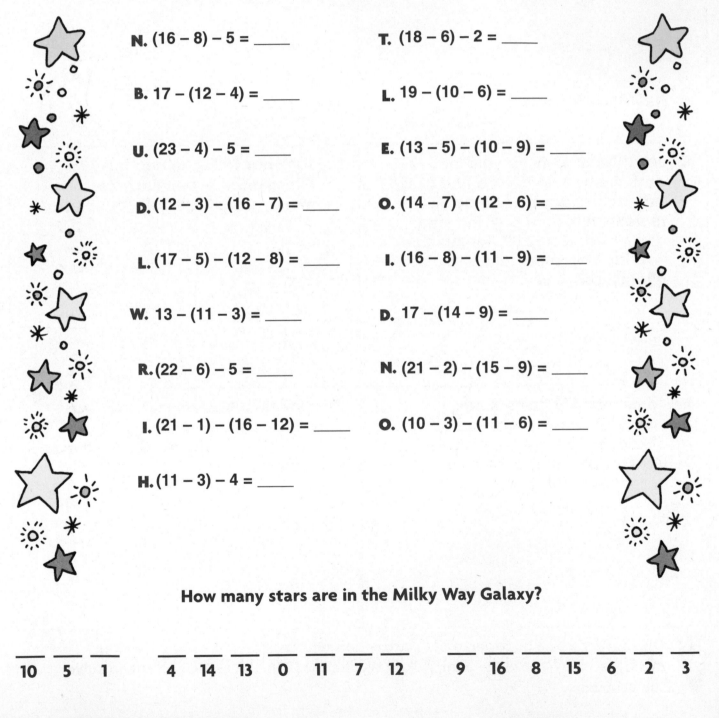

N. $(16 - 8) - 5 =$ _____

T. $(18 - 6) - 2 =$ _____

B. $17 - (12 - 4) =$ _____

L. $19 - (10 - 6) =$ _____

U. $(23 - 4) - 5 =$ _____

E. $(13 - 5) - (10 - 9) =$ _____

D. $(12 - 3) - (16 - 7) =$ _____

O. $(14 - 7) - (12 - 6) =$ _____

L. $(17 - 5) - (12 - 8) =$ _____

I. $(16 - 8) - (11 - 9) =$ _____

W. $13 - (11 - 3) =$ _____

D. $17 - (14 - 9) =$ _____

R. $(22 - 6) - 5 =$ _____

N. $(21 - 2) - (15 - 9) =$ _____

I. $(21 - 1) - (16 - 12) =$ _____

O. $(10 - 3) - (11 - 6) =$ _____

H. $(11 - 3) - 4 =$ _____

How many stars are in the Milky Way Galaxy?

___ ___ ___   ___ ___ ___ ___ ___ ___ ___   ___ ___ ___ ___ ___ ___ ___
10 5   1   4 14 13 0 11 7 12   9 16 8 15 6   2   3

Moon Madness

➡️ *The answer to a subtraction problem is called the **difference**.*

Subtract. Then write the ☽ differences in order to answer the fun fact.

How fast does the moon travel in its orbit? ☽ ☽ ☽ ☽ **m.p.h.**
_____ _____ _____ _____

A. $11 - (15 - 9) =$ _____

$14 - (18 - 9) =$ _____

B. $(15 - 7) - (11 - 5) =$ _____

$17 - (14 - 6) =$ _____

C. $16 - (15 - 8) =$ _____

$18 - (16 - 7) =$ _____

D. $15 - (15 - 8) =$ _____

$(16 - 8) - (10 - 4) =$ _____

E. $(13 - 9) - (11 - 8) =$ _____

$13 - (14 - 7) =$ _____

F. $12 - (13 - 6) =$ _____

$17 - (12 - 3) =$ _____

G. $(17 - 9) - (13 - 8) =$ _____

$(15 - 6) - (12 - 5) =$ _____

H. $18 - (13 - 4) =$ _____

$16 - (17 - 9) =$ _____

I. $14 - (13 - 5) =$ _____

$15 - (16 - 8) =$ _____

J. $12 - (18 - 9) =$ _____

$(20 - 7) - (6 - 2) =$ _____

💡 **On another piece of paper, write subtraction problems with a code to answer this question: What is the diameter of the moon? (2,160 miles) Have a friend solve the problems.**

Chess, Anyone?

To subtract multiple-digit numbers without regrouping, follow these steps.

1. **Subtract the ones column.**

```
  6,48|9|
- 2,16|5|
      |4|
```

2. **Subtract the tens column.**

```
  6,4|8|9
- 2,1|6|5
     |2|4
```

3. **Subtract the hundreds column.**

```
  6,|4|89
- 2,|1|65
    |3|24
```

4. **Subtract the thousands column.**

```
  |6|,489
- |2|,165
  |4|,324
```

Subtract.

6,518 − 1,414	9,842 − 621	7,966 − 3,234	6,549 − 21
4,916 − 4,113	8,385 − 7,224	3,309 − 203	5,977 − 2,863
9,459 − 300	7,749 − 7,637	4,969 − 2,863	3,496 − 3,260
6,839 − 5,324	1,578 − 1,241	8,659 − 46	9,481 − 9,240

© Scholastic Inc.

Checkmate

To subtract with regrouping, follow these steps.

1. **Subtract the ones column. Regroup if needed.**

   $$\begin{array}{r} {\scriptstyle 2\ 11} \\ 4\,\cancel{3}\,\cancel{1} \\ -\ 266 \\ \hline 5 \end{array}$$

2. **Subtract the tens column. Regroup if needed.**

   $$\begin{array}{r} {\scriptstyle 12} \\ {\scriptstyle 3\,\cancel{2}\,11} \\ \cancel{4}\,\cancel{3}\,\cancel{1} \\ -\ 266 \\ \hline 65 \end{array}$$

3. **Subtract the hundreds column. Regroup if needed.**

   $$\begin{array}{r} {\scriptstyle 12} \\ {\scriptstyle 3\,\cancel{2}\,11} \\ \cancel{4}\,\cancel{3}\,\cancel{1} \\ -\ 266 \\ \hline 165 \end{array}$$

Subtract. Cross out the chess piece with the matching difference. The last piece standing is the winner of the match.

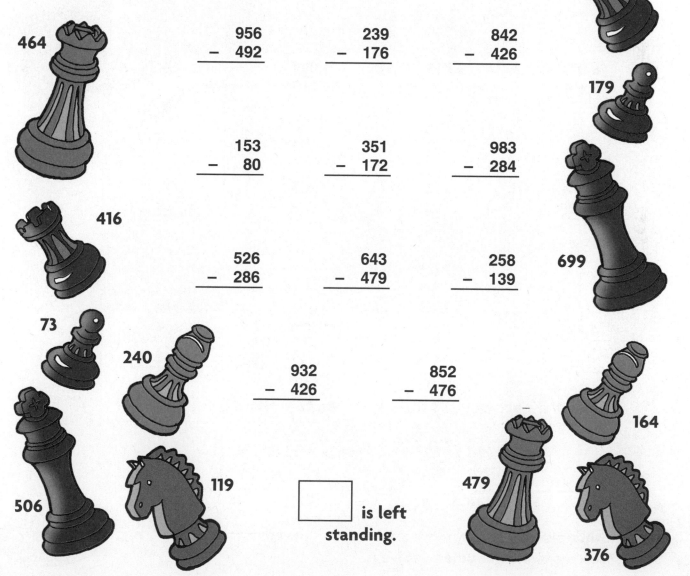

$$\begin{array}{r} 956 \\ -\ 492 \\ \hline \end{array} \qquad \begin{array}{r} 239 \\ -\ 176 \\ \hline \end{array} \qquad \begin{array}{r} 842 \\ -\ 426 \\ \hline \end{array}$$

$$\begin{array}{r} 153 \\ -\ 80 \\ \hline \end{array} \qquad \begin{array}{r} 351 \\ -\ 172 \\ \hline \end{array} \qquad \begin{array}{r} 983 \\ -\ 284 \\ \hline \end{array}$$

$$\begin{array}{r} 526 \\ -\ 286 \\ \hline \end{array} \qquad \begin{array}{r} 643 \\ -\ 479 \\ \hline \end{array} \qquad \begin{array}{r} 258 \\ -\ 139 \\ \hline \end{array}$$

$$\begin{array}{r} 932 \\ -\ 426 \\ \hline \end{array} \qquad \begin{array}{r} 852 \\ -\ 476 \\ \hline \end{array}$$

464   63   179   699   73   240   164   506   119   479   376

_____ is left standing.

Out of the Park!

To subtract with regrouping, follow these steps.

1.
$$
\begin{array}{r}
5\ 10 \\
3,4\,\cancel{6}\,\cancel{0} \\
-\ \ \ \ 876 \\
\hline
4
\end{array}
$$

2.
$$
\begin{array}{r}
15 \\
3\,\cancel{5}\ 10 \\
3,\cancel{4}\,\cancel{6}\,\cancel{0} \\
-\ \ \ \ 876 \\
\hline
84
\end{array}
$$

3.
$$
\begin{array}{r}
13\ \ 15 \\
2\ \cancel{3}\,\cancel{5}\ 10 \\
\cancel{3},\cancel{4}\,\cancel{6}\,\cancel{0} \\
-\ \ \ \ 876 \\
\hline
584
\end{array}
$$

4.
$$
\begin{array}{r}
13\ \ 15 \\
2\ \cancel{3}\,\cancel{5}\ 10 \\
\cancel{3},\cancel{4}\,\cancel{6}\,\cancel{0} \\
-\ \ \ \ 876 \\
\hline
2,584
\end{array}
$$

Subtract. Then use the code to solve the riddle below.

E. 4,622 − 1,284	**E.** 5,198 − 469	**H.** 3,469 − 890
T. 6,077 − 1,258	**A.** 9,617 − 759	**R.** 3,804 − 115
H. 8,941 − 1,895	**N.** 952 − 95	**C.** 7,263 − 4,772 **B.** 7,603 − 3,728
E. 9,550 − 4,298	**L.** 6,451 − 868	**S.** 2,850 − 1,976 **I.** 2,972 − 984

In what part of the ballpark do you find the whitest clothes?

___ ___   ___ ___ ___
1,988 857   4,819 2,579 5,252

___ ___ ___ ___ ___ ___ ___ ___ ___!
3,875 5,583 4,729 8,858 2,491 7,046 3,338 3,689 874

On another piece of paper, write a subtraction problem that requires regrouping two
times. Ask someone at home to solve it.

Touchdown!

Subtract. The final score of the game will be written in the footballs at the bottom of the page.

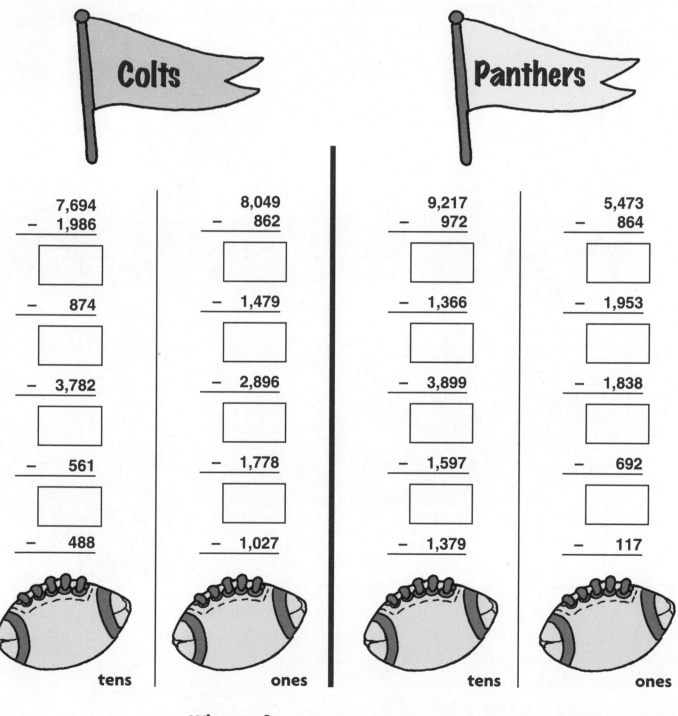

Colts

```
   7,694
 - 1,986
 _____
 [      ]

 -  874
 _____
 [      ]

 - 3,782
 _____
 [      ]

 -  561
 _____
 [      ]

 -  488
 _____
```
tens

```
   8,049
 -   862
 _____
 [      ]

 - 1,479
 _____
 [      ]

 - 2,896
 _____
 [      ]

 - 1,778
 _____
 [      ]

 - 1,027
 _____
```
ones

Panthers

```
   9,217
 -   972
 _____
 [      ]

 - 1,366
 _____
 [      ]

 - 3,899
 _____
 [      ]

 - 1,597
 _____
 [      ]

 - 1,379
 _____
```
tens

```
   5,473
 -   864
 _____
 [      ]

 - 1,953
 _____
 [      ]

 - 1,838
 _____
 [      ]

 -  692
 _____
 [      ]

 -  117
 _____
```
ones

Who won? _____

On another piece of paper, write a series of four subtraction problems that have a final difference equal to your age.

A Funny Fixture

Continue regrouping into the ten thousands column if necessary.

Subtract. Then use the code to find the answer to the riddle below.

E. 63,210 − 11,799	I. 41,392 − 38,164	R. 76,146 − 34,982	E. 12,388 − 9,891
P. 54,391 − 23,689	H. 68,612 − 59,446	T. 97,413 − 89,608	L. 32,602 − 19,561
A. 18,546 − 11,798	G. 92,475 − 76,097	S. 29,816 − 17,909	! 78,752 − 69,275

Why did the man climb up the chandelier?

,

9,166	51,411	11,907		6,748

13,041	3,228	16,378	9,166	7,805

11,907	13,041	2,497	51,411	30,702	2,497	41,164	9,477

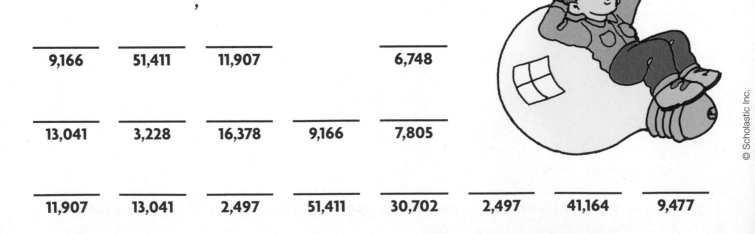

Bright Idea!

Each part of a subtraction problem has a name:

$$3,486 \leftarrow \textbf{minuend}$$
$$-\ 2,371 \leftarrow \textbf{subtrahend}$$
$$1,115 \leftarrow \textbf{difference}$$

Find each missing subtrahend by subtracting the difference from the minuend.

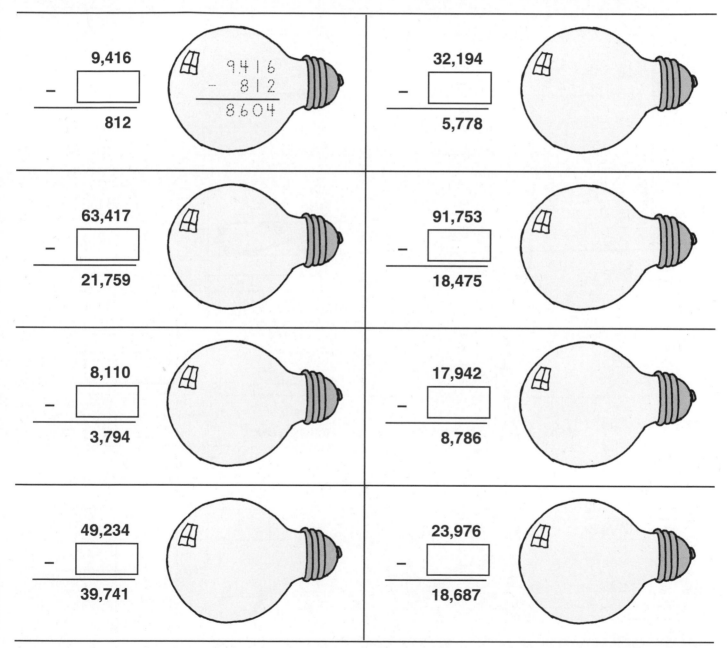

9,416
− [ ]
812

9,416
−   812
8,604

32,194
− [ ]
5,778

63,417
− [ ]
21,759

91,753
− [ ]
18,475

8,110
− [ ]
3,794

17,942
− [ ]
8,786

49,234
− [ ]
39,741

23,976
− [ ]
18,687

On another piece of paper, write two subtraction problems with missing subtrahends.
Ask a friend to solve the problems.

Cross-Number Puzzle

Subtract. Complete the puzzle.

Across

2. 3,016
    − 1,209

6. 246,342
    − 156,129

8. 64,293
    − 28,318

9. 5,249
    − 3,928

10. 36,425
    − 18,929

11. 5,264
    − 3,192

12. 818,462
    − 131,910

14. 3,642
    − 1,813

15. 7,645
    − 1,328

Down

1. 6,429
    − 3,298

3. 9,145
    − 2,189

4. 9,142
    − 1,381

5. 58,142
    − 13,098

7. 76,418
    −39,291

10. 31,642
    − 18,945

13. 814,603
    −148,231

Map It Out

 Always write a long subtraction problem vertically before solving it. When subtracting decimals, write each place value column so the decimal points are aligned.

82.17 − 74.16 =

$$\begin{array}{r} 82.71 \\ -\quad 74.16 \\ \hline \end{array}$$

Write each subtraction problem vertically. Subtract.

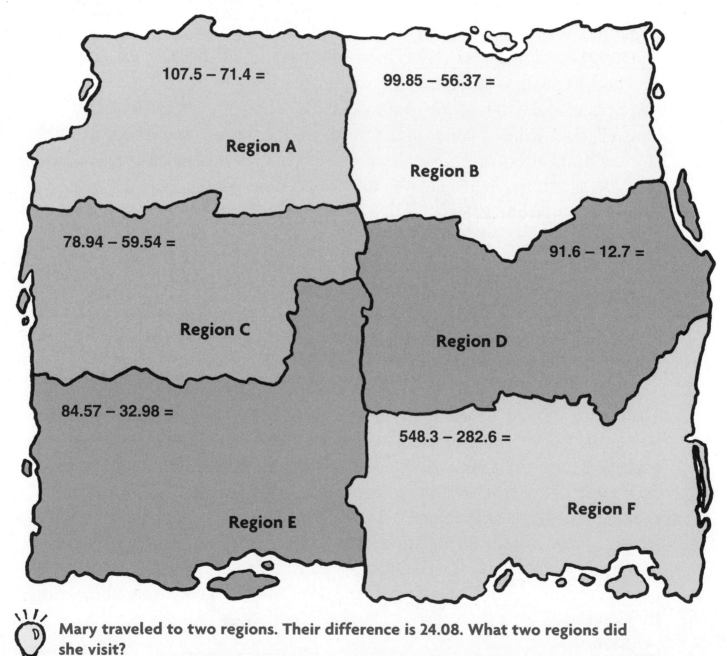

107.5 − 71.4 =

Region A

99.85 − 56.37 =

Region B

78.94 − 59.54 =

Region C

91.6 − 12.7 =

Region D

84.57 − 32.98 =

Region E

548.3 − 282.6 =

Region F

Mary traveled to two regions. Their difference is 24.08. What two regions did she visit?

Sums & Differences

> **Point-scoring in the Inter-Galaxy Football League**
> Touchdown . . . . 6 points
> Touchdown with an extra point . . . . 7 points
> Touchdown with a 2-point conversion . . . . 8 points
> Field Goal . . . . 3 points

The Asteroids played the Constellations. Each team scored a field goal in the first quarter. In the second quarter, the Asteroids scored a touchdown, but missed the extra point. At the half, the Constellations led by 1 point. In the third quarter, the Asteroids made a touchdown with the extra point. The Constellations matched them, and made a field goal, as well. In the fourth quarter, following a Constellation field goal, the Asteroids scored a touchdown with a 2-point conversion.

Who won? _____

By what score? _____

> **Point-scoring in the Inter-Galaxy Basketball League consists of
> 1-point free throws, 2-point goals, 3-point goals, and 4-point goals
> (those made without looking at the basket!).**

The Comets, playing the Meteors, led 22–9 at the end of the first quarter. They led by 7 at the half after scoring two 4-point goals, two 3-point goals, four 2-point goals, and three free throws. In the third quarter, the Meteors had six 2-point goals and four free throws. They also had one more 4-point goal, but one less 3-point goal than the Comets. The Comets had five 2-point goals and no free-throws. They scored 20 points in the quarter. In the last quarter, each team scored the same number of 4-point, 3-point, and 2-point goals. The Comets scored 31 points in that quarter, including four free throws. The Meteors made two fewer free throws than the Comets.

Who won? _____

By what score? _____

© Scholastic Inc.

Follow the Map

Write a number sentence for each problem. Solve.

A. Hannah's family drove 1,246 miles in 2 days. They drove 879 miles the first day. How far did they drive the second day?

B. Joplin is between Wells and Greenville. The distance from Wells to Greenville is 4,128 miles. The distance from Wells to Joplin is 1,839 miles. How far is it from Joplin to Greenville?

C. The Midnight Express travels 6,283 miles. When the train reaches Springfield, it has traveled 2,496 miles. How much farther will the Midnight Express travel?

D. Jacob's scout troop is going camping 947.6 miles from home. The bus breaks down after 289.9 miles. How far is the bus from the campgrounds?

E. Jonesburgh is between Johnsonville and Piper. Johnsonville is 8,612 miles from Piper. Piper is 4,985 miles from Jonesburgh. How far is it from Jonesburgh to Johnsonville?

F. Lola's family drove 2,391 miles to go to the beach. They drove home using another route that was 3,290 miles. How much longer was the second route?

It's a Circus in Here!

To multiply is to use repeated addition. Basic multiplication facts are learned by memorizing.

3 groups of 5 = 5 + 5 + 5 = 3 x 5 = 15

Multiply.

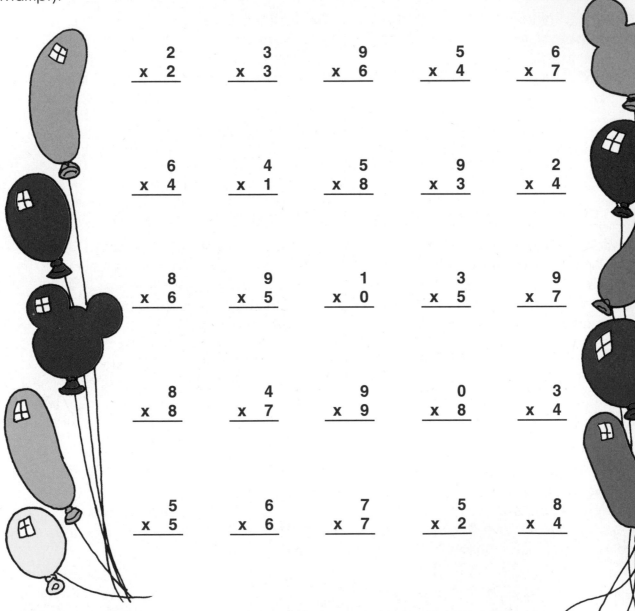

| 2 | 3 | 9 | 5 | 6 |
| x 2 | x 3 | x 6 | x 4 | x 7 |

| 6 | 4 | 5 | 9 | 2 |
| x 4 | x 1 | x 8 | x 3 | x 4 |

| 8 | 9 | 1 | 3 | 9 |
| x 6 | x 5 | x 0 | x 5 | x 7 |

| 8 | 4 | 9 | 0 | 3 |
| x 8 | x 7 | x 9 | x 8 | x 4 |

| 5 | 6 | 7 | 5 | 8 |
| x 5 | x 6 | x 7 | x 2 | x 4 |

On another piece of paper, draw a picture to match this problem: There are 6 clowns. Each clown is holding 7 balloons. Then write the multiplication fact that tells the total number of balloons.

Under the Big Top

*The answer to a multiplication problem is called the **product**.
The numbers being multiplied are called **factors**.*

Multiply. Then use each product and the code to answer the riddles.

What happened to the human cannonball at the circus?

| 4 x 6 | 6 x 3 | | 7 x 7 | 3 x 4 | 8 x 8 | | 8 x 3 | 6 x 8 | 7 x 9 | 2 x 9 | 8 x 7 |

| 6 x 2 | 8 x 9 | 7 x 8 | | 9 x 9 | 8 x 6 | 9 x 7 | 3 x 6 | 7 x 8 | | 7 x 6 | 9 x 8 |

| 5 x 9 | 6 x 4 | 9 x 2 | | 8 x 8 | 4 x 3 | 6 x 6 | 6 x 3 | | 8 x 7 | 2 x 6 | 5 x 5 ! |

What happened to the kid who ran away with the circus?

| 3 x 8 | 2 x 9 | | 4 x 6 | 3 x 4 | 8 x 7 |

| 9 x 5 | 6 x 7 | | 9 x 3 | 7 x 9 | 8 x 6 | 9 x 8 | 5 x 8 |

| 6 x 8 | 5 x 9 | | 3 x 9 | 2 x 6 | 5 x 3 | 9 x 6 ! |

A = 12	H = 24	O = 42
B = 27	I = 48	P = 16
C = 15	J = 4	Q = 28
D = 56	K = 54	R = 63
E = 18	L = 8	S = 64
F = 81	M = 36	T = 45
G = 40	N = 72	U = 0

V = 21
W = 49
X = 1
Y = 25
Z = 2

Come to Costa Rica

To multiply with a 2-digit factor, follow these steps.

1. Multiply the ones
   column.

$$\begin{array}{r} 4\,2 \\ \times\ 3 \\ \hline 6 \end{array}$$

2. Multiply the bottom factor in
   the ones column with the top
   factor in the tens column.

$$\begin{array}{r} 4\,2 \\ \times\ 3 \\ \hline 1\,2\,6 \end{array}$$

Multiply. Use the code to fill in the blanks below.

I. 82 × 4	**O.** 91 × 9	**S.** 21 × 8	**H.** 92 × 3	**J.** 73 × 2
E. 71 × 7	**L.** 53 × 3	**R.** 90 × 8	**C.** 61 × 6	**N.** 11 × 5
A. 32 × 4	**F.** 41 × 9	**T.** 70 × 7	**E.** 52 × 4	**P.** 40 × 8

490 276 208

‾‾‾ ‾‾‾ ‾‾‾

366 128 320 328 490 128 159

‾‾‾ ‾‾‾ ‾‾‾ ‾‾‾ ‾‾‾ ‾‾‾ ‾‾‾

819 369   366 819 168 490 128

‾‾‾ ‾‾‾   ‾‾‾ ‾‾‾ ‾‾‾ ‾‾‾ ‾‾‾

720 328 366 128   328 168

‾‾‾ ‾‾‾ ‾‾‾ ‾‾‾   ‾‾‾ ‾‾‾ .

168 128 55   146 819 168 497

**Costa Rica is in Central America. If a Costa Rican farmer sells 63 pounds of coffee every
day for 3 days. How much will he sell altogether?**

The Faraway Country

To multiply with a 2-digit factor that requires regrouping, follow these steps.

1. Multiply the ones.
   Regroup if needed.
   $7 \times 3 = 21$

2. Multiply the bottom factor in the ones column with the top factor in the tens column. Add the extra tens.
   $6 \times 3 = 18$ $18 + 2 = 20$

Multiply.

A.

48	24	73
x 3	x 7	x 4

B.

57	63	56
x 7	x 9	x 3

C.

98	64	57	35	23	82
x 2	x 8	x 8	x 9	x 8	x 6

D.

95	77	83	96	28	96
x 9	x 6	x 9	x 8	x 4	x 5

Switzerland is famous for the magnificent Swiss Alps. Waterfalls are formed by many of the mountain streams. One of the highest waterfalls is Giessbach Falls. To find out how many meters high this waterfall is, add the products in Row A.

© Scholastic Inc.

A Multiplication Puzzler

Multiply. Circle each product in the puzzle. The products will go across and down.

A. 32   56   70   65   68
   x 8   x 8 x 5 x 4 x 5

B. 81   89   60   69   96
   x 3   x 6 x 5 x 4 x 2

C. 49   78   72   68   24
   x 6   x 4 x 8 x 9 x 9

D. 43   97   91   79   49
   x 5   x 3 x 2 x 3 x 3

6	1	2	9	6	8	2	3	7
9	3	6	3	1	4	7	2	3
7	1	2	5	6	0	6	1	5
2	8	3	0	9	5	4	5	7
6	2	4	3	2	3	2	1	6
0	7	4	3	4	0	6	9	3
1	6	8	1	3	3	1	2	0
7	5	2	9	1	0	4	3	5
5	3	4	3	8	0	2	9	4

The Big City

To multiply with a 3-digit factor that requires regrouping, follow these steps.

1. Multiply the ones. Regroup if needed.

```
    1
  4 7 3
x     6
_____
      8
```

2. Multiply the tens in the top factor. Add the extra tens. Regroup if needed.

```
  4 1
  4 7 3
x     6
_____
    3 8
```

3. Multiply the hundreds in the top factor. Add the extra hundreds.

```
  4 1
  4 7 3
x     6
_____
  2,838
```

Multiply.

A.

463	923	194	630	494	604
x 3	x 4	x 8	x 5	x 2	x 4

B.

325	817	293	168	208	196
x 7	x 6	x 9	x 3	x 8	x 6

C.

305	815	980	155	626	126
x 2	x 5	x 7	x 9	x 3	x 6

A subway train travels 296 miles daily. How far does the train travel in a week?

A Changing Reef

To multiply with zeros, follow these steps.

90	$9 \times 2 = 18$	90	$9 \times 2 = 18$	900	$9 \times 2 = 18$
x 2	Add a zero in the ones place to make 180.	x 20	Add 2 zeros—one in the ones place and one in the tens place.	x 20	Add 3 zeros—one in the ones place, one in the tens place, and one in the hundreds place.

Multiply.

A.

80	60	900	40	120	200
x 7	x 50	x 30	x 11	x 2	x 60

B.

70	120	60	700	50	30
x 7	x 300	x 90	x 60	x 70	x 12

C.

600	40	30	90	200	50
x 80	x 12	x 8	x 50	x 120	x 8

fringing reef   **barrier reef**   **atoll**

The formation of a coral reef starts growing around the top of an undersea volcano forming a fringing reef. As the volcano sinks, it leaves behind a barrier reef. When the volcano sinks below the ocean's surface, an atoll is left. On another piece of paper, write three problems with products to match those on the pictures.

Ship Shape

What are the cheapest
ships to buy?

What To Do

To find the answer to the riddle,
solve the multiplication problems.
Then, match each product with a
letter in the Key below. Write the
correct letters on the blanks below.

1 100 x 23 = _____

2 200 x 17 = _____

3 300 x 31 = _____

4 400 x 44 = _____

5 500 x 19 = _____

6 600 x 27 = _____

7 700 x 35 = _____

8 800 x 18 = _____

9 900 x 50 = _____

Key

3,200 . . . . D	16,200 . . . . B	16,700 . . . . H
17,600 L	3,600 . . . . K	24,500 . . . . O
10,500 I	3,400 . . . . T	12,600 . . . . Y
45,000 . . . . A	9,300 . . . . E	14,400 . . . . A
15,300 . . . . R	9,500 . . . . S	2,300 . . . . S

Riddle
Answer:

" ___ ___ ___ ___   ___ ___ ___ ___ ___ "
5 **9** **4** **3**   **6** **7** **8** **2** **1**

Caught in the Web

Why did the spider join the baseball team?

What To Do

To find the answer to the riddle, solve the multiplication problems. Then, match each product with a letter in the Key below. Write the correct letters on the blanks below.

1 1,000 x 11 = _____

2 2,000 x 12 = _____

3 3,000 x 10 = _____

4 4,000 x 14 = _____

5 5,000 x 20 = _____

6 6,000 x 24 = _____

7 7,000 x 30 = _____

8 8,000 x 32 = _____

9 9,000 x 40 = _____

10 7,500 x 50 = _____

Key

56,000 . . . . H	65,000 . . . . M	30,000 C
11,000 I	144,000 . . . . T	375,000 C
265,000 . . . . B	25,000 . . . . N	10,000 . . . . Y
360,000 . . . . F	256,000 L	100,000 . . . . A
210,000 . . . . E	90,000 . . . . Q	24,000 . . . . S

Riddle Answer:

TO __ __ __ __ __ " __ __ __ __ __ "
     3 **5** **6** **10** **4**   **9** **8** **1** **7** **2**

Purple Blossoms

Solve the problems. ◆ If the answer is between 1 and 250, color the shape yellow. ◆ If the answer is between 251 and 4000, color the shape purple. ◆ If the answer is between 4,001 and 9,000, color the shape pink. ◆ Finish by coloring the other shapes with colors of your choice.

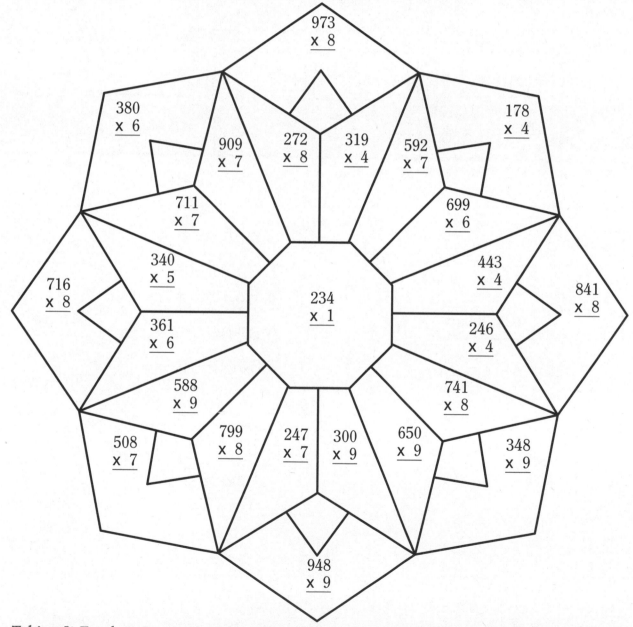

Taking It Further: I am an even number. I have three digits and they are all the same. If you multiply me by 4, all of the digits in the product are 8. What number am I? _____

Stallions in the Stable

Multiply. Use the products to put each stallion back where he belongs. Write the horse's name on the stall door.

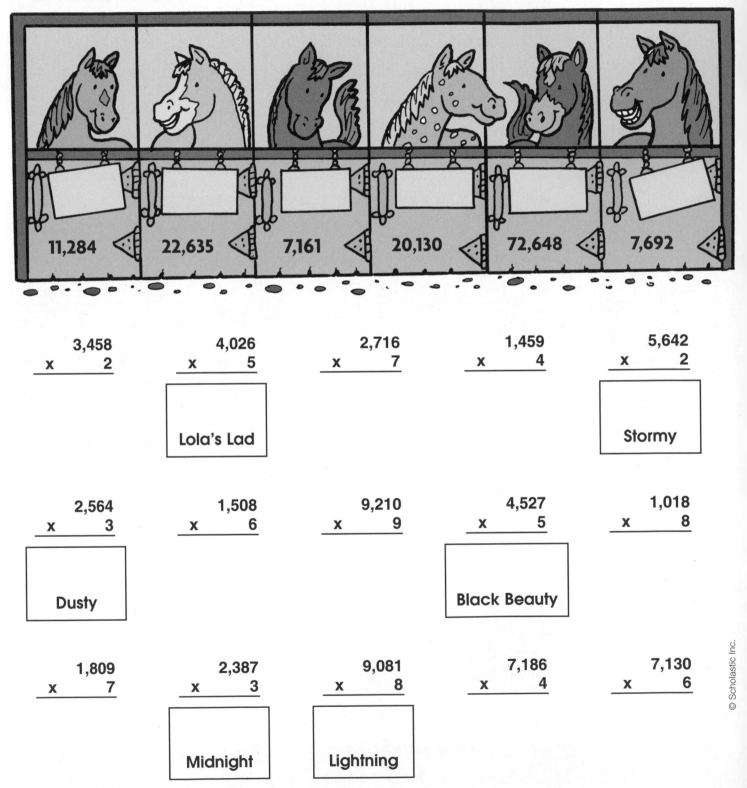

| 11,284 | 22,635 | 7,161 | 20,130 | 72,648 | 7,692 |

3,458	4,026	2,716	1,459	5,642
x 2	x 5	x 7	x 4	x 2

Lola's Lad

Stormy

2,564	1,508	9,210	4,527	1,018
x 3	x 6	x 9	x 5	x 8

Dusty

Black Beauty

1,809	2,387	9,081	7,186	7,130
x 7	x 3	x 8	x 4	x 6

Midnight

Lightning

© Scholastic Inc.

Stop Horsing Around!

To multiply with a 2-digit factor that requires regrouping, follow these steps.

1. Multiply by the ones digit.	2. Place a zero in the ones column..	3. Multiply by the tens digit.	4. Add to find the product.

```
        3                   3                   3                  1
       4 6                 4 6                 4 6                 3
    x   2 6             x   2 6             x   2 6                4 6
    ---------          ---------           ---------          x   2 6
       2 7 6              2 7 6               2 7 6               2 7 6
                             0             +   9 2 0           +   9 2 0
                                                               ---------
                                                                1 , 1 9 6
```

Multiply. Then use the code to answer the riddle below.

G. 32 x 48	T. 67 x 14	S. 53 x 27	I. 96 x 52	A. 83 x 33	D. 49 x 72

M. 39 x 28	E. 56 x 15	N. 83 x 24	R. 75 x 46	K. 96 x 51	H. 84 x 62

What horses like to stay up late?

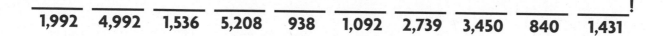

```
_____  _____  _____  _____  _____  _____  _____  _____  _____  _____!
1,992  4,992  1,536  5,208   938   1,092  2,739  3,450   840   1,431
```

Each of Farmer Gray's 24 horses eat 68 pounds of hay. How many pounds of hay do the horses eat altogether?

Famous Landmarks

Which of these landmarks is the tallest? Multiply. Write the ones digit of each product in order to find the height of each landmark. Circle the tallest landmark.

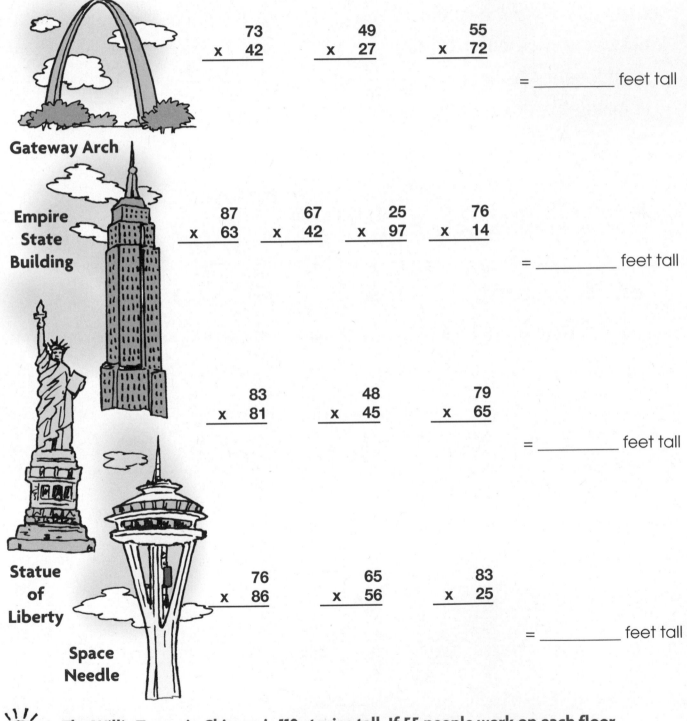

Gateway Arch

$$\begin{array}{r} 73 \\ \times\ 42 \\ \hline \end{array} \qquad \begin{array}{r} 49 \\ \times\ 27 \\ \hline \end{array} \qquad \begin{array}{r} 55 \\ \times\ 72 \\ \hline \end{array}$$

= _____ feet tall

Empire State Building

$$\begin{array}{r} 87 \\ \times\ 63 \\ \hline \end{array} \qquad \begin{array}{r} 67 \\ \times\ 42 \\ \hline \end{array} \qquad \begin{array}{r} 25 \\ \times\ 97 \\ \hline \end{array} \qquad \begin{array}{r} 76 \\ \times\ 14 \\ \hline \end{array}$$

= _____ feet tall

$$\begin{array}{r} 83 \\ \times\ 81 \\ \hline \end{array} \qquad \begin{array}{r} 48 \\ \times\ 45 \\ \hline \end{array} \qquad \begin{array}{r} 79 \\ \times\ 65 \\ \hline \end{array}$$

= _____ feet tall

Statue of Liberty

$$\begin{array}{r} 76 \\ \times\ 86 \\ \hline \end{array} \qquad \begin{array}{r} 65 \\ \times\ 56 \\ \hline \end{array} \qquad \begin{array}{r} 83 \\ \times\ 25 \\ \hline \end{array}$$

= _____ feet tall

Space Needle

💡 **The Willis Tower in Chicago is 110 stories tall. If 55 people work on each floor, how many total people work in the building?**

Soccer Balls

Solve the problems, then choose two colors that you like. ◆ Write the name of one of the colors on each line below. ◆ Color the design. If the answer is even, color the shape _____. If the answer is odd, color the shape _____. ◆ Finish the design by coloring the other shapes with the colors of your choice.

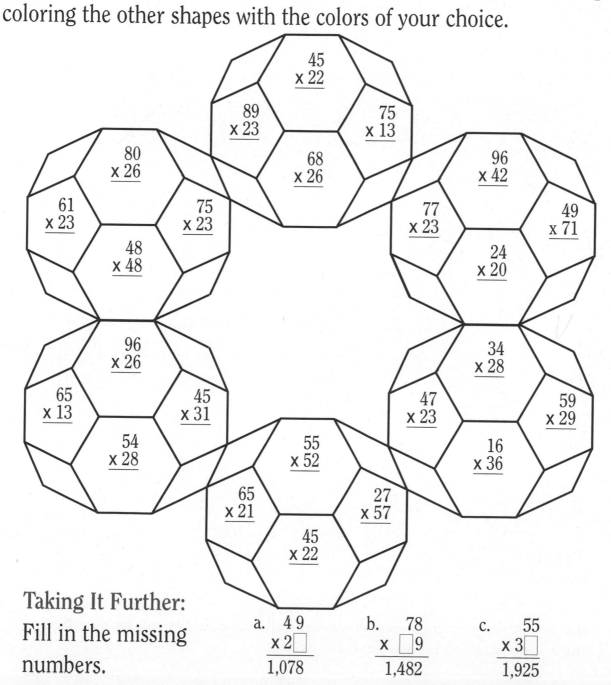

Taking It Further:
Fill in the missing numbers.

a.
```
    4 9
  x 2 □
  ─────
  1,078
```

b.
```
    78
  x □ 9
  ─────
  1,482
```

c.
```
    55
  x 3 □
  ─────
  1,925
```

In the Wink of an Eye

Solve the problems. If the answer is even, connect the dot beside each problem to the heart on the right- and left-hand sides of the circle. If the answer is odd, do nothing. Two lines have been drawn for you.

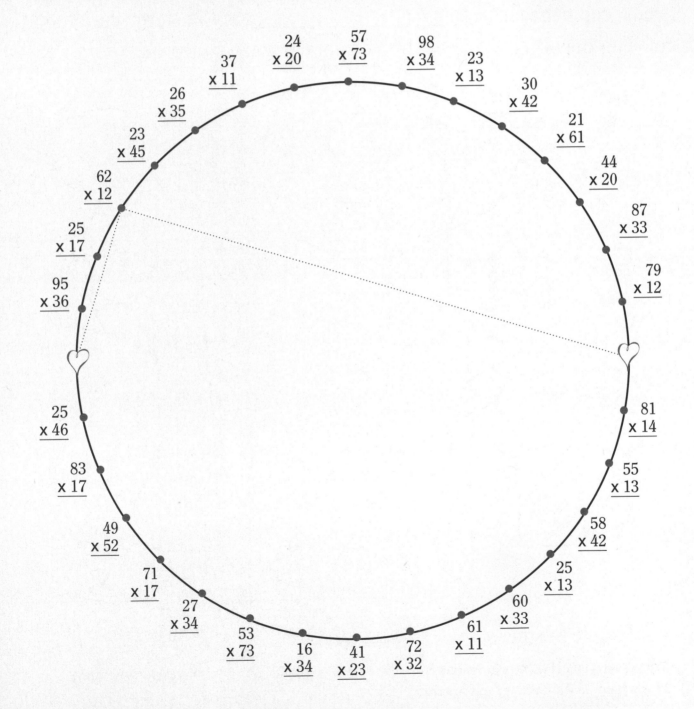

Monumental Multiplication

Multiply.

A.

362	602	452	283	918	473
x 43	x 18	x 22	x 13	x 27	x 55

B.

540	417	308
x 38	x 56	x 61

C.

692	586	918
x 34	x 37	x 86

D.

467	598	861
x 42	x 29	x 73

The Washington Monument has 897 steps. If 42 people climb to the top, how many steps have they climbed altogether?

The Music Store

When a multiplication problem involves money, the product must have a dollar sign and a decimal point. The decimal point is placed between the ones digit and the tenths digit.

```
        6
        2
     $3.71
 x      94
 ─────────
     14.84
 + 333.90
 ─────────
   $348.84
```

Remember to use a dollar sign and a decimal point.

Multiply. Then use the code to answer the riddle below.

N. $1.94
x   23

M. $0.79
x   25

I. $2.06
x   64

O. $0.68
x   45

A. $3.68
x   32

T. $9.54
x   19

F. $0.88
x   72

D. $0.93
x   94

E. $8.15
x   67

S. $7.43
x   92

R. $0.87
x   75

H. $6.92
x   83

Where do musicians buy instruments?

___ ___   ___ ___ ___
$117.76 $181.26 $181.26 $574.36 $546.05

___ ___ ___ ___   ___ ___ ___
$63.36 $131.84 $63.36 $546.05 $117.76 $44.62 $87.42

___ ___ ___ ___   ___ ___ ___ ___ ___!
$87.42 $131.84 $19.75 $546.05 $683.56 $181.26 $30.60 $65.25 $546.05

The Corner Candy Store

Word problems that suggest equal groups often require multiplication.

Write a number sentence for each problem. Solve.

A. Sam bought 4 candy bars at $1.23 each. How much did Sam spend altogether?	**B.** Mr. Johnson, the store owner, ordered 48 boxes of jawbreakers. Each box contained 392 pieces of candy. How many jawbreakers did Mr. Johnson order?
C. Carly's mom sent her to the candy store with 29 party bags. She asked Carly to fill each bag with 45 pieces of candy. How many pieces of candy will Carly buy?	**D.** Thirty-five children visited the candy store after school. Each child spent 57¢. How much money was spent in all?
E. Mr. Johnson keeps 37 jars behind the candy counter. Each jar contains 286 pieces of candy. How many pieces of candy are behind the counter altogether?	**F.** Nick bought each of his 6 friends a milk shake. Each milk shake cost $2.98. How much did Nick spend in all?

© Scholastic Inc.

What's on the Tube?

To divide means to make equal groups. Since multiplication also depends on equal groups, you can use the multiplication facts to help you learn the division facts.

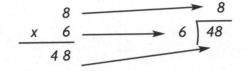

Basic division facts are problems you will learn by memory. Divide.

A. 4)24   4)36   7)56   5)25   9)81   8)24

B. 5)45   8)72   4)28   6)42   6)36   1)9

C. 3)12   7)21   6)48   3)24   8)32   7)63

D. 8)64   7)49   5)30   9)27   6)6   3)15

Divide to learn an interesting fact.

In what year was television invented?

3)3   8)72   7)14   8)64

💡 **Research to find the year something else was invented. On another piece of paper, write four division facts with the year hidden in their quotients.**

Television Division

Each part of a division problem has a name.

$$5 \leftarrow \text{quotient}$$
$$\text{divisor} \rightarrow 9\overline{)45} \leftarrow \text{dividend}$$

Divide.

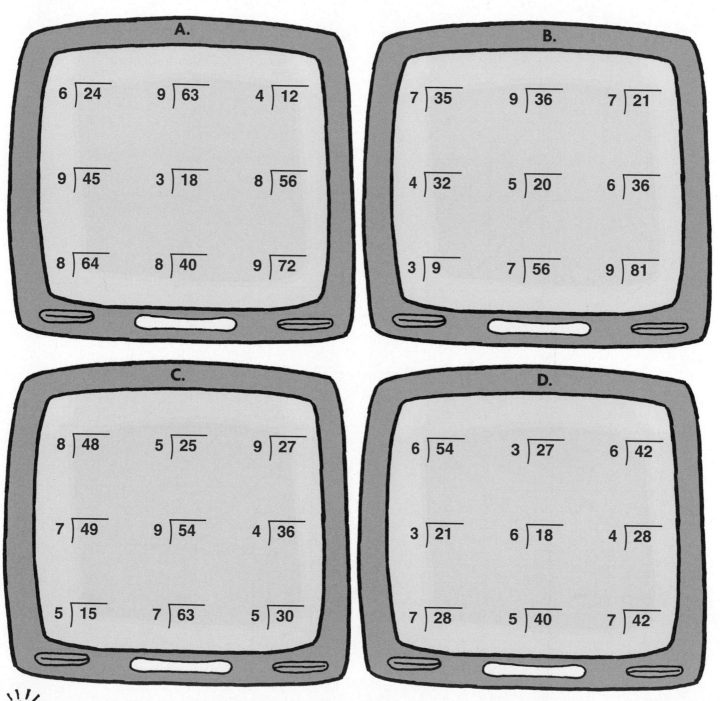

A.

6)24   9)63   4)12

9)45   3)18   8)56

8)64   8)40   9)72

B.

7)35   9)36   7)21

4)32   5)20   6)36

3)9   7)56   9)81

C.

8)48   5)25   9)27

7)49   9)54   4)36

5)15   7)63   5)30

D.

6)54   3)27   6)42

3)21   6)18   4)28

7)28   5)40   7)42

On another piece of paper, write nine division facts with a quotient of 8.

© Scholastic Inc.

Patchwork Diamonds

Solve the problems. ◆ If the answer is between 1 and 6, color the shape green. ◆ If the answer is between 7 and 12, color the shape red. ◆ Finish the design by coloring the other shapes with the colors of your choice.

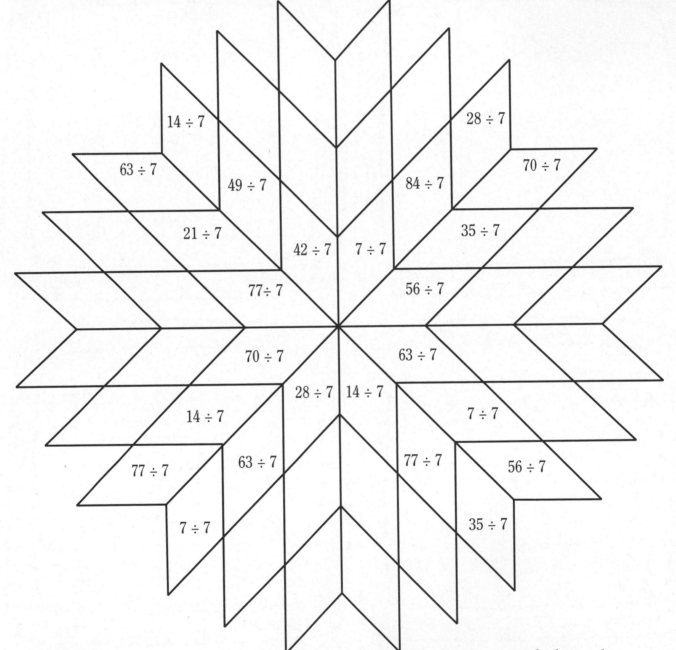

Taking It Further: Jamie is making a quilt with 70 diamond-shaped pieces. If 7 pieces make 1 square, how many squares will her quilt have?

Mirror Image

Solve the problems. Then connect the dot beside each problem to the dot beside its answer.

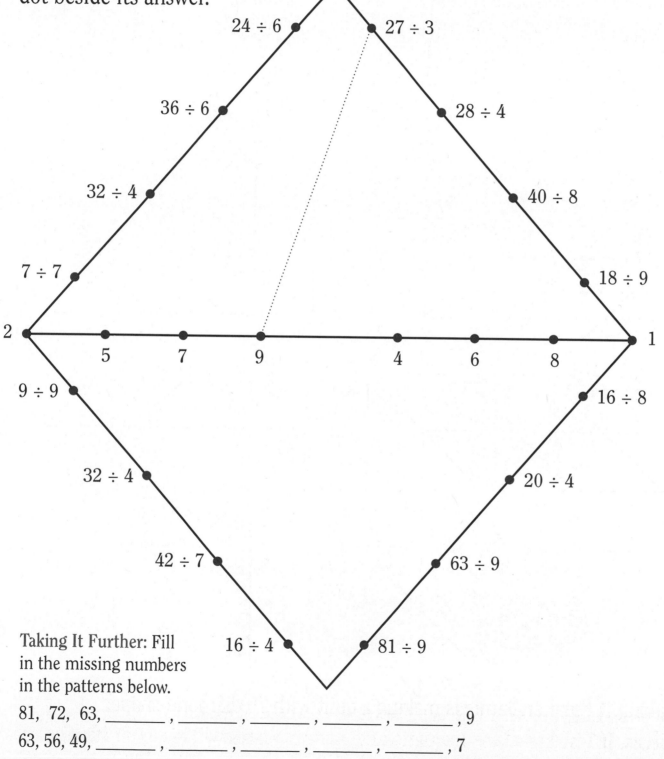

Taking It Further: Fill in the missing numbers in the patterns below.

81, 72, 63, _____ , _____ , _____ , _____ , _____ , 9

63, 56, 49, _____ , _____ , _____ , _____ , _____ , 7

A Barrel of Monkeys

To divide with zeros, follow these samples.

$$
\begin{array}{r} 80 \\ 8\overline{)640} \end{array}
\quad
\begin{array}{l} 64 \div 8 = 8 \\ 0 \div 8 = 0 \\ \text{Add a zero to} \\ \text{make 80.} \end{array}
\qquad
\begin{array}{r} 800 \\ 8\overline{)6400} \end{array}
\quad
\begin{array}{l} 64 \div 8 = 8 \\ 0 \div 8 = 0 \\ 0 \div 8 = 0 \\ \text{Add 2 zeros to} \\ \text{make 800.} \end{array}
$$

Divide.

A. $6\overline{)420}$ $9\overline{)8100}$ $6\overline{)540}$ $5\overline{)4500}$ $3\overline{)2400}$

B. $3\overline{)1800}$ $4\overline{)320}$ $8\overline{)7200}$ $7\overline{)560}$ $5\overline{)400}$

C. $3\overline{)150}$ $4\overline{)360}$ $6\overline{)4800}$ $6\overline{)360}$ $8\overline{)640}$

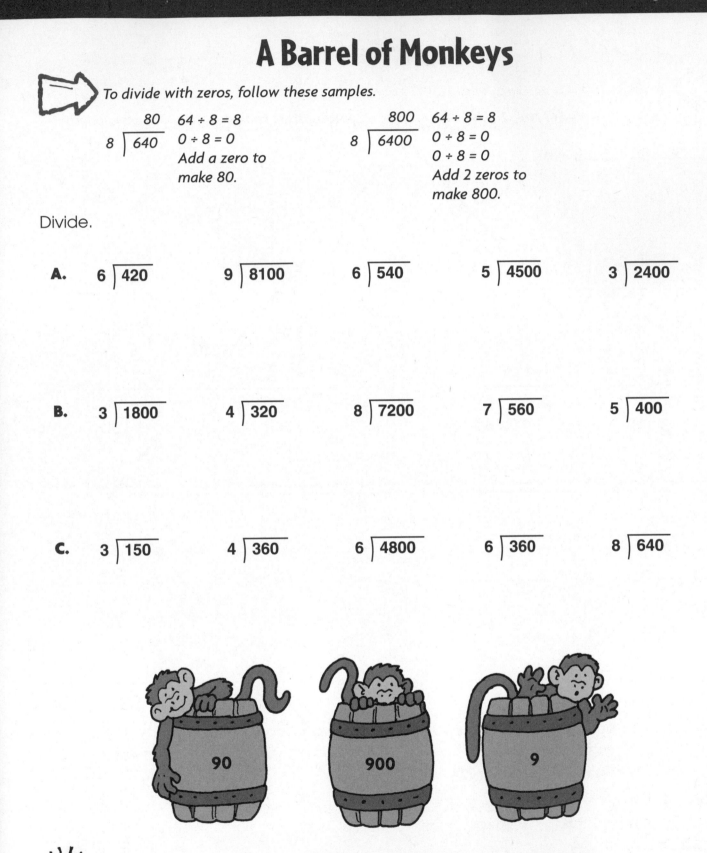

90   900   9

Write three problems with quotients to match those on the barrels.

No Way!

➡ *To divide with remainders, follow these steps.*

1. Does 8 x ___ = 34? No!

$$8\overline{)34}$$

2. Use the closest smaller dividend.
8 x 4 = 32

$$\begin{array}{r} 4 \\ 8\overline{)34} \\ 32 \end{array}$$

3. Subtract to find the remainder.

$$\begin{array}{r} 4 \\ 8\overline{)34} \\ -32 \\ \hline 2 \end{array}$$

4. The remainder is always less than the divisor.

$$\begin{array}{r} 4\ R2 \\ 8\overline{)34} \\ -32 \\ \hline 2 \end{array}$$

Divide. Then use the code to complete the riddle below.

E. $9\overline{)84}$	L. $3\overline{)29}$	S. $7\overline{)67}$	O. $5\overline{)24}$
T. $6\overline{)23}$	N. $6\overline{)47}$	P. $6\overline{)39}$	I. $7\overline{)52}$
O. $4\overline{)19}$	A. $8\overline{)70}$	T. $3\overline{)26}$	S. $9\overline{)55}$
H. $4\overline{)23}$	! $7\overline{)45}$	R. $5\overline{)27}$	N. $8\overline{)79}$

Emily: Yesterday I saw a man at the mall with very long arms. Every time he went up the stairs he stepped on them.

Jack: Wow! He stepped on his arms?

Emily:

___ ___ , ___ ___   ___ ___ ___
7 R5 4 R4   4 R3 9 R7   8 R2 5 R3 9 R3

___ ___ ___ ___ ___ ___
9 R4 3 R5 8 R6 7 R3 5 R2 6 R1 6 R3

Honeycomb

Solve the problems. ◆ If the answer has a remainder between 1 and 4, color the shape black. ◆ If the answer has a remainder between 5 and 8, color the shape red. ◆ Finish the design by coloring the other shapes with the colors of your choice.

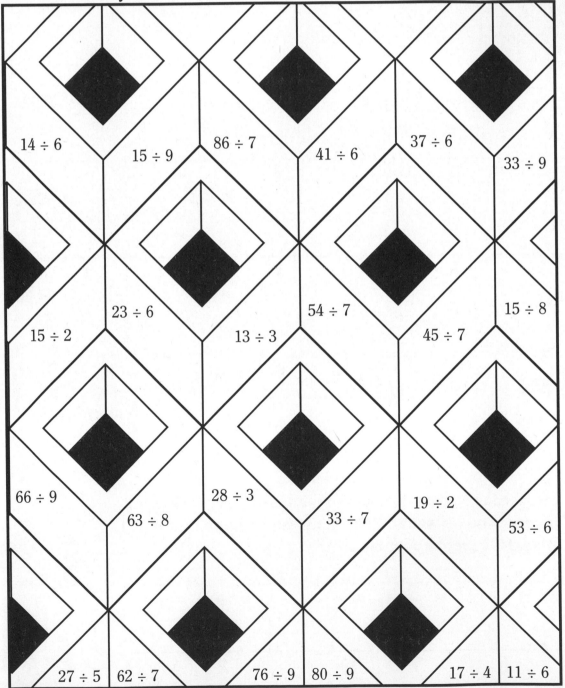

14 ÷ 6   15 ÷ 9   86 ÷ 7   41 ÷ 6   37 ÷ 6   33 ÷ 9

15 ÷ 2   23 ÷ 6   13 ÷ 3   54 ÷ 7   45 ÷ 7   15 ÷ 8

66 ÷ 9   63 ÷ 8   28 ÷ 3   33 ÷ 7   19 ÷ 2   53 ÷ 6

27 ÷ 5   62 ÷ 7   76 ÷ 9   80 ÷ 9   17 ÷ 4   11 ÷ 6

Division Decoder

Riddle: What kind of tools do you use for math?

Find each quotient. Then use the Decoder to solve the riddle by filling in the spaces at the bottom of the page.

Decoder

8	I
3 remainder 2	L
7	W
8 remainder 1	S
6	U
9	A
15 remainder 3	B
4	L
2 remainder 3	D
9 remainder 2	T
1	F
7 remainder 6	N
6 remainder 6	I
2	E
11	O
15 remainder 2	P
2 remainder 5	X
10	C
5	R

❶ 8 ÷ 2 = _____

❷ 10 ÷ 5 = _____

❸ 24 ÷ 4 = _____

❹ 50 ÷ 10 = _____

❺ 72 ÷ 9 = _____

❻ 32 ÷ 10 = _____

❼ 48 ÷ 7 = _____

❽ 29 ÷ 3 = _____

❾ 65 ÷ 8 = _____

❿ 92 ÷ 6 = _____

"M ___ ___ ___ ___ " ___ ___ ___ ___ ___ ___
3   1   8   5   10   6   7   2   4   9

Mousing Around

To divide with a 3-digit dividend, follow these steps.

1.
$$7\overline{)427}$$ quotient 6, 42
$7 \times \underline{} = 42$
$7 \times 6 = 42$

2.
$$7\overline{)427}$$ 6, $-42\downarrow$, 07
Subtract.
Bring down the ones digit.

3.
$$7\overline{)427}$$ 61, $-42\downarrow$, 07, -7, 0
$7 \times \underline{} = 7$
$7 \times 1 = 7$
Subtract.

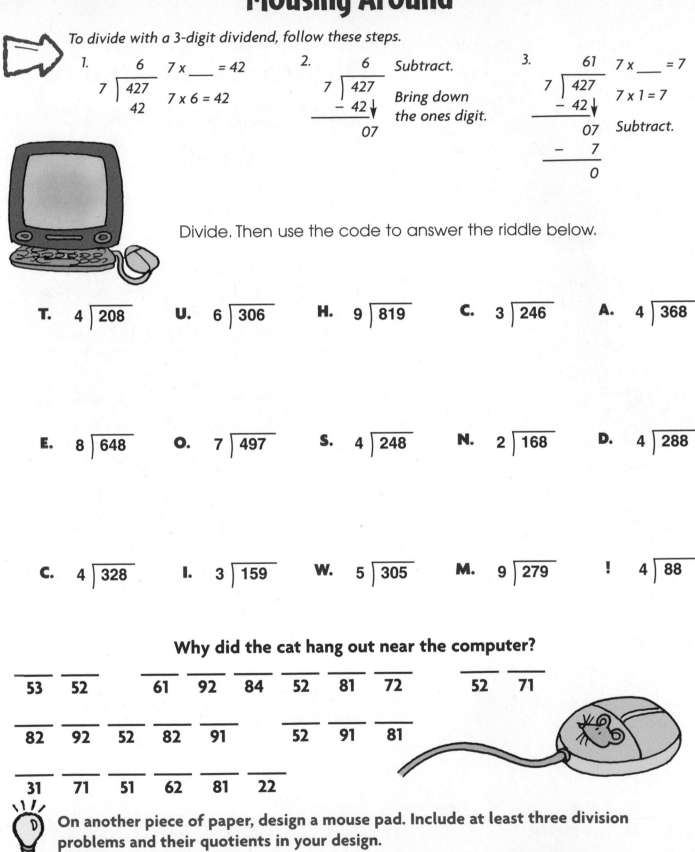

Divide. Then use the code to answer the riddle below.

T. $4\overline{)208}$ **U.** $6\overline{)306}$ **H.** $9\overline{)819}$ **C.** $3\overline{)246}$ **A.** $4\overline{)368}$

E. $8\overline{)648}$ **O.** $7\overline{)497}$ **S.** $4\overline{)248}$ **N.** $2\overline{)168}$ **D.** $4\overline{)288}$

C. $4\overline{)328}$ **I.** $3\overline{)159}$ **W.** $5\overline{)305}$ **M.** $9\overline{)279}$ **!** $4\overline{)88}$

Why did the cat hang out near the computer?

___ ___   ___ ___ ___ ___ ___ ___   ___ ___
53   52   61   92   84   52   81   72   52   71

___ ___ ___ ___ ___   ___ ___ ___
82   92   52   82   91   52   91   81

___ ___ ___ ___ ___ ___
31   71   51   62   81   22

On another piece of paper, design a mouse pad. Include at least three division problems and their quotients in your design.

Surfing the Web

When the divisor has a remainder in the middle of a problem, follow these steps.

1.
$$8\overline{)816}$$ quotient 10, 80
$8 \times \underline{\quad} = 81$
$8 \times 10 = 80$

2.
$$8\overline{)816}$$ quotient 10, $-80\downarrow$, 16
Subtract.
Bring down the ones digit.

3.
$$8\overline{)816}$$ quotient 102, $-42\downarrow$, 07, -7, 0
$8 \times \underline{\quad} = 16$
$8 \times 2 = 16$
Subtract again.

Divide. Use another piece of paper to work the problems.
Then connect each problem to its answer to learn the definitions of some computer terms.

A. $5\overline{)375}$ browser

B. $6\overline{)492}$ byte

C. $2\overline{)216}$ download

D. $3\overline{)249}$ gigabyte

E. $9\overline{)243}$ Internet

F. $8\overline{)288}$ megabyte

G. $4\overline{)424}$ network

H. $6\overline{)564}$ program

I. $7\overline{)532}$ scanner

J. $4\overline{)312}$ virus

K. $9\overline{)486}$ web site

82   an amount of data equal to 8 bits

75   a program to help get around the Internet

54   a place on the Internet's World Wide Web where text and pictures are stored

106   a group of computers linked together so they can share information

36   an amount of information equal to 1,048,516 bytes

27   a worldwide system of linked computers

108   to transfer information from a host computer to a personal computer

83   an amount of information equal to 1,024 megabytes

78   a program that damages other programs and data; often transmitted through telephone lines or shared disks

94   instructions for a computer to follow

76   a device that can transfer words and pictures from a printed page into the computer

Flying Carpet

Solve the problems. ◆ If the answer is between 100 and 250, color the shape red. ◆ If the answer is between 251 and 900, color the shape blue. ◆ Finish the design by coloring the other shapes with the colors of your choice.

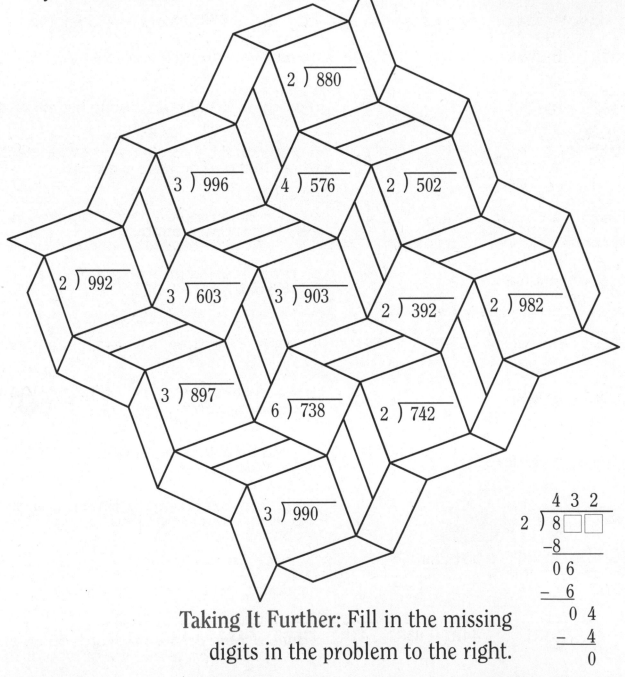

Taking It Further: Fill in the missing digits in the problem to the right.

$$\begin{array}{r} 4\ 3\ 2 \\ 2\ \overline{)\ 8\ \square\ \square} \\ -8 \\ \hline 0\ 6 \\ -\ 6 \\ \hline 0\ 4 \\ -\ 4 \\ \hline 0 \end{array}$$

© Scholastic Inc.

Poolside!

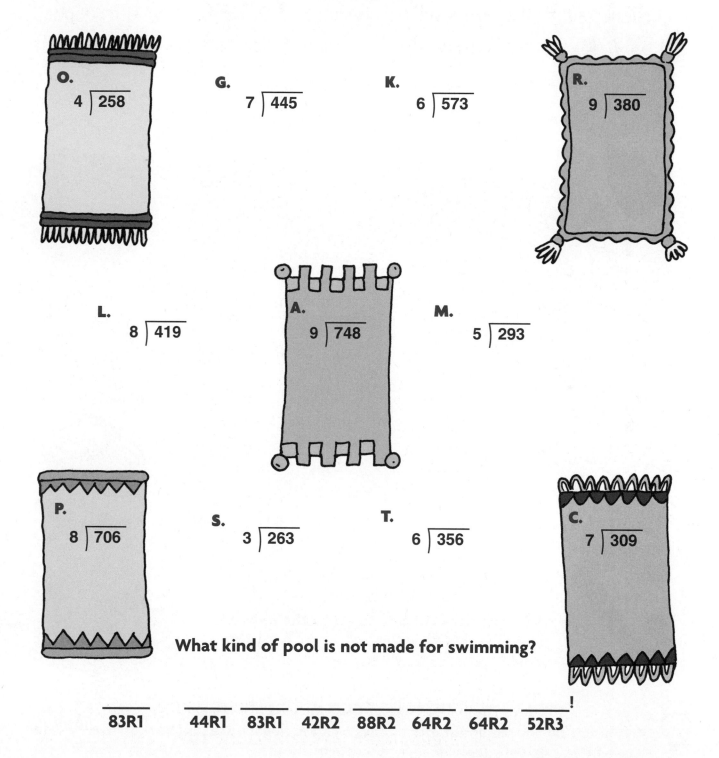

Remember: The remainder is always less than the divisor.

Divide. Then use the code to answer the riddle below.

O. 4) 258

G. 7) 445

K. 6) 573

R. 9) 380

L. 8) 419

A. 9) 748

M. 5) 293

P. 8) 706

S. 3) 263

T. 6) 356

C. 7) 309

What kind of pool is not made for swimming?

_____	_____	_____	_____	_____	_____	_____	_____ !
83R1	44R1	83R1	42R2	88R2	64R2	64R2	52R3

© Scholastic Inc.

Summer Days

Divide. Then use the code to answer the riddle below.

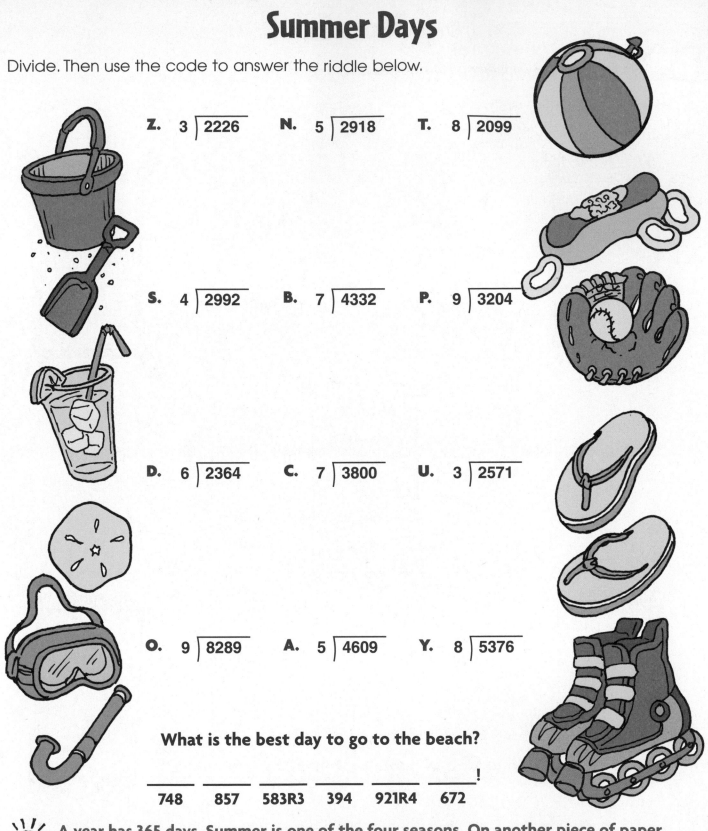

Z. 3) 2226   **N.** 5) 2918   **T.** 8) 2099

S. 4) 2992   **B.** 7) 4332   **P.** 9) 3204

D. 6) 2364   **C.** 7) 3800   **U.** 3) 2571

O. 9) 8289   **A.** 5) 4609   **Y.** 8) 5376

What is the best day to go to the beach?

___ ___ ___ ___ ___ ___!
748 857 583R3 394 921R4 672

💡 **A year has 365 days. Summer is one of the four seasons. On another piece of paper, divide to find the exact number of days that are in each season. Your answer will tell you why our seasons truly change at a specific hour.**

Bone Up on Division

To divide by a 2-digit divisor, follow these steps.

1.
$$15 \overline{)330}$$
  2
  30

15 x ___ = 33
Use the closest
smaller dividend.
x 2 = 30
Put the 2 above
the 3 tens.

2.
$$15 \overline{)330}$$
  2
  − 30 ↓
  30

Subtract.

Bring down
the ones digit.

3.
$$15 \overline{)330}$$
  22
  − 30 ↓
  30
  − 30
  0

15 x ___ = 30
15 x 2 = 30

Subtract
again.

Divide. Write the digit in the ones place with the least amount in each row to find out how many bones an adult human body has.

A. 13 $\overline{)559}$ 16 $\overline{)208}$ 39 $\overline{)468}$ 23 $\overline{)874}$

B. 31 $\overline{)682}$ 46 $\overline{)690}$ 26 $\overline{)858}$ 47 $\overline{)940}$

C. 35 $\overline{)630}$ 27 $\overline{)486}$ 28 $\overline{)756}$ 18 $\overline{)828}$

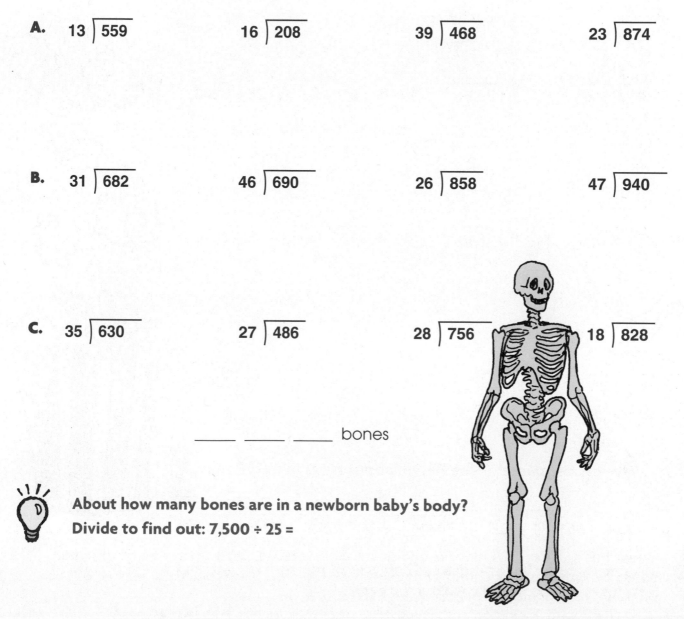

____ ____ ____ bones

About how many bones are in a newborn baby's body?
Divide to find out: 7,500 ÷ 25 =

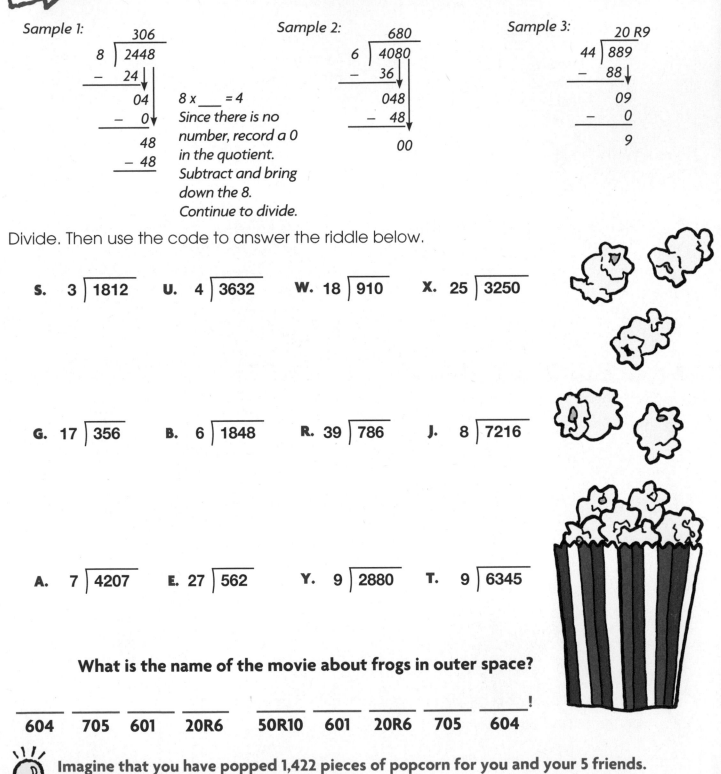

Let's Go to the Show

➡ *Look at each sample to learn how to finish dividing when there is a zero in the quotient.*

Sample 1:

```
       306
  8 ) 2448
    - 24↓
       04
     -  0↓
         48
       - 48
```

8 x ___ = 4
Since there is no number, record a 0 in the quotient. Subtract and bring down the 8. Continue to divide.

Sample 2:

```
       680
  6 ) 4080
    - 36↓
       048
     -  48↓
          00
```

Sample 3:

```
        20 R9
  44 ) 889
     - 88↓
        09
      -  0
         9
```

Divide. Then use the code to answer the riddle below.

S. 3) 1812   **U.** 4) 3632   **W.** 18) 910   **X.** 25) 3250

G. 17) 356   **B.** 6) 1848   **R.** 39) 786   **J.** 8) 7216

A. 7) 4207   **E.** 27) 562   **Y.** 9) 2880   **T.** 9) 6345

What is the name of the movie about frogs in outer space?

___ ___ ___ ___ ___ ___ ___ ___ ___!
604 705 601 20R6   50R10 601 20R6 705 604

💡 Imagine that you have popped 1,422 pieces of popcorn for you and your 5 friends. How many pieces would each person get?

MATH

Comparing & Ordering Numbers

Use the digits in the box to answer each number riddle.
You cannot repeat digits within a number.

1 8 3 4 9 6 2 7

1 I am the number that is 100 greater than 3,362.
What number am I? _____

2 I am the number that is 40 less than the largest number
you can make using five of the digits.
What number am I? _____

3 I am the largest number you can make that is greater than
8,745 but less than 8,750.
What number am I? _____

4 I am the number that is 5,000 greater than the smallest
number you can make using six of the digits.
What number am I? _____

5 I am the smallest number you can make that is greater
than 617,500.
What number am I? _____

6 I am the largest number you can make that is less than
618,400 but greater than 618,300.
What number am I? _____

Sign It!

✎ There are signs with numbers on them almost everywhere you look! They're on street corners and on highways. What if those numbers were written out as words?

Take a look at the street signs below. They all have numbers on them. Each sign has a blank sign next to it. Write the numbers as words on each blank sign. We've done the first one for you.

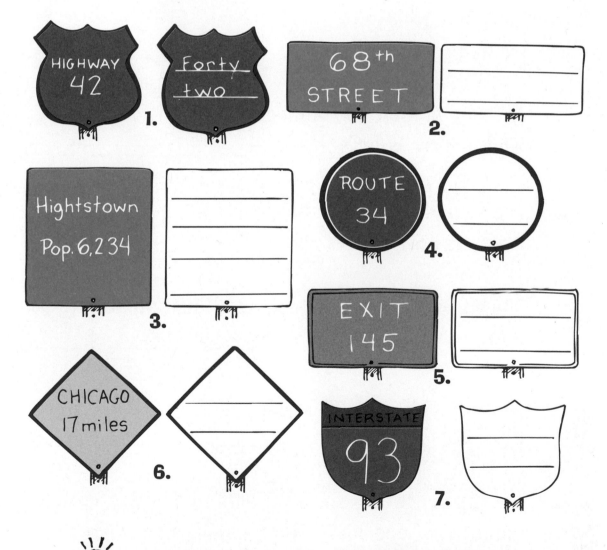

Try writing other numbers as words, such as your address, area code, age, or shoe size.

Mystery Number

Use the digits in the box to answer each number riddle. Digits appear
only once in an answer. Each answer may not use all digits.

2 4 9 6 7 3

 When you subtract a 2-digit number from a 3-digit number,
the difference is 473.
What are the numbers? _____

 The sum of these two numbers is 112.
What are the numbers? _____

 The sum of these two numbers is 519.
What are the numbers? _____

 The difference between these two 3-digit numbers is 263.
What are the numbers? _____

 The sum of these three 2-digit numbers is 184.
What are the numbers? _____

 The difference between two 3-digit numbers is a palindrome
between 200 and 300.
What are the numbers? _____

What Number Am I?

Use the digits in the box to answer each number riddle.
You cannot repeat digits within a number.

1 2 3 4 5 6 7 8 9

 I am the largest 4-digit odd number you can make.
What number am I? _____

 I am the smallest 5-digit even number you can make.
What number am I? _____

 I am the largest 5-digit even number you can make that has a 3 in the thousands place.
What number am I? _____

 I am the smallest 5-digit number you can make that has all odd digits.
What number am I? _____

 I am the largest 6-digit number you can make that has a 1 in the thousands place and a 5 in the ten-thousands place.
What number am I? _____

I am the smallest 6-digit even number you can make that has a 6 in the hundreds place.
What number am I? _____

A Place for Every Number

Look at the numbers in 243. Each number in the group has its own "place" and meaning. For instance, the 2 in 243 is in the hundreds place. That stands for 2 hundreds or 200. The 4 is in the tens place, meaning 4 tens or 40. And the 3 is in the ones place, meaning 3 ones or 3.

DIRECTIONS:

Use a place value chart to put the numbers in this crossnumber puzzle in their places.

ACROSS

A. 3 hundreds 2 tens 6 ones
C. 8 tens 1 one
E. 6 tens 4 ones
F. 4 tens 7 ones
H. 5 hundreds 2 tens 6 ones
J. 9 tens 3 ones
K. 8 tens 9 ones
M. 5 hundreds 4 tens 2 ones
O. 2 thousands 8 hundreds 3 tens 1 one
Q. 9 tens 8 ones
S. 6 hundreds 6 tens 4 ones

DOWN

A. 3 tens 6 ones
B. 2 thousands 4 hundreds 5 tens 7 ones
D. 1 hundred 4 tens 9 ones
G. 7 tens 3 ones
I. 6 thousands 8 hundreds 5 tens 1 one
L. 9 tens 4 ones
N. 2 hundreds 9 tens 6 ones
P. 3 tens 5 ones
R. 8 tens 4 ones

Bee Riddle

Riddle: What did the farmer get when he tried to reach the beehive?

Round each number. Then use the Decoder to solve the riddle by filling in the spaces at the bottom of the page.

Decoder

400 .... **A**
800 .... **W**
30 .... **O**
10 .... **Y**
25 .... **E**
500 .... **I**
210 .... **J**
20 .... **L**
40 .... **C**
700 .... **U**
90 .... **S**
100 .... **T**
600 .... **G**
95 .... **F**
50 .... **N**
550 .... **V**
300 .... **Z**
7 .... **H**
200 .... **Z**

❶ Round 7 to the nearest ten _____

❷ Round 23 to the nearest ten _____

❸ Round 46 to the nearest ten _____

❹ Round 92 to the nearest ten _____

❺ Round 203 to the nearest hundred _____

❻ Round 420 to the nearest hundred _____

❼ Round 588 to the nearest hundred _____

❽ Round 312 to the nearest hundred _____

❾ Round 549 to the nearest hundred _____

❿ Round 710 to the nearest hundred _____

A "B __ __ __ __ __ " __ __ __ __ __ __
     10 5 8 1   4 9 7 3 6 2

When to Estimate

Estimation is a great way to solve many problems.
But some problems need an exact answer. How can you decide?

Read each question below. Think about what kind of answer you need.
Then circle Estimate or Exact Answer.

1. How much sugar do you need to make cookies?	Estimate	Exact Answer
2. How much money could your school play earn?	Estimate	Exact Answer
3. How many plates will you need to serve dinner?	Estimate	Exact Answer
4. How much money will three new tapes cost?	Estimate	Exact Answer
5. How long will it take to get to the airport?	Estimate	Exact Answer
6. How much money is in a bank account?	Estimate	Exact Answer
7. How long would it take you to run a mile?	Estimate	Exact Answer
8. How many kids are in your class?	Estimate	Exact Answer

How Would You Estimate . . .

On another sheet of paper, write about how you would estimate each of these.

...the height of a tree?	...how long it would take to walk from Miami to Seattle?	...how much water you use in a year?
...the number of gumballs in a gumball machine?	...the number of students in your school?	...how much one million pennies would weigh?

© Scholastic Inc.

Super Seven

How can you make the number seven even?

Find the answer by completing the next step in the pattern. Then use the Decoder to solve the riddle by filling in the blanks at the bottom of the page.

Decoder

5	**B**
1	**A**
97	**D**
215	**Y**
22	**W**
124	**H**
31	**I**
2	**P**
115	**A**
120	**C**
50	**N**
4	**E**
60	**S**
232	**M**
26	**T**
100	**R**
32	**F**
57	**E**
34	**K**

1. 10, 7, 4, ___
2. 19, 13, 8, ___
3. 42, 40, 36, 30, ___
4. 56, 54, 50, 42, ___
5. 33, 32, 34, 33, 35, ___
6. 117, 97, 77, ___
7. 205, 175, 150, 130, ___
8. 344, 274, 214, 164, ___
9. 760, 660, 540, 400, 240, ___
10. 512, 490, 457, 413, 358, 292, ___

TA ___ ___ ___ ___ ___ ___ ___ ___ ___ "___".
　　5　2　7　3　1　10　4　8　6　9

© Scholastic Inc.

Pansy's Picture Patterns

✍ Pansy Pattern has lots of hobbies. Her favorite hobby, though, is drawing patterns. There's just one problem. Sometimes Pansy forgets to draw the complete pattern. Maybe you can help. Try filling in the missing pieces in the patterns below.

Root for the Home Team!

Riddle: What do cheerleaders like to drink?

Use the coordinates to identify points on the graph. Then use the point names to solve the riddle by filling in the blanks at the bottom of the page.

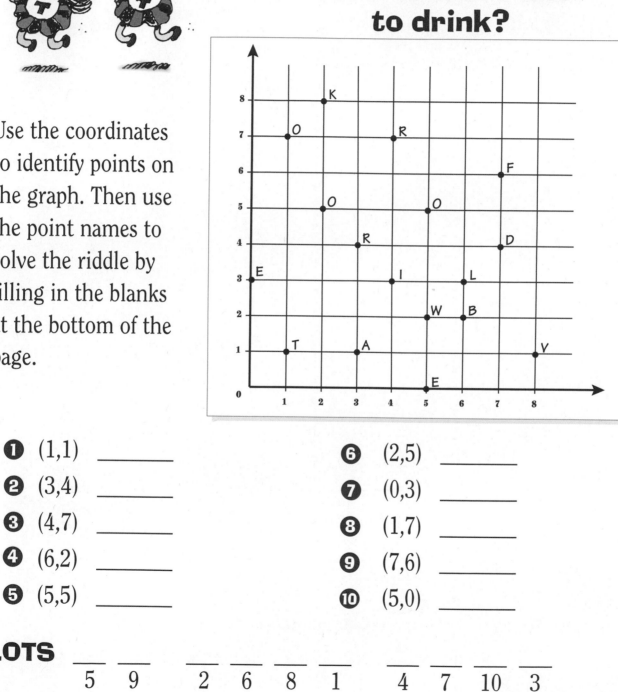

❶ (1,1) _____

❷ (3,4) _____

❸ (4,7) _____

❹ (6,2) _____

❺ (5,5) _____

❻ (2,5) _____

❼ (0,3) _____

❽ (1,7) _____

❾ (7,6) _____

❿ (5,0) _____

LOTS __ __ __ __ __ __ __ __ __ __
     5   9   2 6 8 1   4 7 10 3

Bewitching Math

Solve the problems. Then connect the dot above each problem to the dot beside its answer. The first line has been drawn for you. Some dots will not be used.

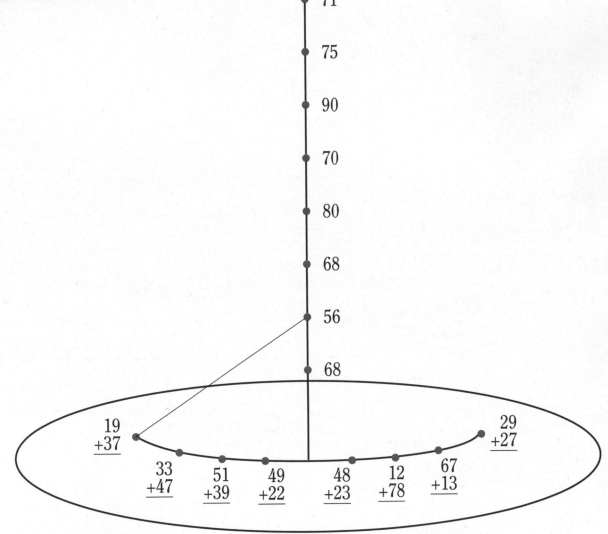

Taking It Further: Fill in the missing numbers in the problems below.

a.
$$\begin{array}{r} 2\square \\ +27 \\ \hline 50 \end{array}$$

b.
$$\begin{array}{r} 53 \\ +2\square \\ \hline 82 \end{array}$$

c.
$$\begin{array}{r} 56 \\ +1\square \\ \hline 73 \end{array}$$

d.
$$\begin{array}{r} 28 \\ +57 \\ \hline \square\square \end{array}$$

e.
$$\begin{array}{r} 43 \\ +\square7 \\ \hline 90 \end{array}$$

f.
$$\begin{array}{r} 45 \\ +\square\square \\ \hline 71 \end{array}$$

Into Infinity

Solve the problems. Then rename the answers in lowest terms.

If the answer is $\frac{1}{4}$, $\frac{1}{8}$, or $\frac{1}{16}$, color the shape purple.

If the answer is $\frac{1}{2}$, $\frac{1}{3}$, or $\frac{1}{7}$, color the shape blue.

If the answer is $\frac{2}{3}$, $\frac{3}{4}$, or $\frac{7}{8}$, color the shape green.

If the answer is $\frac{3}{5}$, $\frac{4}{5}$, or $\frac{5}{7}$, color the shape yellow.

If the answer is $\frac{9}{10}$ or $\frac{11}{12}$, color the shape red.

Finish the design by coloring the other shapes with colors of your choice.

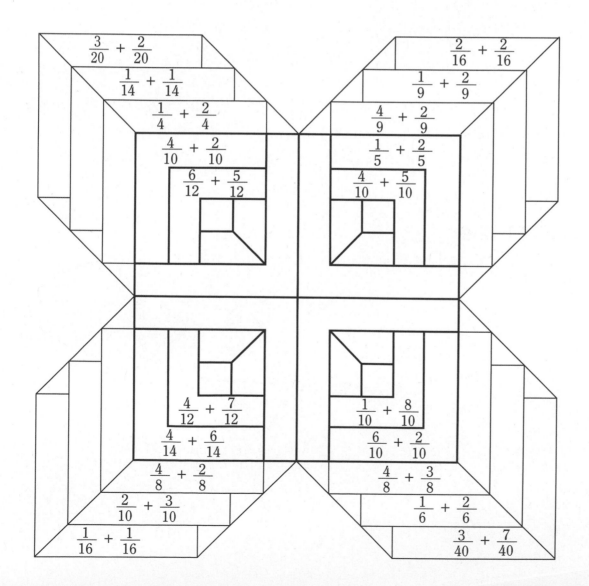

Food Fractions

ACTIVITY GOAL

Identify the fraction represented in each shape to complete a riddle.

HELPFUL HINT!

• The denominator of each fraction represents the total
amount of parts in the shape. The shaded parts represent
the numerator. A food item can help illustrate this strategy.

EXAMPLE

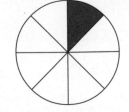

There are 8 slices of pie shown here (/8) the denominator. The
shaded area represents how many pieces of the pie you can eat
(1/) the numerator. The fraction represented in this picture is 1/8.

TRY THIS!

Draw a pizza on another piece of paper, then cut out the circle. Cut the pizza into six equal
pieces. Using your paper pizza, make the following fractions: 1/2, 2/6, 5/6, 1/3.
Now divide your pizza between you and two imaginary friends. Did you each get the same
amount? _____

MORE SWEET FUN!

Color 1/3 of these 12 pieces of candy. What fraction of the candy is left? _____

Now that you've reviewed fractions, duck into action and name a few fractions to solve the
riddle on the following page!

© Scholastic Inc.

Duck Into Action With Fractions

✏ Why don't ducks like to get mail? Fractions can help you find the answer. Each of the shapes below represent a fraction and a letter. To figure out each fraction, compare the number of shaded spaces in the shape to the total number of spaces.

Example: is the same as 2/6. Next, write the letter that is underneath each shape on the corresponding blank below. You will use some letters several times. Now get quacking!

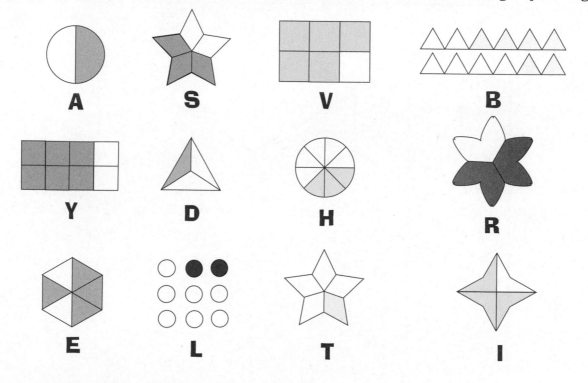

Why don't ducks like to get mail?

___ ___ ___ ___   ___ ___ ___ ___ ___ ___ ___

1/5   3/8   4/6   6/8   1/2   2/9   2/3   4/6   1/2   1/3   6/8

___ ___ ___ ___   ___ ___ ___ ___ ___.

3/8   1/2   5/6   4/6   6/12   3/4   2/9   2/9   3/5

Trefoil

Solve the problems. ◆ Rename the answers in lowest terms. ◆ If the answer is $\frac{1}{2}$ or greater, color the shape red. ◆ If the answer is less than $\frac{1}{2}$, color the shape blue. ◆ Finish the design by coloring the other shapes with the colors of your choice.

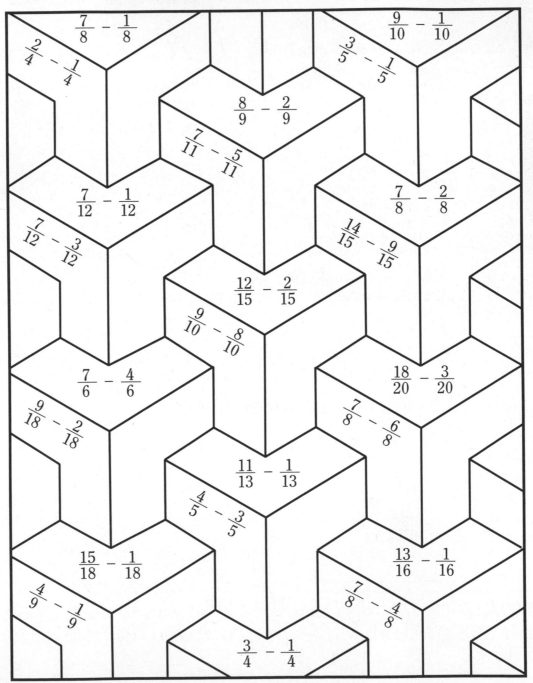

© Scholastic Inc.

White Socks, Black Socks

Figure it out!

1. Rowena Pig is wearing 1 white sock and 1 black sock. What fraction of the socks she's wearing is white? What fraction is black?

_____

2. Rowena puts 7 socks in the washing machine. Four of them are black and 3 are white. What fraction of the socks is black? What fraction is white?

_____

3. Rowena hangs 8 socks out to dry. Two of the socks are black and 6 are white. What fraction is black? Write your answer in simplest form.

_____

4. Judy Frog brings 6 socks on a trip. One third of the socks are red. The rest are green. How many socks are red? How many are green?

_____

5. Six out of 10 socks are blue. The rest are red. What fraction of the socks is red? Write your answer in simplest form.

_____

SUPER CHALLENGE: Judy has 12 socks. One third of them are white. One fourth of them are red. The rest are yellow. How many socks are yellow? How many socks are white and red?

Decimals Around the Diamond

Baseball fans always argue about who's the best player. Everybody seems to have a favorite!

When it comes to finding the best hitter, though, no one can argue with batting averages. The batting average shows how often a baseball player gets a hit. It is a 3-digit decimal number, and looks like this: .328, .287, .311, .253. The larger the batting average is, the better the hitter is.

Rank	Player (Team)	2015 Batting Average
☐	Yunel Escobar (Washington Nationals)	.314
☐	A. J. Pollock (Arizona Diamondbacks)	.315
☐	Buster Posey (San Francisco Giants)	.318
☐	Bryce Harper (Washington Nationals)	.330
☐	Paul Goldschmidt (Arizona Diamondbacks)	.321
☐	Miguel Cabrera (Detroit Tigers)	.338
☐	Joey Votto (Cincinnati Reds)	.314
☐	Dee Gordon (Miami Marlins)	.333
☐	Xander Bogaerts (Boston Red Sox)	.320
☐	Jose Altuve (Houston Astros)	.313

Decimals are numbers between 0 and 1. They are written to the right of the ones place. Decimals always have a decimal point to the left of them.

decimal point — tenths place — hundredths place — thousandths place

What to Do:

Read the chart of baseball players' batting averages from 2015. Rank the batting averages. This means number the batting averages in order from highest to lowest. (See Home Plate for help.) Write the numbers 1 to 10 in the boxes next to the names—1 for the highest average, 10 for the lowest. Ready? Play ball!

HOME PLATE

To rank decimal numbers:
- Start at the left.
- Compare the digits in the same place.
- Find the first place where the digits are different.
- The number with the smaller digit is the smaller number. Example: Rank .318 and .312

.318
⇕⇕⇕
.312

So .312 is smaller than .318.

Across-and-Down Decimals

Complete the crossnumber puzzle as if it were a crossword puzzle. Give each digit and decimal point its own square. Remember to align the decimal points and add any necessary zeros, then proceed as if you were adding whole numbers.

ACROSS

A.	1.3 + 2.4
C.	2.2 + 2.18
E.	.3 + .25
F.	.3 + .3
G.	.56 + .34
J.	.4 + .17
K.	6.93 + .23
L.	1.18 + 3.12

DOWN

A.	1.44 + 1.7
B.	23.11 + 53.18
C.	2.25 + 2.25
D.	6.5 + 1.6
F.	.1604 + .11
H.	20.8 + 3.5
I.	1.367 + .333
J.	.2 + .16

Change Arranger

When you make change, always start with the price. Count on from the price. Start with the coins that have the least value. Write the change from these purchases.

1. LAWN GAME

AMOUNT GIVEN $ 5.00
PRICE 3.45

CHANGE $ _____

2. YO-YO

AMOUNT GIVEN $ 3.00
PRICE 2.77

CHANGE $ _____

3. BIKE HELMET

AMOUNT GIVEN $10.00
PRICE 7.55

CHANGE $ _____

4. SOAP BUBBLES

AMOUNT GIVEN $ 2.00
PRICE 1.52

CHANGE $ _____

5. VIDEO GAME

AMOUNT GIVEN $ 20.00
PRICE 7.30

CHANGE $ _____

6. ACTION TOY

AMOUNT GIVEN $10.00
PRICE 6.49

CHANGE $ _____

7. SUNGLASSES

AMOUNT GIVEN $4.00
PRICE 3.68

CHANGE $ _____

8. BACKPACK

AMOUNT GIVEN $20.00
PRICE 9.35

CHANGE $ _____

9. JUMP ROPE

AMOUNT GIVEN $4.00
PRICE 3.17

CHANGE $ _____

10. MARKERS

AMOUNT GIVEN $5.00
PRICE 2.43

CHANGE $ _____

Money Magic Puzzle

Round your answers to the nearest dollar. Circle the correct amount, then fill in the puzzle.

ACROSS:

A.	$16.98 + $18.99	$36	$26
C.	$24.85 + $29.99	$65	$55
E.	$21.99 + $8.95	$31	$41
G.	$218.04 + $67.90	$286	$386
I.	$53.75 + $40.98	$105	$95
K.	$7.99 + $19.70	$28	$22
L.	$99.98 + 99.57	$300	$200
M.	$65.75 + $20.90	$87	$97
O.	$9.69 + $32.99	$40	$43
P.	$588.95 + $14.90	$704	$604
Q.	$3.75 + $9.99	$13	$14
R.	$428.70 + $50.90	$480	$520

DOWN:

B.	$28.59 + $33.95	$69	$63
C.	$39.25 + $18.70	$58	$42
D.	$376.35 + $184.50	$521	$561
F.	$7.28 + $11.69	$19	$16
H.	$199.80 + $224.99	$525	$425
J.	$399.95 + $126.99	$527	$566
M.	$5.85 + $76.95	$83	$75
N.	$39.80 + $13.99	$54	$62
O.	$26.98 + $16.89	$44	$49
P.	$48.95 + $18.99	$68	$66

Time for Play

✏ The dogs in the neighborhood play in the park at the same time every day. Today, some are running around trees and others are playing catch with their owners. But most of them are busy doing something else—chasing another dog! What time were they chasing the dog? Equivalent measurements can help you find the answer.

DIRECTIONS:

- There are two answers next to each question. Circle the letter after the correct answer.
- When you've finished, write each circled letter in the blanks below the riddle. Be sure to write the letters in order.

1.	How many weeks are in a year?	34	**L**	52	**T**
2.	How many inches are in a foot?	12	**W**	36	**A**
3.	How many centimeters are in a meter?	100	**E**	1000	**O**
4.	How many nickels are in a dollar?	40	**M**	20	**N**
5.	How many days are in a year?	365	**T**	245	**S**
6.	How many inches are in a yard?	36	**Y**	24	**B**
7.	How many ounces are in a pound?	16	**A**	12	**I**
8.	How many hours are in a day?	48	**C**	24	**F**
9.	How many years are in a decade?	50	**H**	10	**T**
10.	How many cups are in a pint?	2	**E**	4	**U**
11.	How many quarts are in a gallon?	4	**R**	8	**D**
12.	How many feet are in a mile?	5,280	**O**	2,160	**G**
13.	How many seconds are in a minute?	30	**J**	60	**N**
14.	How many millimeters are in a meter?	1,000	**E**	1500	**P**

What time is it when twenty dogs run after one dog?

___ ___ ___ ___ ___ ___ ___   ___ ___ ___ ___ ___ ___   ___ ___ ___

Come up with an equivalent measurement problem of your own.

© Scholastic Inc.

Measure by Measure

Josie is surrounded by all kinds of measuring tools. But she's not sure which tool does what! Sure, she knows that a ruler measures the length of something. But she doesn't realize that all the other tools around her are used for measuring things too. Try giving Josie a hand.

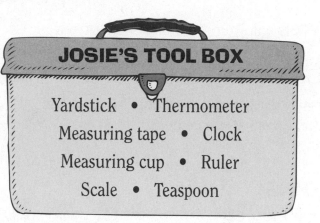

JOSIE'S TOOL BOX

Yardstick • Thermometer
Measuring tape • Clock
Measuring cup • Ruler
Scale • Teaspoon

DIRECTIONS:

Take a look at the list of measuring tools in Josie's Tool Box. Use the list to answer the questions below.

1. What tool could Josie use to measure the weight of a pumpkin? _____

2. What tool could Josie use to measure the width of her math book?

_____

3. Josie plans to watch one of her favorite television shows. What tool could help her measure the length of each commercial that appears during that show?

_____

4. Josie has an awful cough. What tool could she use to measure the amount of cough syrup she should take? _____

5. If Josie's mom wants to find out Josie's temperature, which tool could she use?

_____

6. Say Josie wanted to make a cake. What tool could she use to measure the milk she needs to put in the cake mix? _____

7. What tool could Josie use to measure the height of her brother's tree house?

_____

8. What tool could Josie give her dad to measure the length of their living room?

_____

Choose four of the measuring tools in Josie's Tool Box. Make a list of things you could measure with each of those tools.

Picnic Area

What to Do:

Area measures the number of square units inside a shape. Find the area of each ant family's picnic blanket by counting the number of squares on the blanket. Then answer the following questions.

Remember—area is measured in square units, such as square centimeters. My blanket's area is four square units.

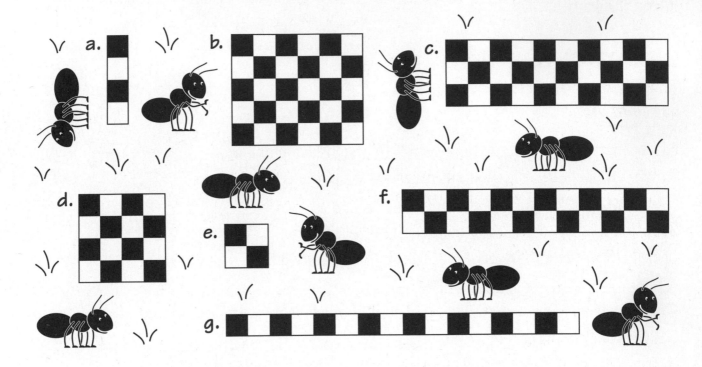

1. Which pairs of blankets have the same area?

   _____ and _____

   _____ and _____

   _____ and _____

2. Which two blankets can you put together to make a rectangle with an area of 20?

   _____

3. Which three blankets can you put together to make a rectangle with an area of 50?

   _____

4. What is the total area of all of the ants' blankets?

   _____

Perimeter and Area Zoo

A shape doesn't have to be a square or a rectangle to have perimeter and area. The animals in this zoo are different shapes. Can you find each animal's perimeter and area?

Remember: To find perimeter, count the sides of the units. To find area, count the number of whole units.

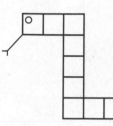

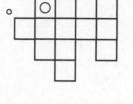

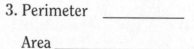

1. Perimeter _____

   Area _____

2. Perimeter _____

   Area _____

3. Perimeter _____

   Area _____

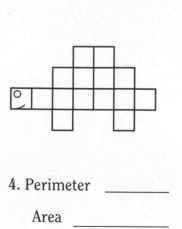

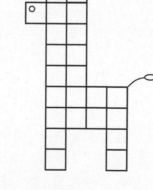

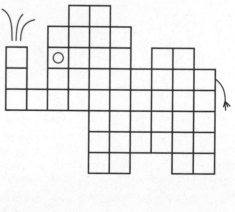

4. Perimeter _____

   Area _____

5. Perimeter _____

   Area _____

6. Perimeter _____

   Area _____

Angles From A to Z

Angles are hiding everywhere—even in the words you're reading now. When two straight lines meet, they make an angle. There are three kinds of angles:

- The corner of a square or rectangle makes a right angle.

- Angles that are smaller than right angles are called acute angles.

- Angles that are larger than right angles are called obtuse angles.

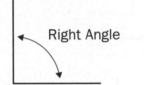

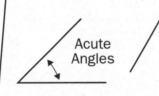

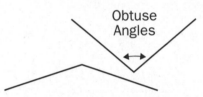

Take a look at the letters below. Circle each angle you see in the letters. Tell whether it is right, acute, or obtuse.

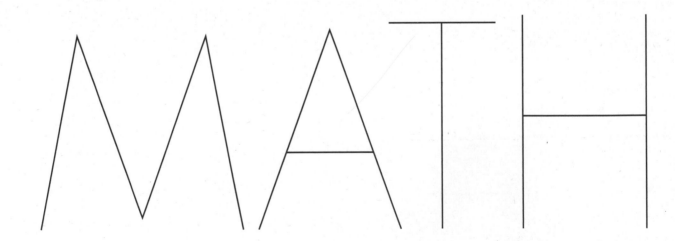

Measuring and Classifying Angles

Use a protractor to measure each angle.
Then decide whether it should be classified as acute, obtuse, or right.

Classifying Angles

Right angle: looks like the corner of a square. It measures exactly 90°.

Obtuse angle: wider than a right angle. It measures greater than 90° but less than 180°.

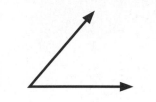

Acute angle: narrower than a right angle. It measures greater than 0° but less than 90°.

Straight angle: two rays that make what looks like a straight line. It measures 180°.

1.

Angle measurement: _____

Angle classification: _____

2.

Angle measurement: _____

Angle classification: _____

3.

Angle measurement: _____

Angle classification: _____

4.

Angle measurement: _____

Angle classification: _____

5.

Angle measurement: _____

Angle classification: _____

Flying Through the Air

What is the last thing that the trapeze flier wants to be?

Find the symmetrical shapes. Then use the Decoder to solve the riddle by filling in the blanks at the bottom of the page.

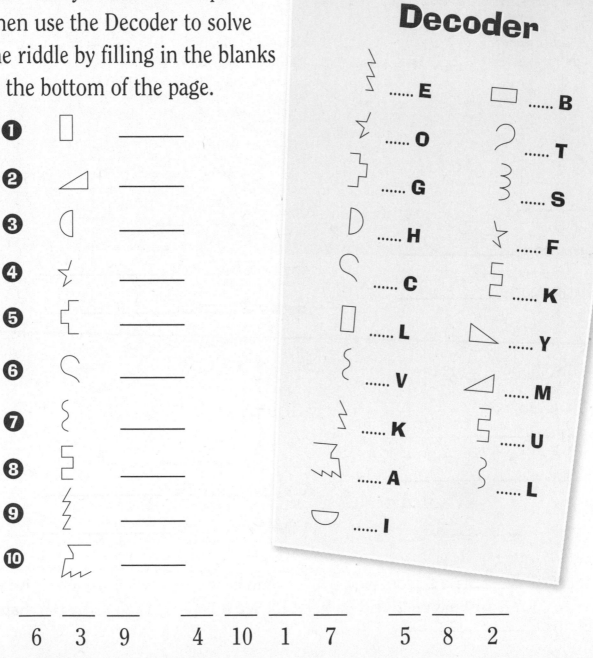

1 _____

2 _____

3 _____

4 _____

5 _____

6 _____

7 _____

8 _____

9 _____

10 _____

Decoder

⚡ ...... E   ▭ ...... B

...... O   ...... T

...... G   ...... S

...... H   ...... F

...... C   ...... K

...... L   ...... Y

...... V   ...... M

...... K   ...... U

...... A   L

...... I

___ ___ ___   ___ ___ ___ ___   ___ ___ ___
 6   3   9   4   10 1   7   5   8   2

Shape Up!

✏ How well do you know geometric shapes? Here's your chance to test yourself. Take a look at the shape in each statement. Fill in the blank spaces with the correct answers. When you're done, write the letters in the shaded squares on the spaces provided to solve the riddle.

What did the alien eat for lunch?

1. An ⬡ has __ ▨ __ __ ▨ sides.

2. This triangle has an angle that is the opposite of obtuse.
    It's an ▨ __ __ ▨ angle.

3. The __ __ __ ▨ __ __ __ __ __ of this rectangle is fourteen.

4. The ▨ ▨ __ __ of this rectangle is twelve. ³⟦ ⟧⁴   ³⟦ ⟧⁴

5. This shape ⬜ is a __ __ __ __ __ .

6. This shape ⬛ is a __ __ ▨ __ .

7. This shape △ is a __ __ __ ▨ __ __ __ __.

8. This shape ◯ is a __ __ ▨ __ __ __ .

9. These shapes ⬡⬠⬡ have many sides.
    They are called __ __ __ __ __ __ __ ▨ .

What did the alien eat for lunch?

__ __ __   __ __ __ __ __   __ __ __   __ __ __ __ .

Draw a geometric shape not included in this activity on a piece of paper. Give it to a friend. See if he or she can name the shape.

Terrific Tessellations

What do math and art have in common? Everything—if you're making tessellations!

A tessellation (tess-uh-LAY-shun) is a design made of shapes that fit together like puzzle pieces. People use tessellations to decorate walls and floors, and even works of art.

This sidewalk is formed from rectangles.

Hexagons form this beehive.

Here is a tessellation made from more than one shape.

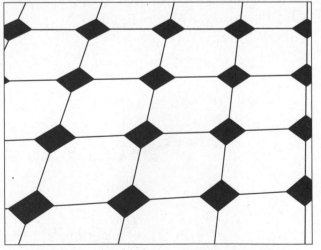

Squares and octagons form a tile floor.

Terrific Tessellations

You Need:
heavy paper ◆ scissors
tape ◆ crayons

What to Do:
Here's how you can make your own tessellation.

1. Start with a simple shape like a square. (Cut your shape from the heavy paper). Cut a piece out of side A . . .

2. . . . and slide it over to side B. Make sure it lines up evenly with the cut out side, or your tessellation won't work. Tape it in place on side B.

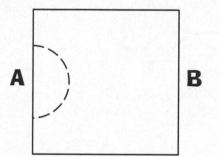

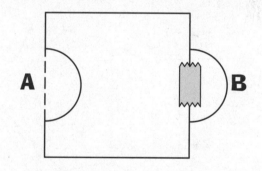

3. If you like, do the same thing with sides C and D. Now you have a new shape.

4. Trace your new shape on paper. Then slide the shape so it fits together with the one you just traced. Trace it again. Keep on sliding and tracing until your page is filled. Decorate your tessellation.

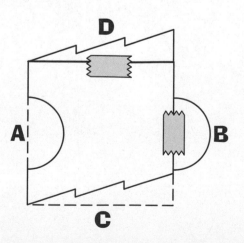

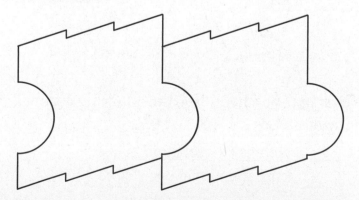

Kaleidoscope of Flowers

If the number has a 5 in the ones place, color the shape green.
If the number has a 5 in the tenths place, color the shape pink.
If the number has a 5 in the hundredths place, color the shape yellow.
Finish the design by coloring the other shapes with colors of your choice.

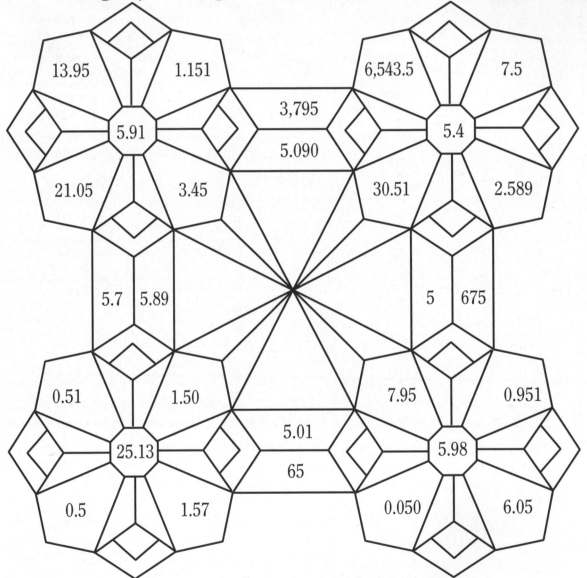

Taking It Further: Place the following decimals in the correct places on the lines below the dots: 4.9, 1.7, 2.5, and 0.2.

© Scholastic Inc.

Answer Key

READING COMPREHENSION

Pages 12–13
Answers will vary. Sample main ideas: Letter one—Except for the bugs, Tyler and his new friends are having fun at camp.; Letter two—Tyler's mom is worried about his bug bites, and she wants him to start being nice to the other campers.; Letter three—Tyler is having a great time at camp, has some new friends, and is having fun playing tricks on other campers.; Letter four—Steven is sad he could not go to camp and remembers the fun he had at camp last year.

Pages 14–15
1. A; 2. D; 3. B; 4. B; 5. C

Pages 16–17
1. between Virginia and Maryland on the Potomac River; 2. Answers will vary. Possible answers: capital of the United States, symbol of our country's history, home of many important historic landmarks; 3. George Washington, Abraham Lincoln, Thomas Jefferson, and Franklin D. Roosevelt; 4. Americans who fought in the Korean War and Vietnam War; 5. The National World War II Memorial; 6. to honor Americans who fought in World War II; 7. about four years—1941–1945; 8. Rainbow Pool, two giant arches, ring of stone columns, wall covered with stars; 9. Americans who died fighting in World War II; 10. Bob Dole; 11. the value of freedom; 12. many businesses, private groups, and schools

Pages 18–19
1. formal; 2. residence; 3. reception; 4. entertained; 5. adorned; 6. guide; 7. wing; 8. mansion; 9. tour; 10. incredible; 11. huge; 12. visitors; 13. vary; five hundred seventy

Pages 20–21
1. classed; 2. unique; 3. fascinating; 4. strike; 5. enamored; 6. eventually; 7. accumulated; 8. carting; 9. slinky; 10. creature; 11. Cassidy loves large, dangerous snakes. 12. a diamondback rattlesnake

Pages 22–23
1. Southwest: many-storied homes; steep-walled canyons; buttes; Arizona, New Mexico, and southern Colorado; Apache and Navajo; Both: made pottery; hunting; excellent craftspeople; corn, beans, and squash; Eastern Woodlands: wigwams and longhouses; fishing; cold winters, warm summers; Iroquois and Cherokee; bordered what is now Canada; 2. large, multiple-family dwellings; 3. The northern parts had cold winters.

Pages 24–25
1. Arizona: Tonto National Forest, Phoenix, very hot, Apache Trail, Grand Canyon; Massachusetts: Old State House, Freedom Trail, mild climate, Boston, Cape Cod; 2. building sandcastles, beach, Meteor Crater, Freedom Trail; 3. Their parents love hot weather. Zach and Emily do not. 4. You can walk on the Freedom Trail; you must drive along the Apache Trail. 5. Emily likes to boogie board, and Zach likes to body surf. 6. Zach thinks he might be able to find the missing object. Emily thinks he is crazy to think he might find it.

Pages 26–27
1. Picture order: 5, 1, 6, 3, 4, 2, Sentences will vary.
2.

a	p	r	t	e	i	c
c	o	l	e	s	a	b
m	u	s	i	i	n	l
g	l	y	l	c	p	r
e	d	e	i	t	c	e
o	d	v	s	e	b	r
i	s	l	l	i	o	n

Pages 28–29
1. 7, 3, 4, 2, 1, 5, 6; 2. Answers will vary. 3. prank, party, delicious; 4. because water makes the chocolate lose its creaminess; 5. tortilla, apricot jam, green fruit roll, cashews, chocolate chips; 6. Maria "sweetly" tricked her friends on April Fools' Day. 7. vanilla ice cream, marshmallow fluff, yellow pudding; 8. black olives, green peppers, mushrooms

Pages 30–31
1. hard worker, brave, fast-thinking, quick-acting; 2. scared, helpless, sick, alarmed; 3. Answers will vary. 4. Both: good students; Lindsay: persistent, dependable; Erica: frightened, grateful, appreciative; 5. Henry Heimlich; 6. Mount Waialeale; 7. just under 2"; 8. Answers will vary.

Pages 32–33
1. positive: He sees his friend, Eric., He learns Home Run Harvey is the coach.; negative: He could not play baseball with his friends., He sees a player on his new team strike out. 2. He would not get to see his friends and have Coach Dave whom he loved. 3. when he saw Eric; 4. Answers will vary. 5. excited, remorseful; 6. What Juan thought was going to be a negative experience soon looked like it could be a positive one. 7. Answers will vary.

Pages 34–35
1. Tuesday and Wednesday; 2. Monday; 3. Answers will vary. Suggested answers: go to the movies, go to the mall, go bowling, go to a museum, go to the library; 4. Wednesday, Thursday, Friday; 5. Answers will vary. Possible answer: They are probably not pleased. They want to do all kinds of outdoor activities, and it is going to be cold and rainy. 6. no clouds with a high of 82; It is the best forecast for doing outside activities. 7. lingering; 8. athletic, energetic; 9. goggles, sunglasses, cooler with drinks, sunscreen; 10. Paragraphs will vary.

Pages 36–37
main characters: the colonists; setting: east coast of America; problem: The colonists wanted their independence from Britain. solution: Delegates met to try to help gain independence from Britain. When their efforts did not work, they agreed to go to war.

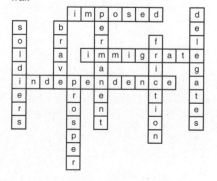

Pages 38–39
1. B, C, A; 2. a. E, C; b. C, E; c. E, C; d. E, C;
3. Since it was a beautiful day, Janie and
Jake's mom was taking them to the beach.
4. Janie: because Hayley had recently had
Janie over to play; Jake: because he
and Charlie went everywhere together;
5. Answers will vary.

Page 40
1. Jupiter; 2. Uranus; 3. Neptune;
4. Earth; 5. Saturn; 6. Mercury;
7. Mars; 8. Venus

Page 41
Grant: Washington; Spencer: Arizona;
Kara: Pennsylvania;
Jack: Massachusetts; All live in Maine.

Pages 42–43
1. to run errands and shop;
2. Answers will vary.

Pages 44–45
Chart: Dairy—milk, yogurt, ice cream,
cheese, milkshake; Vegetables—carrots,
peas, corn, broccoli, cauliflower; Grains—
oatmeal, wheat bread, rice, crackers, pasta;
Fruits—banana, apple, grapes, strawberries,
pear; Meat & Fish—chicken nuggets,
ham, hamburger, fish sticks, pork chops;
Fats/Sweets—chocolate chip cookies,
candy bar, doughnuts, chocolate cake,
cheesecake;
1. She eats right and exercises.
2. hamburger, chicken, ribs;
3. Answers will vary. 4. E, C;
5. Katie: banana, oatmeal; Jimmy: candy
bar, ham, corn; Toni: chocolate chip cookies,
chicken nuggets, carrots; Anna: fish sticks,
pear

Page 46
1. spring; 2. Mother's Day; 3. because they
are having a sale; 4. Answers will vary.
Possible answer: It was spring. Many people
shop for plants in the spring, so a sale would
not be needed. 5. because they are buy one
get one free; 6. because the sale ends
Tuesday

Page 47
1. They love it. 2. They are sad., They do
not they will do without their good friends.
3. They think it sounds like a fun, interesting
part of the country.
4.

Pages 48–49
1. Most whales are enormous creatures.
2. Whales might look a lot like fish, but the
two are very different. 3. Whales can be
divided into two groups—baleen and
toothed. 4. Blubber is very important to
whales and has many purposes. 5. Most
whales are enormous creatures. Whales
might look a lot like fish, but the two are
very different. Whales can be divided into
two groups—baleen and toothed. Blubber
is very important to whales and has many
purposes. 6. Whale: can hold breath for long
time, tail fin sideways, lungs; Fish: gills, live
in ponds, tail fin up and down; Both: live in
oceans, people love to watch

Pages 50–51
1. O, O, F, O, F, F, F, O; 2. Answers will vary.
3. Answers will vary. 4. brave, strong, daring,
athletic; 5. climbing poles, ice axes,
breathing masks; 6. Answers will vary.
7. Answers will vary.

Pages 52–53
1. to entertain; 2. Working is not what the
author would choose to do. 3. The author
wants to escape from worries and be free
like animals. 4. worries, chores, homework;
5. bird: fly, float, sing, play, soar; dolphin:
splash, play, dive, flip; bear: jump, climb,
sleep, run, play, fish; dog: play ball, jump,
run, roll over, fetch, rest, catch;
6. F, O, F, F, O

Page 54
1. to persuade; 2. Answers will vary.
3. Answers will vary. Possible reasons:
Students would get around more quickly.,
Students would learn more., It would lead to
better health. 4. Answers will vary.

GRAMMAR

Page 56
A. 1. declarative   4. imperative
   2. interrogative   5. exclamatory
   3. imperative   6. interrogative
B. 1. incomplete   4. incomplete
   2. complete   5. complete
   3. complete
C. 1. Sarah stood at the edge of the square.
   2. The sword slide out of the stone.

Page 57
A. 1. interrogative, ?   3. imperative, .
   2. exclamatory, !   4. declarative, .
B. 1. listened, declarative 3. pass, imperative
   2. play, interrogative 4. won,
                              exclamatory
C. Answers will vary.

Page 58
1. b   3. c   5. c   7. c   9. a
2. b   4. a   6. b   8. a   10. b

Page 59
A. 1. A small family | lived on a faraway
      planet.
   2. The family's two children | played near
      the space launch.
   3. The little girl | dreamed about life on
      Earth.
   4. Huge spaceships | landed daily on the
      planet.
   5. The spaceships mechanics | repaired
      huge cargo ships.
   6. Twinkling stars | appeared in the black
      sky.
B. 1. The planet's inhabitants | lived in
      underground homes.
   2. A special machine | manufactures air
      inside the family's home.
   3. The athletic girl | jumped high into the
      air.
   4. Many toys and games | cluttered the
      children's playroom.
   5. The children's father | described
      weather on Earth.
C. 1. The underground home contained
      large,comfortable rooms.
   2. The playful child rolled his clay into a
      ball.

Page 60
A. 1. My whole <u>family</u> 4. <u>Everyone</u>
   2. The warm, sunny <u>day</u> 5. The <u>people</u> in
   3. My cousin <u>Fred</u> the park
B. 1. <u>watched</u> the space shuttle
      on TV this morning
   2. <u>rocketed</u> into space at 6:00 a.m.
   3. <u>released</u> a satellite into space.
   4. <u>circled</u> Earth for three days.
   5. <u>landed</u> smoothly on Monday at noon.
C. Answers will vary.

Page 61
1. b   3. a   5. b   7. a   9. b
2. c   4. c   6. b   8. c   10. c

Page 62
A. 1. Pig One, Pig Two, and Pig Three
   2. bears, rabbits, and pigs
   3. Carrots, beets, and squash
   4. Teddy and Osito
   5. brothers and sisters
B. 1. cleaned and peeled
   2. laughed and giggled
   3. waited and watched
   4. weeds and waters
   5. writes and edits
C. 1. buys and reads, CP
   2. authors and illustrators, CS

Page 63
A. 1. teacher, students; The teacher and her
      students visited the ocean.
   2. Seagulls, Pelicans;
      Seagulls and pelicans flew overhead.
   3. Seashells, Seaweed; Seashells and
      seaweed littered the sand.
   4. Carlos, Tanya; Carlos and Tanya ran on
      the beach
B. 1. paints, draws; The artist paints and
      draws sea life.
   2. collect, decorate; I collect and decorate
      driftwood.
   3. swim, dive; Seals swim and dive near
      the pier.

Page 64
A. 1. a   2. b   3. a   4. c   5. b
B. 1. c   2. a   3. c   4. b   5. b

Page 65
A. 1. simple   3. compound 5. simple
   2. compound 4. simple   6. compound
B. 1. <u>Connor had seen many parks in his
      life</u>, but <u>he never had seen a park like
      this one.</u>
   2. <u>Dad brought a pair of binoculars</u>, and
      <u>Nate used them to look for animals.</u>
   3. <u>He saw his first live bear</u>, and <u>the hair
      stood up on his arms.</u>
   4. <u>It was an exciting moment</u>, but <u>it only
      lasted a second.</u>
   5. <u>The bear was no bear at all</u>, and <u>Felicia
      was embarrassed.</u>
   6. <u>He hadn't seen a bear</u>, but <u>he kept
      looking.</u>

Page 66
A. 1. <u>One day we were in the park,</u> (and) <u>we
      saw two ducks swimming by.</u>
   2. <u>We watched the ducks for a while,</u> (but)
      <u>they disappeared into the tall grass.</u>
   3. <u>The ducks might have gone to a nest,</u>
      (or) <u>they could have swum to the shore.</u>
   4. <u>We walked along the grassy bank,</u> (but)
      <u>we could not find them anywhere.</u>
   5. <u>We sat down on the dock,</u> (and) <u>out
      came the ducks again.</u>
   6. <u>One adult duck led six ducklings
      around the pond,</u> (and) <u>the other adult
      followed behind the babies.</u>
B. 1. but   3. and   5. or
   2. but   4. and
C. Answers will vary.

Page 67
A. 1. b   2. b   3. a   4. b   5. a
B. 1. a   2. b   3. a   4. b   5. c

Page 68
A. 1. farmer, house, road
   2. farmer, wheat, soybeans, corn
   3. fields, crop
   4. crops, rows
   5. plants, farmer, weeds, bugs
B. 1. John Vasquez, Tulsa, Oklahoma
   2. Vasquez Farm, Rising J Horse Ranch
   3. Mr. Vasquez, Sally
   4. Joker
   5. October, Vasquez Farm, Harvest
      Celebration
C. 1. the street, park
      We walked down Oak Street to Blair
      Park.
   2. aunt, the city
      My Aunt Ellen lives in Denver.

Page 69
A. 1. (story, celebrations);
      Atlanta Constitution
   2. (movie, poodles);
      Three Dogs on a Summer Night
   3. (campfire); "She'll Be Comin' 'Round
      the Mountain"
   4. (friend, grandparents); <u>August, John,
      Germany</u>
   5. (family, beach); <u>Memorial Day</u>
B. Common nouns: newspaper, city, day,
   magazine, park, book, month
   Proper nouns: <u>The Sun News</u>, Chicago,
   Tuesday, <u>Cobblestone</u>, Yellowstone
   National Park, <u>Young Arthur</u>, July

Page 70
1. b   3. b   5. a   7. b   9. a
2. c   4. c   6. c   8. c   10. a

Page 71
A. 1. door, cap, bat, game   4. team
   2. bat, shoulder   5. day, foul, homer
   3. fence, dugout
B. 1. uncles, feet   4. brothers, sisters, cousins
   2. bases   5. teams, playoffs
   3. players
C. 1. (season); <u>teams, players; awards</u>
   2. (hitter), (catcher), (teammate); <u>games</u>
   3. (mother), (father), (assembly); <u>parents</u>
   4. (glove); <u>achievements</u>

Page 72
A. 1. (homework) (night), (story); <u>friends</u>
   2. (home); <u>friends</u>
   3. (cat); <u>dogs, birds, pals</u>
   4. <u>adventures, pets, buddies</u>
   5. (teacher), (story); <u>classes</u>
B. Singular nouns:
   1. chair   3. tooth   5. foot
   2. mouse   4. sheep   6. man
   Plural Nouns:
   1. chairs   3. teeth   5. feet
   2. mice   4. sheep   6. men
C. Answers will vary.

Page 73
1. b   3. b   5. c   7. b   9. a
2. c   4. a   6. c   8. a   10. b

Page 74
A. 1. <u>The fourth graders;</u> (they)
   2. <u>Ada;</u> (she)
   3. <u>Juan, Jill, and I;</u> (We)
B. 1. <u>the author;</u> her
   2. <u>the fourth graders; them</u>
   3. <u>information; it</u>
C. 1. (I), <u>you</u>   2. (You), <u>me</u>   3. (he), us

Page 75
A. 1. We; S   4. I; S   7. them; O
   2. us; O   5. it; O   8. She; S
   3. You; S   6. her; O
B. 1. They sent a postcard to us.
   2. It was addressed to him.
C. Answers will vary.

Page 76
A. 1. a   2. c   3. b   4. a   5. b
B. 1. a   2. b   3. a   4. b   5. b

Page 77
A. 1. my   3. their   5. her   7. Our
   2. his   4. my   6. your
B. 1. My   3. her   5. our
   2. their   4. his   6. my

Page 78
A. 1. mine   3. yours   5. her
   2. your   4. ours
B. 1. our   4. my   7. your
   2. her   5. his   8. our
   3. their   6. My or His
C. Answers will vary.

Page 79
1. d   3. b   5. d   7. b   9. c
2. c   4. c   6. b   8. d   10. a

Page 80
A. 1. wrote   4. weave   7. tie   10. wished
   2. painted   5. knits   8. learned
   3. twisted   6. stretched   9. made
B. 1. hopped   3. slurped
   2. pounded   4. sewed
C. Answers will vary.

Page 81
A. 1. use   3. imagine   5. amazes
   2. tie   4. invented
B. 1. lounge   3. gulp   5. staple
   2. gallop   4. drag

Page 82
A. 1. b   3. a   5. a
   2. c   4. b
B. 1. b   3. a   5. a
   2. b   4. b

Page 83
A. 1. past   5. present   9. future
   2. past   6. future   10. present
   3. future   7. present   11. past
   4. past   8. past
B. 1. Gum acted as an eraser.
   2. Unfortunately, pure rubber cracked in cold weather.
   3. Goodyear licensed the process to shoe companies.

Page 84
A. 1. wears   4. hurt   7. buys
   2. make   5. cause   8. want
   3. teaches   6. places
B. With Most Singular subjects: laces, designs, reaches, erases
   With Plural Subjects: lace, design, reach, erase

Page 85
A. 1. c   2. a   3. c   4. b   5. c
B. 1. a   2. c   3. b   4. a   5. c

Page 86
A. 1. will happen   6. will handle
   2. has equipped   7. was talking
   3. was polishing   8. had helped
   4. had tinkered   9. is wearing
   5. was gathering   10. will need
B. 1. had (asked); past
   2. will (drop); future
   3. is (learning); present
   4. will (enjoy); future
   5. has (eaten); past
   6. are (taking); present

Page 87
A. 1. was cooking   4. is tasting
   2. had added   5. will add
   3. have prepared   6. have arrived
B. 1. will bake   4. had planted
   2. has picked   5. have tossed
   3. is picking   6. are planning
C. Answers will vary.

Page 88
1. a   3. c   5. b   7. b   9. a
2. a   4. a   6. c   8. b   10. c

Page 89
A. 1. (I) am (reader)
   2. (books) are (nonfiction)
   3. (bookstore) is (one)
   4. (books) are (interesting)
   5. (owner) is (knowledgeable)
   6. (name) is (Terry baldes)
   7. (Mr. Baldes) was (inventor, scientist)
   8. (windows) were (attractive)
   9. (event) was (appearance)
   10. (friends) are (admirers)
B. 1. is   3. were   5. were
   2. was   4. are
C. Answers will vary.

Page 90
A. 1. was, S   5. were, P   9. were, P
   2. were, P   6. are, P   10. was, S
   3. are, P   7. is, S   11. am, S
   4. is, S   8. are, P
B. 1. is   2. are   3. are   4. is
C. Answers will vary.

Page 91
1. c   3. c   5. a   7. a   9. b
2. b   4. b   6. b   8. b   10. a

Page 92
A. 1. bought   4. rode   7. took
   2. made   5. shook   8. thought
   3. came   6. heard   9. broke
B. 1. heard   4. broke   7. shook
   2. made   5. rode
   3. bought   6. came

Page 93
A. 1. have chosen   6. have gone
   2. has brought   7. had heard
   3. have eaten   8. have ridden
   4. has hidden   9. has bought
   5. had taken
B. 1. heard   4. ridden   7. brought
   2. taken   5. chosen
   3. gone   6. bought

Page 94
A. 1. b   2. a   3. c   4. a   5. b
B. 1. a   2. c   3. a   4. b   5. c

Page 95
A. 1. (colorful), (dark); many
   2. (small); few
   3. (strange), (unusual); one
   4. (mysterious)
   5. (big), (dark); four
   6. (rare), (new)
   7. (tiny), (large), (cold)
   8. (amazing); several
B. Sample answers are given.
   1. small, mysterious
   2. big, large
   3. sandy, small, long
   4. new
   5. underwater, several, many
C. Answers will vary.

Page 96
A. Sample answers are given.
   1. big, hungry
   2. fuzzy, orange, little
   3. missing, tasty
   4. plastic, red; red-headed, young
   5. more, tasty, good
B. 1. gray, shaggy, dark   4. soft, shady
   2. some, droopy   5. enormous, large
   3. little, quiet
C. Answers will vary.

Page 97
Answers will vary.

Page 98

1. a	3. b	5. a	7. a	9. b
2. c	4. b	6. b	8. a	10. c

Page 99

A. 1. older   4. quieter   7. brightest
   2. loudest   5. higher   8. saddest
   3. biggest   6. softer
B. 1. hottest; more than two
   2. warmer; two
   3. colder; two
   4. tallest; more than two
   5. longer, two
   6. friendliest; more than two
   7. younger; two
   8. liveliest; more than two

Page 100

1. funniest   7. more challenging
2. funnier   8. most challenging
3. busier   9. more tiring
4. busiest   10. most tiring
5. more exciting   11. more delicious
6. most exciting   12. most delicious

Page 101

1. a	3. b	5. a	7. a	9. a
2. b	4. a	6. b	8. a	10. b

Page 102

A. 1. (of) mountains, rivers, and lakes.
   2. (on) the walls (of) his room
   3. (to) the scenes (in) the pictures
   4. (on) a camping trip
   5. (in) a backpack and knapsack
   6. (from) his father's mug
   7. (in) the mountains (for) hours
   8. (at) the Lost Lake
   9. (on) their journey
   10. (at) a quiet place (for) the night
   11. (in) a tent
   12. (from) the wind and rain
   13. (to) his father
   14. (on) their camping trip
B. 1. Answers will vary.

Page 103

A. 1. in   3. on   5. at
   2. with 4. for 6. into
B. Answers will vary.
C. Answers will vary.

Page 104

1. a	3. b	5. c	7. a	9. c
2. c	4. a	6. c	8. b	10. b

Page 105

A. 1. Tucker, lives; present
   2. It, opens; present
   3. Tucker, collected; past
   4. mouse, filled; past
   5. Tucker, sits; present
   6. He, watches; present
   7. boy, worked; past
   8. They, sell; present
B. 1. crowd, passes; singular
   2. Trains, run; plural
   3. Papa, waits; singular
   4. station, feels; singular
   5. People, rush; plural
   6. Mama, Papa, make; plural

Page 106

A. 1. Crickets, (make)
   2. males, (produce)
   3. I, (listen)
   4. You, (hear)
   5. Mario, (finds)
   6. mother, (calls)
B. 1. Mario wants the cricket for a pet.
   2. He wishes for a pet of his own.
   3. Crickets seem like unusual pets
     to his mother.
   4. Maybe insects scare her!

Page 107

A. 1. b   3. a   5. a
   2. b   4. b
B. 1. c   3. c   5. b
   2. a   4. b

Page 108

A. 1. "I really like tall tales!"
   2. "Davy Crockett is my favorite
     character,"
   3. "Who likes Sally Ann Thunder Ann
     Whirlwind?"
B. 1. "I am a big fan of hers."
   2. I added, "Sally can even sing a wolf
     to sleep."
   3. "How did Sally tame King Bear?"
   4. "Sally really ought to be in the movies,"
C. 1. "What kind of person is Sally?" asked
     Davy Crockett.
   2. The schoolmarm replied, "Sally is a
     special friend."
   3. "She can laugh the bark off a pine
     tree," added Lucy.
   4. The preacher said, "She can dance a
     rock to pieces."
   5. "I'm very impressed!" exclaimed Davy.
D. Answers will vary.

Page 109

A. 1. "Well,   3. "Yes,
   2. "Oh, Ed,   4. "Thank you,
B. 1. "Kim, your posters for the talent
     contest are terrific!"
   2. She replied, "Thank you, Doug, for
     your kind words."
   3. Our teacher asked, "Meg, will you play
     your guitar or sing?"
   4. "Oh, I plan to do both," said Meg.
   5. "Will you perform your juggling act this
     year Roberto?"
   6. "No, I want to do a comedy routine,"
C. 1. "Kit, which act did you like best?"
     asked Mina.
   2. He replied, "Oh, I enjoyed the singing
     pumpkins and the tap dancing
     elephants."
   3. "Well, I liked the guitar player,"
     said Mina.
D. Answers will vary.

Page 110

Possible answers: Mateo announced,
"They're closing school for two days."
"That's fantastic!" shouted Melissa. "I'm so
happy!"; "Let's sell cupcakes to raise money
for the team," suggested Beth. "I think that's
a great idea," said Paul.

Page 111

1. b	3. b	5. a	7. a	9. a
2. a	4. c	6. b	8. c	10. b

Page 112

A. 1. shouted, (Later)
   2. hit, (yesterday)
   3. got, (soon)
   4. tried, (earlier)
   5. went, (Then)
B. 1. fell, (everywhere)
   2. piled, (up)
   3. were trapped, (inside)
   4. tunneled, (out)
   5. traveled, (there)
C. 1. never, when   3. inside, where
   2. underground, where 4. Soon, when

Page 113

A. 1. <u>talked</u>, (happily)
2. <u>squawked</u>, (sharply)
3. <u>greeted</u>, (warmly)
4. <u>guided</u>, (expertly)
5. <u>wrote</u>, (regularly)
6. <u>recorded</u>, (faithfully)
7. <u>responded</u>, (personally)
8. <u>looked</u>, (eagerly)
9. <u>jumped</u>, (quickly)
10. <u>snorkeled</u>, (easily)
11. <u>saw</u>, (clearly)
12. <u>gazed</u>, (intently)
13. <u>surrounded</u>, (Swiftly)
14. <u>chased and nipped</u>, (playfully)

B. Sample answers are given.
1. bellowed loudly.
2. swam gracefully.

Page 114

A. 1. a   2. b   3. b   4. c   5. a
B. 1. c   2. b   3. a   4. a   5. b

WRITING

Page 116
Sentences will vary.

Page 117
A. (left to right) S, P; S, P; P, P; S, P; S, S; P, S; P, P; S, S; B. 1. Half a loaf is better than none. 2. One good turn deserves another. 3. One rotten apple spoils the whole barrel. 4. The show must go on. 5. Every cloud has a silver lining. 6. The early bird catches the worm. 7. A rolling stone gathers no moss. 8. Haste makes waste.

Pages 118–119
1. S; 2. E; 3. S; 4. Q; 5. C; 6. E; 7. C; 8. E; 9. Q; 10. C; 11. S; 12. Q; Sentences will vary.

Page 120
1. Did you know that the whale shark can grow to a length of 60 feet? 2. That's about as long as two school buses parked end to end! 3.These huge creatures are not a threat to humans like some other sharks are. 4. Whale sharks float near the surface to look for plankton and tiny fish. 5. Imagine how amazing it must be to swim alongside a whale shark. 6. There are an estimated 27,000 known species of fish in the world. 7. Is the dwarf pygmy goby one of the smallest of all these species? 8. This species of goby is less than a half-inch long when it is fully grown! 9. This tiny fish makes its home in the seas and rivers of Asia.

Page 121
1. Are numbers that cannot be divided evenly by 2 called odd numbers? 2. Can all even numbers be divided evenly by 2? 3. Is 0 considered an even number? 4. Are numbers that have 0, 2, 4, 6, or 8 in the ones place even numbers? 5. Do odd numbers end in 1, 3, 5, 7, or 9? 6. Is the number 317,592 an even number because it ends in 2? 7. Is the sum always an even number when you add two even numbers? 8. Is the sum of two odd numbers also an even number? 9. Does the same rule apply if you subtract an odd number from an odd number? 10. Can you figure out all the rules for working with odd and even numbers?

Page 122
Think about the fastest car you've ever seen in the Indianapolis 500 race. That's about how fast a peregrine falcon dives. It actually reaches speeds over 200 miles an hour. How incredibly fast they are! Peregrine falcons are also very powerful birds. Did you know that they can catch and kill their prey in the air using their sharp claws? What's really amazing is that peregrine falcons live in both the country and in the city. Keep on the lookout if you're ever in New York City. Believe it or not, it is home to several falcons.

Page 123
Answers will vary.

Page 124
Sentences will vary.; The simple sentence will be: The team cheered.

Page 125
Answers and sentences will vary.

Page 126
1. My sister Annie has always participated in sports, and many say she's a natural athlete. 2. Soccer, basketball, and softball are fun, but she wanted a new challenge. 3. My sister talked to my brother and me, and we were honest with her. 4. I told Annie to go for it, but my brother told her to stick with soccer or basketball. 5. Will Dad convince her to try skiing, or will he suggest ice skating?

Page 127
1. The Caspian Sea, the world's largest lake, covers an area about the same size as Montana. 2. The Komodo dragon, a member of the monitor family, can grow to a length of 10 feet. 3. Our closest star, the sun, is estimated to be more than 27,000,000°F. 4. Ronald W. Reagan, our nation's 40th president, worked as a Hollywood actor for almost 30 years. 5. Georgia, the state that grows the most peanuts, harvests over 2 billion pounds each year. 6. Jackie Robinson, who played for the Brooklyn Dodgers, was the first African American to play in the major leagues.

Page 128
1. My brothers built a tree house in the old oak tree in our backyard. 2. Jim made a sturdy rope ladder for the tree house. 3. Kyle bought a gallon of brown paint. 4. Kyle and Jim finished painting the walls in an hour. 5. Jim painted a "no trespassing" sign on the tree house door. 6. A curious squirrel leaped from a branch into their tree house. 7. The unexpected visitor startled my unsuspecting brothers. 8. The frightened squirrel leaped out of the tree house in a big hurry.

Page 129
1. While I waited for my parents to get home, I watched a movie. 2. My brother was in his room because he had homework to do. 3. Before the movie was over, the power went out. 4. Since this happens all the time, I wasn't concerned. 5. I didn't mind the dark at first until I heard a scratching sound. 6. When I found my flashlight, I started to look around. 7. I was checking the living room when I caught Alex trying to hide.

Page 130
Sentences will vary.

Page 131
1. I'd like a bike, a pair of in-line skates, and a snowboard for my birthday. 2. Well, my friend, you can't always have what you want when you want it. 3. No, but I can always hope! 4. My friends and I skate all year long and snowboard during the winter. 5. I used to like skateboarding, but now I prefer snowboarding and in-line skating. 6. What sports, games, or hobbies do you enjoy most, Jody? 7. I learned to ski last year, and now I'm taking ice-skating lessons. 8. Skiing, ice skating, and skateboarding are all fun things to do. 9–12: Examples will vary.

Page 132

1. While Gina answered the phone, Marta watched for the bus. 2. Just as Gina said, "Hello," the caller hung up. 3. Unless they hurried, the girls were going to miss the one o'clock show. 4. By the time they got to the corner, the bus had already come and gone. 5. After the girls had waited a half hour, the next bus to town finally showed up. 6. Since they missed the earlier show, the girls decided to catch the four o'clock show. 7. Since Gina bought the tickets first, they wouldn't have to stand in line later. 8. Even though it was early, Gina and Marta were at the theater by three o'clock. 9. Once they were inside, they bought a tub of popcorn and drinks.

Page 133

Possible sentences: 1. Did you know that the United States is the top meat-eating country in the world? Each person consumes about 260 pounds of meat each year. Beef is the most commonly eaten meat. 2. Have you ever noticed that Abraham Lincoln faces right on a penny? He is not the only president on a U.S. coin who does. Thomas Jefferson faces right on newer nickels too. 3. It would be fantastic to have a robot to do all my chores, help do my homework, and play games. I really think the day will come. Unfortunately, it won't come soon enough for me.

Page 134

How would **you** like to go to school on Saturdays? If you lived in the **country** of Japan, that's just where you'd be each Saturday morning. I have a **friend** who lives in Japan. Yuichi explained that **students** attend classes five and one-half **days** a week. The **half** day is on Saturday. I was also surprised to **learn** that the Japanese school **year** is one of the longest in the world—over 240 days. It begins in the **month** of April. While we have over two months off each **summer**, students in Japan get their **vacation** in late July and August. School then **begins** again in fall and ends in March. The people of **Japan** believe that a good **education** is very important. Children are required to attend school from the age of six to the **age** of fifteen. They have elementary and middle schools just like we do. Then most **students** go on to **high** school for another three years. Yuichi says that students work very **hard** because the standards are so high. He and some of his friends even **take** extra classes after school. They all want to get into a good **college** someday.

Page 135

Starting Over
Today started off badly and only got worse. Everyone in my family woke up late this morning. I had only 15 minutes to get ready and catch the bus. I dressed as fast as I could, grabbed an apple and my backpack, and raced to get to the bus stop on time. Fortunately, I just made it. Unfortunately, the bus was pulling away when several kids pointed out that I had on two different shoes. At that moment, I wanted to start the day over.

Page 136

Sentences and topics will vary.

Page 137

Topic sentences will vary.

Page 138

Topic sentences will vary.

Page 139

Topic sentence: Tony Hawk was an extraordinary skateboarder.
Supporting sentences: He turned professional when he was only 14 years old. Now retired, Tony made history in 1999 by landing a trick called the "900" at the Summer X Games.
Closing sentence: Tony Hawk may just be the greatest skateboarder ever.
Paragraphs will vary.

Page 140

Topic sentence: Yesterday our science class went on a field trip to a pond.
Unrelated supporting sentences: Next month we're going to the ocean.; That will be fun.; One of the boys accidentally fell in.; He was really embarrassed.

Page 141

Supporting sentences will vary.

Page 142

Paragraphs will vary.

Page 143

1. O; 2. F; 3. F; 4. O; 5. F; 6. O;
Fact and opinion sentences will vary.

Page 144

Paragraphs will vary.

Page 145

Responses and paragraphs will vary.

Page 146

Responses will vary.

Page 147

1. Max had forgotten to check the pot of stew heating up on the stove. 2. Effects: the stew boiled over; the bottom of the pot was scorched; smoke filled the kitchen; dinner was ruined; and Max was in trouble; Paragraphs will vary.

Page 148

Paragraphs will vary.

Page 149

Overused words in paragraph: good, nice, little, big, bad, hard, afraid, sad; Synonyms will vary.

Page 150

Verbs: 1. went; 2. ran; 3. blew; 4. cleaned; 5. laughed; 6. ate; 7. liked; 8. slept; 9. looked; Synonyms will vary.; Exact verbs and sentences will vary.

Page 151

Responses will vary.

Page 152

Responses will vary.

Page 153

Responses will vary.

Page 154

Responses will vary.

Page 155

Responses will vary, but all should include commas and quotation marks around the direct words of speakers.

Pages 156–157

1. Chester Greenwood; 2. 3; 3. Who was Chester Greenwood?; 4. 5; Outlines will vary.

Page 158

Responses will vary.

CHARTS, TABLES & GRAPHS

Mathematics

Page 160
1. b
2. c
3. d
4. a
5. a

Page 161
1. 60 in.
2. 24 pounds
3. Teresita and Pablo
4. Size 5
5. The sizes get larger, or the numbers increase.

Page 162
1. b
2. a
3. c
4. d

Page 163
1. a
2. d
3. b
4. d

Page 164
1. a
2. a
3. b
4. c

Page 165
1. Computer
2. 30
3. Automobile and telephone
4. 20

Page 166
1. a
2. c
3. b
4. b

Page 167
1. 2
2. Vermont
3. 1
4. 16

Page 168
1. b
2. d
3. b
4. c

Page 169
1. 5
2. 3
3. Nature
4. 31
5. The Science badge is probably most difficult because it has been earned by the fewest scouts.

Page 170

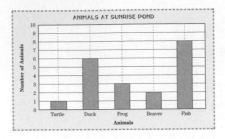

Page 171
1. Science museum
2. 5
3. Water park and amusement park
4. Amusement park
5. Example: The water park would get the fewest votes; the science museum would get a lot more votes.

Page 172
1. d
2. a
3. d
4. b
5. c

Page 173
1. 21
2. Thursday
3. 8
4. 29
5. About 13 books

Page 174
1. 16 in.
2. 5 in.
3. 20 sq. in.
4. 3.5 in.
5. Example: The area of a square increases rapidly as the sides of the square become longer.

Reading/Language Arts

Page 175
1. c
2. a
3. d
4. c
5. a

Page 176
1. Hiking, camping
2. 4
3. Lilac Lake and Mead Canyon
4. Mead Canyon
5. Underwood Park

Page 177
1. a
2. c
3. b
4. c

Page 178
1. Amy Grows Up
2. $2.95
3. 5
4. Dinosaur Dig, $4.50

Page 179
1. b
2. a
3. d
4. d

Page 180
1. c
2. a
3. b
4. d

Social Studies

Page 181
1. 2
2. July
3. 5
4. Spring
5. April

Page 182
1. c
2. b
3. d
4. c
5. a

Page 183
1. Verrazano-Narrows
2. Mackinac Straits, Michigan
3. California, 1937
4. 3,500 feet
5. Delaware Memorial and Tacoma Narrows

Page 184
1. Olympia
2. 1890
3. Oregon
4. Lark Bunting
5. Oregon
6. Sagebrush
7. Idaho and Nevada both have the mountain bluebird.

Page 185
1. Logs are chipped into small pieces.
2. Wood pulp is cleaned and beaten into slush.
3. Step 4, Screen
4. Heat is used to cook the wood chips and to dry the web.

Page 186
1. 60 houses
2. Franklin County
3. Langham County
4. 25 houses
5. The answer should show 4 1/5 house symbols.

Page 187
1. c
2. d
3. b
4. c
5. b

Page 188
Examples of Correct Responses:
1.

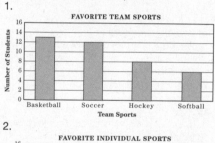

2.

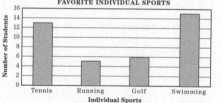

Page 189
1. b
2. d
3. d
4. b
5. a
6. c

Page 190
1. About 1200
2. About 400
3. About 2400
4. 1940–1960
5. Example: The population grew steadily from 1900 to 1980, and then it began to decline.
6. Probably between 2,000 and 2,200

Page 191
1. a
2. c
3. d
4. c
5. Example: Winding became unnecessary in 1930 when electric clocks were invented.

Science
Page 192
1. 5:26 am
2. August 4
3. June 23
4. 10 minutes
5. July 14
6. The sun rises later each day and sets earlier.

Page 193
1. 68°F, 42°F
2. Tuesday
3. Friday and Saturday
4. Partly cloudy
5. 1.5 inches
6. Example: It was warm until Wednesday, and then it got cooler each day. It got cloudy and rainy on Thursday and Friday.

Page 194
1. b
2. c
3. b
4. d
5. a

Page 195
1. Alberto
2. Erin
3. Gert
4. Dorian
5. Example: In each year, names alternate between male and female. In even-numbered years, the first name is male. In odd-numbered years, the first name is female.

Page 196
1. 50 mph
2. 25 mph
3. Cheetah
4. 40 mph
5. Elephant, deer, zebra, lion, cheetah

Page 197
1. d
2. b
3. a
4. d
5. c

Page 198
1. 37°F
2. 64°F
3. July
4. January
5. 47°F
6. Example: The average temperature rises steadily each month from January through July, and then it drops steadily from July through December.

MAPS

Pages 200–201
1. state border
2. Cheyenne
3. Nevada
4. Montana, Idaho
5. Idaho
6. southeast
7. northwest
8. southeast
9. north
10. southwest

Page 203
1. four
2. Southern Hemisphere
3. Prime Meridian
4. north
5. equator
6. It's an imaginary center line on which Earth turns.
7. North America, Asia, Europe, or Africa
8. Asia, Australia, Africa, Europe, and Antarctica

Page 205
1. A world map is flat, a globe is round.
2. Mercator
3. Robinson
4. Mercator
5. Robinson; answers will vary.

Pages 206–207
1. Washington Monument
2. D1
3. Virginia Avenue
4. D1, E1, E2
5. Potomac River
6. E2
7. B2
8. State Department
9. B3
10. A2

Pages 208–209

1. Anchorage
2. 30° N
3. Brasilia
4. equator
5. Nairobi
6. Addis Ababa
7. northern latitudes
8. About 10 degrees
9. 35°N and 35°S
10. 70

Pages 210–211

1. north to south
2. west
3. Manaus
4. 30°E
5. Kinshasa
6. Prime Meridian
7. It is on the other side of Earth.
8. 15°W and 45°E
9. false
10. true
11. true
12. true

Pages 212–213

1. a
2. b
3. b
4. a
5. 300 miles
6. 300 miles, about 500 kilometers
7. about 450 miles
8. 400 kilometers
9. about 800

Pages 214–215

1. 1 mile
2. 2 miles
3. 2 1/4 miles, 4 1/2 miles
4. Map A
5. Map B
6. Map B
7. Map A: 300 miles; Map B: 150 miles
8. Map B just shows part of Texas.
9. Beaumont, Fort Worth
10. 300 miles
11. Map A

Page 217

1. desert
2. northern part
3. Small; it would be hard to live in the desert.
4. light green
5. mostly woodland and shrub
6. Algeria, Egypt

Pages 218–219

1. volcano
2. mountain
3. hill
4. plain
5. valley
6. plateau
7. canyon
8. isthmus
9. cape
10. peninsula
11. gulf
12. bay
13. strait

Pages 220–221

1. 1,000–2,000 feet
2. Cougar Ridge; 5,000 feet
3. green
4. about 4,000 feet
5. about 2,500 feet
6. the north side; 5,000 feet
7. at 2,500 feet
8. the east side, 4,000 feet
9. Answers will vary.

Page 222

1. 0 to 1,000 feet
2. Hawaii
3. mountains
4. 0-1,000 feet
5. Nihau, Molokai, Lanai, Kahoolawe

Page 223

1. Haiti, Dominican Republic
2. green
3. Dominican Republic; mountains
4. 0 to 1,000 feet
5. 1,000 to 5,000 feet
6. northwest

Page 225

1. false
2. true
3. true
4. false
5. true
6. true
7. true
8. true

Pages 226–227

1. Harness and Saddlemaker, C4
2. Apothecary, I3
3. Cooper, E2
4. Printer, F3
5. Windmill, E2
6. Wetherburn's Tavern, G4
7. Milliner, G3
8. Blacksmith, F4
9. Bake Shop, H3
10. Silversmith, H3

Pages 228–229

1. 80
2. 380
3. Missouri, South Dakota
4. state or county road
5. 3 or 20
6. 30 and 35
7. Des Moines, Ames
8. Possible answer: 29 north to 80 east to 35 north to 18 east

Page 231

1. southeast
2. 50s
3. Minneapolis
4. Los Angeles, Miami
5. Possible answer: warm coat
6. rain and a cold front
7. San Francisco
8. yes

Page 233

1. Warm or hot summers, cold winters; Wet
2. Southeast; Pacific Coast; Hawaii
3. three
4. Cool summers, cold winters; Wet. Cool summers, cold winters; Very dry. Cool summers, mild winters; Wet.
5. Hot summers/mild or warm winters; Wet
6. Cool summers, cold winters; Wet
7. drier
8. Answers will vary.

Pages 234–235

1. northwest
2. red dot
3. Supe Valley
4. Andes
5. inland
6. Thailand, Laos; Vietnam
7. Siem Reap
8. northwest
9. about 150 miles
10. Tonle Sap

Pages 236–237
1. Montana, Wyoming, Idaho
2. five
3. west
4. Yellowstone River
5. Yellowstone Lake
6. about 50–60 miles

Pages 238–239
1. Michigan, Wisconsin
2. WV
3. Atlantic Ocean
4. Cornhusker State; corn
5. Washington; Maine
6. Louisiana
7. because it has a sunny climate

Page 240
1. 0°
2. Ecuador, Colombia, Brazil
3. Southern Hemisphere
4. 80°W
5. woodland and shrub
6. along the western coast
7. forest and farmland
8. near the Amazon River

Page 241
1. 1,000 to 2,000 feet
2. 500 to 1,000 feet
3. Harney Peak in the western part of state
4. 2,000 to 5,000 feet
5. higher
6. 0 to 500 feet

Page 242

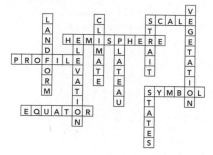

Science

Page 246
rhinoceroses, erupted, fossil, scattered, preserved

Page 247
comical, species, stomachs, evolved, sunlight

Pages 248–249

"Elephants like music," says musician and neuroscientist David Sulzer. "If you play music, they'll come over." At a conservation center in Thailand, he saw this for himself. He watched elephant trainers sing to the animals to soothe them. Sulzer already knew that elephants could recognize melodies. He wondered if they would play music themselves.

So Sulzer collected a band of elephants at the center to find out. He first built a variety of huge, unbreakable percussion instruments the elephants could play with their trunks or feet. He built 22 such instruments. These included drums, gongs, flutes, cymbals, and king-sized xylophones the elephants could play with a large mallet. Sulzer's instruments resemble traditional Thai ones and sound like them, too.

Sulzer soon found that elephants were indeed musicians: They could bang, stomp, tap, and blow to play distinct musical notes. With the help of the trainers, Sulzer got his elephant orchestra to play Thai melodies the tuskers recognize.

The Thai Elephant Orchestra has been a success. They have made three albums. And they'll play for peanuts (or bananas or apples). But the best part is that these talented musicians help raise much-needed money to house and protect other endangered elephants.

1. B; Sample answer: At the end of the article, the author talks about raising money "to house and protect endangered elephants." 2. C; Sample answer: It's the only choice that refers to the elephants, who are at the center of this article. 3. Sample answer: This article explains how David Sulzer used what he observed about elephants and his knowledge of music to answer a question. *Will elephants play music?* He built huge handmade instruments and taught elephants to play them. This took place in Thailand at a conservation center, which earned money by selling albums the Thai Elephant Orchestra made. 4. Sample answer: I know that elephants like peanuts, so one meaning is that the elephants earn their pay in peanuts for working in the orchestra. But the expression of doing something "for peanuts" means to do something for very little pay.

Page 250
similar, newborn, rodents, chief, hibernate

Pages 251-255
Investigation 1: If this were a real food chain, in the following year, the depleted mouse population would mean less food for the booming snake population. If they couldn't get other food, the number of snakes would crash.; This simulation is like a real food chain in that there are multiple species that rely on one another for food (Step 10). The fate of one species affects the fate of the others. It is different because a real food chain is much more complicated. There are many more kinds of plants and animals, and no animal produces a baby animal for every single meal it has.
Investigation 2: Food webs will vary but should include at least 10 living things. Game should be clear enough to teach how food webs work.

Pages 256-257

If you have ever spent any time with dogs, you have noticed how much better their sense of smell is than yours. They can smell things before you do. They can detect smells that you cannot. But how does a dog's sense of taste compare with ours? Their sense of taste is not as good as ours. You get one clue simply by watching them gobble up food as if they are starving and don't seem to even taste what they are wolfing down. Well, dogs just don't seem to care much about taste. That's because they have fewer taste buds than you do.

Taste buds are groups of cells that let us know how things taste. They tell us whether foods are sweet, salty, sour, bitter, or savory. Taste buds are located on the surface of the tongue. There are also some on the roof of the mouth and in the back of the mouth. The more taste buds you have, the better your sense of taste is. Whereas humans have about 9,000 of these, canines have about 1,700.

But compared to cats, dogs are foodies. Poor cats have only about 470 taste buds in their mouths.

1. C; Sample answer: This paragraph talks about how much better dogs can smell than we can. I used context clues in the text to figure out that C is the correct answer. Also, detect reminds me of *detective*, and detectives try to identify clues. 2. C; Sample answer: In paragraph 3, the author writes, "the more taste buds you have, the better your sense of taste is." 3. Sample answer: I think it means to gobble the food down as fast as possible. It probably comes from wolves in the wild eating very quickly before others try to take their food. 4. Accept reasonable responses. Sample answer: I might call the essay "All About Taste Buds" because it is mostly about how the number of taste buds affects how well an animal can taste different flavors.

Page 258
Titles and added words may vary.;
2. eardrum, Parts of the Eye; 3. root, Parts of a Flower; 4. battery, Simple Machines; 5. kilogram, Metric Measures of Length; 6. geometry, Branches of Science; 7. plaque, Types of Teeth; 8. volume, Tools for Measuring; 9. baking soda, Gases; 10. circus, Kinds of Clouds; 11. gosling, Names for Groups of Animals; 12. climate, Areas of Land; 13. hibernation, Stages of an Insect's Life Cycle; 14. seal, Reptiles

Page 259
1. complex; 2. kingdom; 3. mold or mushroom; 4. obtain; 5. fungi; 6. c; 7. e; 8. a; 9. d; 10. b

Page 260
3, 4, 2, 1; b; 1. e; 2. h; 3. a; 4. f; 5. b; 6. g; 7. d; 8. c

Pages 261–262
1. Answers will vary. 2. nectar, detect, secretes, exoskeleton; 3. b, a, a

Page 263
decorate, quality, insulation, oxygen, chemical

Page 264
1. C; 2. solid, liquid and gas; 3. C; 4. solid; 5. in the air and in steam; 6. B

Page 265
1. B; 2. A; 3. A; 4. Waves can bring in and drop off elements to build it up.; 5. pebbles, sand, mud; 6. It can erode the land.

Page 266
1. C; 2. 1. turn sweat to steam 2. cloud you vision 3. burst you ear drums 4. stop your heart; 3. 30; 4. stay inside, avoid metal pipes, stay away from corded phones, computers, and other electrical equipment; 5. C

Pages 267–271
Investigation 1: The surface of the sand starts out even. After gentle waves, your child may notice that it is no longer smooth. There may be a dip where the lower part of the beach has eroded away. The sand under the water may have bumps or dips, depending on how the sand has washed and shifted.

Investigation 2: Your child will likely see enough erosion in Step 3 to shift or wash away the buildings.; Erosion-control methods may include any real life methods such as planting materials into the sand (similar to the roots of dune plants, which help anchor sand in place), covering the sand with fabric or other material (which is similar to erosion-control matting), or hoisting the buildings up on stilts.; Answers will vary, but beachgoers generally like flat, sandy beaches with easy access to the water and a view of the horizon. Animals need to live and find food on the beach, including under the sand. Sea turtles need to be able to crawl from the water onto the sand and then dig a hole in order to lay their eggs.

Pages 272–273

Do thoroughfares in your area ice over in winter? Are sidewalks treacherous for walking? If so, would you ever think to grab a jar of pickles?

Icy roads can be dangerous. Cities and towns spend heavily each winter spreading rock salt on roads to melt the ice. However, the problem with using rock salt is that it is hazardous to the environment. Salt seeps into the ground and into our fresh water, damaging plants and trees. Salt also harms wildlife and pets.

This challenge has pushed transportation departments in some states to seek safer materials to use. One solution is to replace rock salt with *brine*. Brine is salty water. It is found in the juice of beets, pickles, potatoes, and cheese. Brine has three advantages over rock salt. First, it causes less harm to the environment. It also works better than rock salt at very low temperatures. Moreover, using brine saves money for taxpayers.

Indiana has begun to use beet brine to melt ice on its roadways. Surfaces in Tennessee are being de-iced with potato brine. New Jersey ice is being melted with pickle brine. Cheese brine is now used to combat Wisconsin's icy streets. Yes, states may have found an effective answer to a slippery problem.

1. B; Sample answer: I saw the word brine in the middle of paragraph 3 and a definition of it: brine is salty water. 2. D; Sample answer: In paragraph 2, I read that salt can harm pets, plants, wildlife, and our water. 3. Sample answer: Roads and sidewalks get icy, which makes travel dangerous. But using rock salt to melt the ice harms the environment. 4. Sample answer: The article says that brine is safer for the environment, that it works better than rock salt at low temperatures, and is less expensive than rock salt.

Page 274
1. C; 2. clockwise; 3. warm air is pushed upward quickly by a colder mass.; 4. up to 200 miles per hour; 5. in a basement, in a bathtub, under a sturdy piece of furniture

Pages 275–279
Investigation 1: Your child should see very little whipped cream "magma" as he or she models the transform boundary. There should be much more whipped cream "magma" as your child models divergent and convergent boundaries.; Both divergent and convergent boundaries are associated with volcanoes.
Investigation 2: Answers will vary depending on materials used.

Pages 280–281
1. Sample answer: There are more ingredients to be added (lines 19–26).
2. Sample answer: The first list gives the materials you need for the project. The numbered list tells you the steps to follow in order. 3. Sample answer: A big antacid tablet might not fit through the top of the soda bottle. And step 3 says to add one piece at a time and wait for the bubbling to stop before adding the next one. Maybe it has to do with what the bubbling does, and a whole tablet at once might bubble over (lines 21–26). 4. C; Sample answer: I imagined lava burbling, which made me think of thick bubbles in slow motion. So, I picked oatmeal cooking because that's what you see when you make it on a stove. 5. C; Sample answer: The picture at the top and the introduction gave me the idea that a lava lamp was something new and fun that people liked.

Page 282

```
W N K T S U N A M I N G Q
R F L O O D S V X V E L S
M P A W W E L A S N E A U
U M N C R U A L I E R C E
D F D T L V X A N D O I G
S U S J M V W N K Y T E L
L M L I U O J C H O K V A
I W I N D L S H L L I C
D H D P G C T E L E N W I
E G E Q H A L S E N H I E
H S J K N K T S A M W R
E R U P T I O N S D B O S
K A Q R N C B U S Y Q Z B
```

Pages 283–287

Investigation 1: When the light patch is aimed at a wall and the water is calm, your child will likely see reddish orange on one side of the light patch and purplish blue on the other. "Catching" the light on a white sheet of paper and tilting the paper will cause the patch to spread out, which may allow your child to see a wider range of colors. Moving the paper toward the mirror will make the patch smaller and the colors less visible. At some point, your child will probably see only white light. Catching the light with black paper will make the light dimmer because much of it is being absorbed by the black. However, some light will still be reflected.; Vantablack absorbs almost all light, so the light patch would not be visible.

Investigation 2: Your child will likely not get "classic" results using amateur equipment. However, he or she will probably be able to see that putting all three lights together makes something very close to white. Your child may see some of these colors more clearly when looking at the colored shadows created in Step 10. Each color light produces a different color shadow. Where the hand blocks just one light, he or she will see the sum of the other two. And where it blocks two lights, he or she will see the remaining light. The differences in color are highlighted when they see all three colors together.

Page 288

1. The main idea is how a rainbow forms.; 2. C; 3. Sunlight shines on the rain droplets and it gets separated into the colors of the spectrum.; 4. 7; 5. red, orange, yellow, green, blue, indigo, violet; 6. Yes

Pages 289–293

Investigation 1: When the air inside the can is heated by the warm water, it will expand and push up on the balloon skin. Your child will see the skin go from flat to domed. When the air is cooled, it will contract and pull down on the balloon skin, leaving a bowl shape.

Investigation 2: When the balloon floats to the ceiling, it is less dense than the air around it. When the balloon touches the floor, it is denser than the air.

Page 294

pressure, gorilla, weightless, peaceful, vivid

Page 295

1. astronaut; 2. revolution; 3. galaxy; 4. rotate; 5. astronomy; 6. asteroids; 7. gravity; 8. solar; 9. Saturn; 10. Mercury; 11. atmosphere

Pages 296–297

1. E, C, C, E; 2. built, astronomical, transported, nutrients, solar, assembled; four most requested foods of astronauts: shrimp cocktail, lemonade, steak, brownies; 3. conducting experiments; 4. Possible answer: because the ISS is a project that allows some of the world's finest scientists to work together, exploring space for the world's future

Pages 298–299

Nature demands that living things must eat to survive. This might seem easy in a modern world of freezers, supermarkets, and restaurants. But in the past, the problem was that much food spoiled before anyone could eat it. Our ancestors knew that without food, they would die. So they needed to find ways to treat foods to make them last. They had to preserve enough food in good times to survive harsh winters, droughts, natural disasters, and seasonal shortages.

One early answer to making food last was pickling. *Pickling* is a way to preserve foods by curing them in vinegar and/or salt to prevent spoiling. Vinegar is an acid that kills most bacteria. Salt dries food out and aids in the growth of "good" bacteria that protect against the "bad" bacteria that cause rot. Nearly every culture in the world developed pickled foods.

Science has since proven that pickling not only makes food last longer, it also makes some of it easier to digest. In fact, certain foods become more nutritious after they have been pickled. Pickling can also convert inedible foods, such as some roots or plants, into healthy new forms.

1. A; Sample answer: The end of the article talks about converting inedible foods into healthy foods, so I assume they are changing things we couldn't eat into things we can. Also, I know that the prefix *in*- means "not," and *edible* means you can eat it. 2. D; Sample answer: I know that pork is a kind of meat, and salting it would help it last longer. I don't think that vinegar or salt would make the other choices last longer— or taste good to eat! 3. Sample answer: I think the author wants to show that foods are pickled in all cultures of the world. The chart offers a look at some of them. 4. Sample answer: Preserving food has been a challenge throughout history, and another meaning of the word *pickle* is a problem or bad situation. So, "worldwide pickle" refers to the method of preserving food done all around the world, and also suggests the problem itself.

Pages 300–301

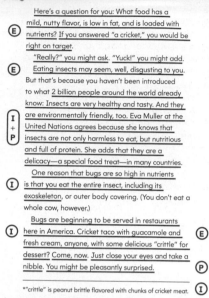

Here's a question for you: What food has a mild, nutty flavor, is low in fat, and is loaded with nutrients? If you answered "a cricket," you would be right on target.

"Really?" you might ask. "Yuck!" you might add. Eating insects may seem, well, disgusting to you. But that's because you haven't been introduced to what 2 billion people around the world already know: Insects are very healthy and tasty. And they are environmentally friendly, too. Eva Muller at the United Nations agrees because she knows that insects are not only harmless to eat, but nutritious and full of protein. She adds that they are a delicacy—a special food treat—in many countries.

One reason that bugs are so high in nutrients is that you eat the entire insect, including its exoskeleton, or outer body covering. (You don't eat a whole cow, however.)

Bugs are beginning to be served in restaurants here in America. Cricket taco with guacamole and fresh cream, anyone, with some delicious "crittle" for dessert? Come, now. Just close your eyes and take a nibble. You might be pleasantly surprised.

*"crittle" is peanut brittle flavored with chunks of cricket meat.

1. B; Sample answer: The context clue let me know that a *delicacy* is a special food treat. I'd be most likely to have a delicacy at a holiday party than at any of the other times described. 2. B; Sample answer: Even if this is true, the article doesn't include this information. But it does mention all the other choices. 3. Sample answer: The writer starts by asking a question whose answer is not what you'd expect. I think this is done to grab readers' attention and make them curious to know more. 4. Sample answer: The author uses a playful, funny, entertaining approach to give information about an unusual topic. It sounds like the author would be willing to try an insect meal because it is nutritious and also supports this as a good idea for the environment.

Pages 302–303

When a person drops otherwise edible food on the floor, you might hear someone yell, "Five-second rule!" This is the belief that if you retrieve food from the floor in five seconds or less, it's still safe to eat. Is this a legitimate fact you can accept as true? Or is it simply an excuse not to waste that tasty brownie? High school senior Jillian Clarke wanted to know. She conducted a controlled scientific experiment to test this notion.

Clarke got smooth and rough tiles of equal size. First, she cleaned them thoroughly. Then she contaminated them with samples of the *E. coli* bacteria. She chose cookies and gummy bears as the test foods. In turn, she dropped one of each on the tainted tiles, picked each up in five seconds or less, and tested for the presence of *E. coli* on the foods.

The results left no doubt. Clarke found a transfer of germs in less than five seconds. Common sense prevails: It's simply not safe to eat food that has fallen on the floor. For her work, Clarke received a joke prize for "research that first makes you laugh, then makes you think."

1. C; Sample answer: The paragraph describes edible food versus food that is contaminated and not safe to eat. So *edible* has to do with food. Floor tiles are not food. 2. A; Sample answer: The caption of the picture explains that eating *E. coli* can make you sick. 3. Sample answer: She found that germs do attach to foods in less than five seconds, which means that the five-second rule isn't reliable. 4. Sample answer: I think *tainted* means infected with something or made unsafe. It's a synonym for contaminated. Clarke *contaminated* the tiles with *E. coli*, which tainted them.

Pages 304–305

What if you scrape your shin or a pet claws you by mistake? Alas, accidents occur to everyone. Minor wounds need TLC—tender loving care—and sufficient time to mend. Luckily, you can manage most small wounds without visiting a hospital; that's why it's a good idea to have basic first-aid supplies on hand at home.

① The [first] thing to do is to stop any bleeding immediately. Small cuts and scrapes usually close on their own. If not, cover the wound with a clean cloth or bandage. Then press gently on it until the bleeding stops. This could take a few seconds or minutes.

② [Next,] it's essential to rinse the wound to avoid infection. Use lukewarm water and mild soap to gently clean the area; repeat to remove dirt and grit. If needed, wet some cotton or gauze with alcohol or peroxide and lightly clean again. Dry the area thoroughly.

③ [Then,] cover the wound to keep out harmful germs using a bandage, gauze pad, or other type of clean cover, but don't make it too tight.

④ [Finally,] be kind to your wound. Try not to bump it.

⑤ [When] the bandage gets wet or dirty, replace it.

⑥ [After] a scab forms, expose the wound to fresh air so it can finish healing.

1. A; Sample answer: It takes time for a wound to heal so the other choices don't make sense. The word *enough* was the best choice to mean the same as *sufficient*. 2. B; Sample answer: Each of the other choices describes something to do earlier in the process of caring for a wound. 3. Sample answer: You need to clean the wound to help avoid infection and cover it to keep germs from getting into the wound before it is healed. 4. Sample answer: I think that the advice in this article is only for minor wounds. The author repeats the words *minor* and *small*. And I know that some injuries—like a broken leg or bad burn—need a doctor or a hospital visit.

Page 306

1. how bones develop and evolve; 2. cartilage-minerals and collagen makes them strong; 3. minerals and collagen; 4. they start out solid then may change to become hollow; 5. they grow from the minerals from the food we eat; 6. loss of minerals and collagen

Addition, Subtraction, Multiplication & Division

Page 308

1. 19; 2. 42; 3. 54; 4. 35; 5. 66
6. 165; 7. 245; 8. 368; 9. 768; 10. 1,323
What sickness can't you talk about until it's cured? Laryngitis

Page 309

102 + 49 = 151; 311 + 219 = 530
315 + 669 = 984; 452 + 266 = 718
167 + 267 = 434; 202 + 179 = 381
177 + 114 = 291; 372 + 109 = 481
345 + 166 = 511; 201 + 99 = 300
99 + 246 = 345; 397 + 119 = 516
245 + 345 = 590; 548 + 328 = 876
756 + 145 = 901; 219 + 79 = 298
Taking It Further: 750, 900, 1,050

Page 310

A. 13, 14; B. 18, 14; C. 16, 12; D. 15, 14; E. 15, 15; F. 15, 13; G. 17, 17; H. 19, 15; I. 17, 14; J. 15, 20; K. 20, 22;
(6 + 3) + 7 = 16 pieces

Page 311

18	18	17	19	15
16	18	15	15	17
17	18	18	16	16
17	22	18	15	19
17	15	18	18	18

Page 312

A. 3,569, 9,876;
B. 9,982, 7,949, 7,860, 91,798;
C. 86,992, 90,749, 89,994, 77,787;
D. 581,998, 774,862, 567,990, 694,939, 959,596; 29,028 feet

Page 313

A. 15,981, 19,341, 10,397, 8,990;
B. 12,218, 12,188, 11,929, 10,984;
C. 18,990, 16,767, 20,310, 16,971;
D. 17,759, 15,984, 14,487, 18,510;
39,651 feet

Page 314

Z. 1,371; B. 632; R. 1,211; Q. 1,522; S. 1,201; X. 761; I. 9,107; C. 4,053; Y. 10,155; A. 14,024; Y. 9,122; L. 103,468; P. 76,076; E. 82,373; F. 92,228; D. 539,396; Q. 651,951; R. 1,059,472; THEY ARE BIRDS OF PREY.

Page 315

H. 9,122; L. 12,548; I. 18,975; A. 17,531; E. 10,322; O. 17,200; C. 18,506; T. 14,123; M. 13,590; N. 130,752; U. 111,110; Y. 182,920; R. 136,131; THE BALD EAGLE IS FOUND ONLY ON THE NORTH AMERICAN CONTINENT.

Page 316

W. 7,901; T. 12,300; P. 7,148; N. 12,885; O. 11,695; E. 15,019; H. 15,994; R. 10,404; S. 9,207; ! 9,816; A. 8,915; U. 11,303; ONE WEARS TROUSERS. THE OTHER PANTS!

Page 317

A. 6,741 + 3,382 = 10,123, 9,443 + 9,817 = 19,260, 4,578 + 5,361 = 9,939, 2,227 + 6,973 = 9,200;
B. 3,841 + 4,064 = 7,905, 7,024 + 9,438 = 16,462, 9,810 + 9,385 = 19,195, 7,426 + 7,923 = 15,349;
C. 1,773 + 158 = 1,931, 3,654 + 6,474 = 10,128, 4,284 + 3,821 = 8,105, 8,863 + 2,317 = 11,180;
D. 3,948 + 9,265 = 13,213, 9,759 + 8,724 = 18,483, 7,558 + 9,948 = 17,506, 4,595 + 6,628 = 11,223; 38,369 + 42,510 = 80,879 pieces

Page 318

A. $92.83; G. $92.53; U $114.60; O. $63.87; B. $72.25; N. $170.78; E. $157.35; R. $69.37; M. $168.72; C. $765.09; S. $980.05; T. $670.09; D. $477.07; Y. $616.34; F. $1,216.40; W. $1,000.68; BECAUSE MONEY DOESN'T GROW ON TREES!

Page 319

1. 1,804; 2. 689; 3. 1,063; 4. 2,133; 5. 3,489; 6. 8,234; 7. 7,538; 8. 8,292; 9. 5,429; 10. 10,439
What's the best thing to eat in a bathtub? Sponge cake

Page 320

1. Deluxe Scraps
2. Kibble or Mouse Crumbs
3. Mouse Crumbs
4. Table Scraps and Mouse Crumbs
5. Crumbs & Cheese and Deluxe Scraps
Super Challenge: Woovis can't buy three items with $5. The cheapest three items cost a combined $5.67.

Page 321

A. $69.95; B. $118.00; C. $23.88; D. $18.58; E. $178.75; F. $5.25

Page 322
N. 3; T. 10; R. 9; L. 15; W. 14; E. 7; D. 0; O.
1; L. 8; I. 6; W. 5; D. 12; R. 11; N. 13; I. 16;
O. 2; H. 4; TWO HUNDRED BILLION

Page 323
2237 m.p.h.; A. 5, 5; B. 2, 9; C. 9, 9; D. 8, 2;
E. 1, 6; F. 5, 8; G. 3, 2; H. 9, 8; I. 6, 7; J. 3, 9

Page 324
5,104, 9,221, 4,732, 6,528; 803, 1,161,
3,106, 3,114; 9,159, 112, 2,106, 236;
1,515, 337, 8,613, 241

Page 325
464, 63, 416; 73, 179, 699; 240, 164, 119;
506, 376; 479 is left standing.

Page 326
E. 3,338; E. 4,729; H. 2,579; T. 4,819;
A. 8,858; R. 3,689; H. 7,046; N. 857;
C. 2,491; B. 3,875; E. 5,252; L. 5,583;
S. 874; I. 1,988; IN THE BLEACHERS!

Page 327
First Column: 5,708, 4,834, 1,052, 491, 3;
Second Column: 7,187, 5,708, 2,812, 1,034, 7;
Third Column: 8,245, 6,879, 2,980, 1,383, 4;
Fourth Column: 4,609, 2,656, 818, 126, 9;
Panthers

Page 328
E. 51,411; I. 3,228; R. 41,164; E. 2,497;
P. 30,702; H. 9,166; T. 7,805; L. 13,041;
A. 6,748; G. 16,378; S. 11,907; ! 9,477;
HE'S A LIGHT SLEEPER!

Page 329
8,604; 26,416; 41,658; 73,278; 4,316; 9,156;
9,493; 5,289

Page 330
Across: 2. 1,807; 6. 90,213; 8. 35,975;
9. 1,321; 10. 17,496; 11. 2,072; 12. 686,552;
14. 1,829; 15. 6,317; Down: 1. 3,131;
3. 6,956; 4. 7,761; 5. 45,044; 7. 37,127;
10. 12,697; 13. 666,372

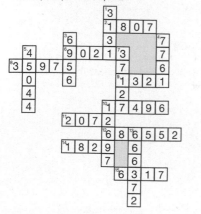

Page 331
A. 36.1, B. 43.48, C. 19.40; D. 78.9;
E. 51.59; 265.7; Mary visited Regions
B and C.

Page 332
Asteroids, 24–23; Comets, 98–96

Page 333
A. 367 miles; B. 2,289 miles; C. 3,787 miles;
D. 657.7 miles; E. 3,627 miles; F. 899 miles

Page 334
4, 9, 54, 20, 42; 24, 4, 40, 27, 8; 48, 45, 0,
15, 63; 64, 28, 81, 0, 12; 25, 36, 49, 10, 32;
6 x 7 = 42 balloons

Page 335
HE WAS HIRED AND FIRED ON THE SAME
DAY!; HE HAD TO BRING IT BACK!

Page 336
I. 328; O. 819; S. 168; H. 276; J. 146; E. 497;
L. 159; R. 720; C. 366; N. 55; A. 128; F. 369;
T. 490; E. 208; P. 320; THE CAPITAL OF
COSTA RICA IS SAN JOSE.; 189 pounds
of coffee

Page 337
A. 144, 168, 292; B. 399, 567, 168; C. 196,
512, 456, 315, 184, 492; D. 855, 462, 747,
768, 112, 480; 604 meters

Page 338
A. 256, 448, 350, 260, 340; B. 243, 534, 300,
276, 192; C. 294, 312, 576, 612, 216; D.
215, 291, 182, 237, 147

6	1	2	9	6	8	2	3	7
9	3	6	3	1	4	7	2	3
7	1	2	5	6	9	6	1	5
2	8	3	0	9	5	4	5	7
6	2	4	3	2	3	2	1	6
0	7	4	3	4	0	6	9	3
1	6	8	1	3	3	1	2	0
7	5	2	9	1	0	4	3	5
5	3	4	3	8	0	2	9	4

Page 339
A. 1,389, 3,692, 1,552, 3,150, 988, 2,416;
B. 2,275, 4,902, 2,637, 504, 1,664, 1,176;
C. 610, 4,075, 6,860, 1,395, 1,878, 756;
2,072 miles

Page 340
A. 560, 3,000, 27,000, 440, 240, 12,000;
B. 490, 36,000, 5,400, 42,000, 3,500, 360;
C. 48,000, 480, 240, 4,500, 24,000, 400

Page 341
1. 2,300; 2. 3,400; 3. 9,300; 4. 17,600
5. 9,500; 6. 16,200; 7. 24,500; 8. 14,400
9. 45,000
What are the cheapest ships to buy?
"Sale"boats

Page 342
1. 11,000; 2. 24,000; 3. 30,000; 4. 56,000;
5. 100,000; 6. 144,000; 7. 210,000
8. 256,000; 9. 360,000; 10. 375,000
Why did the spider join the baseball team?
To catch "flies"

Page 343
973 x 8 = 7784; 380 x 6 = 2280
909 x 7 = 6363; 178 x 4 = 712
272 x 8 = 2176; 319 x 4 = 1276
592 x 7 = 4144; 711 x 7 = 4977
699 x 6 = 4194; 716 x 8 = 5728
340 x 5 = 1700; 234 x 1 = 234
443 x 4 = 1772; 841 x 8 = 6728
361 x 6 = 2166; 246 x 4 = 984
588 x 9 = 5292; 741 x 8 = 5928
508 x 7 = 3556; 799 x 8 = 6392
247 x 7 = 1729; 300 x 9 = 2700
650 x 9 = 5850; 348 x 9 = 3132
948 x 9 = 8532
Taking It Further: 222

Page 344
6,916, 20,130, 19,012, 5,836, 11,284; 7,692,
9,048, 82,890 22,635, 8,144; 12,663, 7,161,
72,648, 28,744, 42,780; Stormy, Black
Beauty, Midnight, Lola's Lad, Lightning,
Dusty

Page 345
G. 1,536; T. 938; S. 1,431; I. 4,992; A. 2,739;
D. 3,528; M. 1,092; E. 840; N. 1,992;
R. 3,450; K. 4,896; H. 5,208; NIGHTMARES!;
1,632 pounds

Page 346
3,066, 1,323, 3,960; 630 feet; 5,481, 2,814,
2,425, 1,064; 1,454 feet; 6,723, 2,160, 5,135;
305 feet; 6,536, 3,640, 3,071; 605 feet;
Empire State Building should be circled.;
6,050 people

© Scholastic Inc.

Page 347

45 x 22 = 990; 89 x 23 = 2047
75 x 13 = 975; 68 x 26 = 1768
80 x 26 = 2080; 61 x 23 = 1403
75 x 23 = 1725; 48 x 48 = 2304
96 x 42 = 4032; 77 x 23 = 1771
49 x 71 = 3479; 24 x 20 = 480
96 x 26 = 2496; 65 x 13 = 845
45 x 31 = 1395; 54 x 28 = 1512
34 x 28 = 952; 47 x 23 = 1081
59 x 29 = 1711; 16 x 36 = 576
55 x 52 = 2860; 65 x 21 = 1365
27 x 57 = 1539; 45 x 22 = 990
Taking It Further: a. 2; b. 1; c. 5

Page 348

57 x 73 = 4161; 98 x 34 = 3332
23 x 13 = 299; 30 x 42 = 1260
21 x 61 = 1281; 44 x 20 = 880
87 x 33 = 2871; 79 x 12 = 948
81 x 14 = 1134; 55 x 13 = 715
58 x 42 = 2436; 25 x 13 = 325
60 x 33 = 1980; 61 x 11 = 671
72 x 32 = 2304; 41 x 23 = 943
16 x 34 = 544; 53 x 73 = 3869
27 x 34 = 918; 71 x 17 = 1207
49 x 52 = 2548; 83 x 17 = 1411
25 x 46 = 1150; 95 x 36 = 3420
25 x 17 = 425; 62 x 12 = 744
23 x 45 = 1035; 26 x 35 = 910
37 x 11 = 407; 24 x 20 = 480

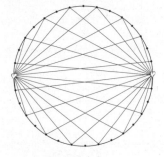

a. 9; b. 7; c. 2; d. 2

Page 349

A. 15,566, 10,836, 9,944, 3,679, 24,786,
26,015; B. 20,520, 23,352, 18,788;
C. 23,528, 21,682, 78,948; D. 19,614,
17,342, 62,853; 37,674 steps

Page 350

A. $44.62; M. $19.75; I. $131.84; O. $30.60;
A. $117.76; T. $181.26; F. $63.36; D. $87.42;
E. $546.05; S. $683.56; R. $65.25;
H. $574.36; AT THE FIFE AND DIME STORE!

Page 351

A. $4.92; B. 18,816; C. 1,305;
D. $19.95; E. 10,582; F. $17.88

Page 352

A. 6, 9, 8, 5, 9, 3; B. 9, 9, 7, 7, 6, 9;
C. 4, 3, 8, 8, 4, 9; D. 8, 7, 6, 3, 1, 5; 1928

Page 353

A. 4, 7, 3, 5, 6, 7, 8, 5, 8;
B. 5, 4, 3, 8, 4, 6, 3, 8, 9;
C. 6, 5, 3, 7, 6, 9, 3, 9, 6;
D. 9, 9, 7, 7, 3, 7, 4, 8, 6;
8 ÷ 1 = 8, 16 ÷ 2 = 8, 24 ÷ 3 = 8,
32 ÷ 4 = 8, 40 ÷ 5 = 8, 48 ÷ 6 = 8,
56 ÷ 7 = 8, 64 ÷ 8 = 8, 72 ÷ 9 = 8

Page 354

14 ÷ 7 = 2; 28 ÷ 7 = 4;
63 ÷ 7 = 9; 49 ÷ 7 = 7;
84 ÷ 7 = 12; 70 ÷ 7 = 10;
21 ÷ 7 = 3; 42 ÷ 7 = 6;
7 ÷ 7 = 1; 35 ÷ 7 = 5;
77 ÷ 7 = 11; 56 ÷ 7 = 8;
70 ÷ 7 = 10; 63 ÷ 7 = 9;
14 ÷ 7 = 2; 28 ÷ 7 = 4;
14 ÷ 7 = 2; 7 ÷ 7 = 1;
77 ÷ 7 = 11; 63 ÷ 7 = 9;
77 ÷ 7 = 11; 56 ÷ 7 = 8;
7 ÷ 7 = 1; 35 ÷ 7 = 5
Taking It Further: 10 squares

Page 355

24 ÷ 6 = 4; 27 ÷ 3 = 9; 36 ÷ 6 = 6;
28 ÷ 4 = 7; 32 ÷ 4 = 8; 40 ÷ 8 = 5;
7 ÷ 7 = 1; 18 ÷ 9 = 2; 9 ÷ 9 = 1;
16 ÷ 8 = 2; 32 ÷ 4 = 8; 20 ÷ 4 = 5;
42 ÷ 7 = 6; 63 ÷ 9 = 7; 16 ÷ 4 = 4;
81 ÷ 9 = 9

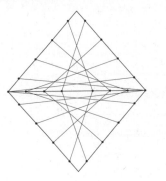

Taking It Further: 54, 45, 36, 27, 18; 42, 35,
28, 21, 14

Page 356

A. 70, 900, 90, 900, 800; B. 600, 80, 900, 80,
80; C. 50, 90, 800, 60, 80

Page 357

E. 9 R3; I. 9 R2; S. 9 R4; O. 4 R4; T. 3 R5;
N. 7 R5; P. 6 R3; I. 7 R3; O. 4 R3; A. 8 R6;
T. 8 R2; S. 6 R1; H. 5 R3; ! 6 R3; R. 5 R2;
N. 9 R7; NO, ON THE STAIRS!

Page 358

14 ÷ 6 = 2R2; 15 ÷ 9 = 1R6; 86 ÷ 7 = 12R2
41 ÷ 6 = 6R5; 37 ÷ 6 = 6R1; 33 ÷ 9 = 3R6
15 ÷ 2 = 7R1; 23 ÷ 6 = 3R5; 13 ÷ 3 = 4R1
54 ÷ 7 = 7R5; 45 ÷ 7 = 6R3; 15 ÷ 8 = 1R7
66 ÷ 9 = 7R3; 63 ÷ 8 = 7R7; 28 ÷ 3 = 9R1
33 ÷ 7 = 4R5; 19 ÷ 2 = 9R1; 53 ÷ 6 = 8R5
27 ÷ 5 = 5R2; 62 ÷ 7 = 8R6; 76 ÷ 9 = 8R4
80 ÷ 9 = 8R8; 17 ÷ 4 = 4R1; 11 ÷ 6 = 1R5

Page 359

1. 4; 2. 2; 3. 6; 4. 5; 5. 8; 6. 3 remainder 2
7. 6 remainder 6; 8. 9 remainder 2
9. 8 remainder 1; 10. 15 remainder 2
What kind of tools do you use for math?
"Multi"pliers

Page 360

T. 52; U. 51; M. 91; C. 82; A. 92; E. 81;
O. 71; S. 62; N. 84; D. 72; C. 82; I. 53;
W. 61; M. 31; ! 22; IT WANTED TO
CATCH THE MOUSE!

Page 361

A. 75; B. 82; C. 108; D. 83; E. 27; F. 36;
G. 106; H. 94; I. 76; J. 78; K. 54

Page 362

880 ÷ 2 = 440; 996 ÷ 3 = 332; 576 ÷ 4 = 144
502 ÷ 2 = 251; 992 ÷ 2 = 496; 603 ÷ 3 = 201
903 ÷ 3 = 301; 392 ÷ 2 = 196; 982 ÷ 2 = 491
897 ÷ 3 = 299; 738 ÷ 6 = 123; 742 ÷ 2 = 371
990 ÷ 3 = 330
Taking It Further:

```
     432
2 ) 864
   - 8
     06
    - 6
     04
    - 4
      0
```

Page 363

O. 64 R2; G. 63 R4; K. 95 R3; R. 42 R2;
L. 52 R3; A. 83 R1; M. 58 R3; P. 88 R2;
S. 87 R2; T. 59 R2; C. 44 R1; A CARPOOL!

Page 364

Z. 742; N. 583 R3; T. 262 R3; S. 748;
B. 618 R6; P. 356; D. 394; C. 542 R6;
U. 857; O. 921; A. 921 R4; Y. 672;
SUNDAY!; 91 R1 days

Page 365

A. 43, 13, 12, 38; B. 22, 15, 33, 20;
C. 18, 18, 27, 46; 206 bones; 300 bones

Page 366

S. 604; U. 908; W. 50 R10; X. 130;
G. 20 R16; B. 308; R. 20 R6; J. 902;
A. 601; E. 20 R22; Y. 320; T. 705;
STAR WARTS!; 237 pieces of popcorn

MATH

Page 368

1. 3,462; 2. 98,724; 3. 8,749
4. 128,467; 5. 617,823; 6. 618,397

Page 369

1. forty two; 2. sixty eighth
3. six thousand two hundred thirty four
4. thirty four; 5. one hundred forty five
6. seventeen; 7. ninety three

Page 370

1. 496, 23; 2. 49, 63; or 43, 69
3. 23, 496; or 26, 493; or 93, 426; or 96, 423
4. 732, 469; 5. 23, 64, 97; or 23, 67, 94; or
24, 63, 97; or 24, 67, 93; or 27, 63, 94; or
27, 64, 93; 6. 674, 392

Page 371

1. 9,875; 2. 12,346; 3. 93,876
4. 13,579; 5. 951,876; 6. 123,648

Page 372

Page 373

1. 10; 2. 20; 3. 50; 4. 90; 5. 200
6. 400; 7. 600; 8. 300; 9. 500; 10. 700
What did the farmer get when he tried to
reach the beehive?
A "buzzy" signal

Page 374

1. Exact Answer; 2. Estimate
3. Exact Answer; 4. Estimate
5. Estimate; 6. Exact Answer
7. Estimate; 8. Exact Answer
How Would You Estimate...
Answers will vary. Ask your child to explain
his or her estimation method in their writing.

Page 375

1. 1; 2. 4; 3. 22; 4. 26; 5. 34
6. 57; 7. 115; 8. 124; 9. 60; 10. 215
How can you make the number seven even?
Take away the "s."

Page 376

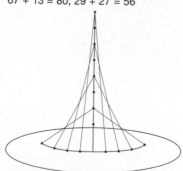

Page 377

1. T; 2. R; 3. R; 4. B; 5. O
6. O; 7. E; 8. O; 9. F; 10. E
What do cheerleaders like to drink?
Lots of root beer

Page 378

19 + 37 = 56; 33 + 47 = 80; 51 + 39 = 90
49 + 22 = 71; 48 + 23 = 71; 78 + 12 = 90
67 + 13 = 80; 29 + 27 = 56

Taking It Further: a. 3; b. 9; c. 7; d. 85;
e. 4; f. 26

Page 379

3/20 + 2/20 = 1/4; 2/16 + 2/16 = 1/4
1/14 + 1/14 = 1/7; 1/9 + 2/9 = 1/3
1/4 + 2/4 = 3/4; 4/9 + 2/9 = 2/3
4/10 + 2/10 = 3/5; 1/5 + 2/5 = 3/5
6/12 + 5/12 = 11/12; 4/10 + 5/10 = 9/10
4/12 + 7/12 = 11/12; 1/10 + 8/10 = 9/10
4/14 + 6/14 = 5/7; 6/10 + 2/10 = 4/5
4/8 + 2/8 = 3/4; 4/8 + 3/8 = 7/8;
2/10 + 3/10 = 1/2; 1/6 + 2/6 = 1/2
1/16 + 1/16 = 1/8; 3/40 + 7/40 = 1/4

Pages 380–381

T H E Y A L R E A D Y
1/5 3/8 4/6 6/8 1/2 2/9 2/3 4/6 1/2 1/3 6/8

H A V E B I L L S.
3/8 1/2 5/6 4/6 6/12 3/4 2/9 2/9 3/5

Page 382

7/8 – 1/8 = 3/4; 9/10 – 1/10 = 4/5
2/4 – 1/4 = 1/4; 3/5 – 1/5 = 2/5
8/9 – 2/9 = 2/3; 7/11 – 5/11 = 2/11
7/12 – 1/12 = 1/2; 7/8 – 2/8 = 5/8
7/12 – 3/12 = 1/3; 14/15 – 9/15 = 1/3
12/15 – 2/15 = 2/3; 9/10 – 8/10 = 1/10
7/6 – 4/6 = 1/2; 18/20 – 3/20 = 3/4
9/18 – 2/18 = 7/18; 7/8 – 6/8 = 1/8
11/13 – 1/13 = 12/13; 4/5 – 3/5 = 1/5
15/18 – 1/18 = 7/9; 13/16 – 1/16 = 3/4
4/9 – 1/9 = 1/3; 7/8 – 4/8 = 3/8;
3/4 – 1/4 = 1/2

Page 383

1. 1/2 white, 1/2 black
2. 4/7 black, 3/7 white
3. 1/4 black
4. 2 red socks, 4 green socks
5. 2/5 red
Super Challenge: 5 yellow socks,
7 red and white socks

Page 384

Here is the correct ranking from highest
to lowest:
1–Miguel Cabrera (.338); 2–Dee Gordon
(.333); 3–Bryce Harper (.330); 4–Paul
Goldschmidt (.321); 5–Xander Bogaerts
(.320); 6–Buster Posey (.318); 7–A. J. Pollock
(.315); 8–Yunel Escobar (.314);
9–Joey Votto (.314); 10–Jose Altuve (.313)

Page 385

ACROSS: A. 3.7; C. 4.38; E. .55; F. .6;
G. .9; J. .57; K. 7.16; L. 4.3
DOWN: A. 3.14; B. 78.29; C. 4.5; D. 8.1;
F. .2704; H. 24.3; I. 1.7; J. .36

Page 386
1. $1.55; 2. 23¢; 3. $2.45; 4. 48¢; 5. $12.70
6. $3.51; 7. 32¢; 8. $10.65; 9. 83¢; 10. $2.57

Page 387

Page 388
1. 52; 2. 12; 3. 100; 4. 20; 5. 365; 6. 36
7. 16; 8. 24; 9. 10; 10. 2; 11. 4; 12. 5,280
13. 60; 14. 1,000
Answer: TWENTY AFTER ONE

Page 389
1. scale; 2. ruler; 3. clock; 4. teaspoon
5. thermometer; 6. measuring cup
7. yardstick; 8. measuring tape

Page 390
1. a and e (4); b and c (30); d and g (16)
2. a and d; 3. a, b, and d; 4. 124

Page 391
1. perimeter: 20; area: 9
2. perimeter: 24; area: 13
3. perimeter: 22; area: 11
4. perimeter: 24; area: 15
5. perimeter: 32; area: 23
6. perimeter: 44; area: 48

Page 392
Your child can examine each angle in the letters MATH and determine whether it is right, acute, or obtuse.

Page 393
1. 50°, acute
2. 145°, obtuse
3. 170°, obtuse
4. 60°, acute
5. 90°, right

Page 394

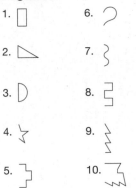

What is the last thing that the trapeze flier wants to be?
The fall guy

Page 395
1. eight; 2. acute; 3. perimeter; 4. area
5. square; 6. cube; 7. triangle; 8. circle
9. polygons
Answer: IT ATE MARS BARS.

Pages 396–397
Tessellate patterns will vary.

Page 398
Taking It Further:

0.2   1.7   2.5   4.9